MW00387654

The Certified Quality Technician Handbook

Also available from ASQ Quality Press:

The Uncertainty of Measurements: Physical and Chemical Metrology Impact and Analysis
S. K. Kimothi

Managing the Metrology System, Second Edition
Robert C. Pennella

Glossary and Tables for Statistical Quality Control, Third Edition
ASQ Statistics Division

How to Analyze Data with Simple Plots
ASQ Statistics Division

Root Cause Analysis: Simplified Tools and Techniques
Bjørn Andersen and Tom Fagerhaug

The Quality Toolbox
Nancy R. Tague

Quality Audit Handbook, Second Edition
ASQ Quality Audit Division

The Certified Quality Technician Handbook

Donald W. Benbow, Ahmad K. Elshennawy, and H. Fred Walker

ASQ Quality Press
Milwaukee, Wisconsin

The Certified Quality Technician Handbook
Donald W. Benbow, Ahmad K. Elshennawy, and H. Fred Walker

Library of Congress Cataloging-in-Publication Data

Benbow, Donald W., 1936–
The certified quality technician handbook / Donald W. Benbow, Ahmad K. Elshennawy, and H. Fred Walker.
p. cm.
Includes bibliographical references and index.
ISBN 0-87389-558-4 (acid-free)
1. Production management—Quality control. I. Elshennawy, Ahmad K. II. Walker, H. Fred, 1963– III. Title.

TS156.B4654 2003
658.5'62—dc21 2002154534

10 9 8 7 6 5 4 3 2 1

ISBN 0-87389-558-4

Publisher: William A. Tony
Acquisitions Editor: Annemieke Koudstaal
Project Editor: Paul O'Mara
Production Administrator: Gretchen Trautman
Special Marketing Representative: Robin Barry

ASQ Mission: The American Society for Quality advances individual, organizational, and community excellence worldwide through learning, quality improvement, and knowledge exchange.

Attention Bookstores, Wholesalers, Schools and Corporations: ASQ Quality Press books, videotapes, audiotapes, and software are available at quantity discounts with bulk purchases for business, educational, or instructional use. For information, please contact ASQ Quality Press at 800-248-1946, or write to ASQ Quality Press, P.O. Box 3005, Milwaukee, WI 53201-3005.

To place orders or to request a free copy of the ASQ Quality Press Publications Catalog, including ASQ membership information, call 800-248-1946. Visit our Web site at www.asq.org or http://qualitypress.asq.org .

Printed in the United States of America

Printed on acid-free paper

American Society for Quality
ASQ®

Quality Press
600 N. Plankinton Avenue
Milwaukee, Wisconsin 53203
Call toll free 800-248-1946
Fax 414-272-1734
www.asq.org
http://qualitypress.asq.org
http://standardsgroup.asq.org
E-mail: authors@asq.org

Table of Contents

List of Figures and Tables

Chapter I

Chapter II

Chapter III

Foreword

Writing the *Certified Quality Technician Handbook (CQTH)* was a project completed by Mr. Don Benbow, Dr. Ahmad Elshennawy, and Dr. H. Fred Walker. Contributions to the CQTH were also provided by two technical experts: Dr. George Schrader and Mr. Robert Dovich.

Primary authorship responsibility for the *CQTH* was allocated as follows:

Chapter I:	Quality Concepts and Tools	Don Benbow
Chapter II:	Statistical Techniques	Don Benbow
	Statistical Inference	H. Fred Walker
Chapter III:	Metrology and Calibration	Ahmad Elshennawy
		With contributions by George Schrader
Chapter IV:	Inspection and Test	Ahmad Elshennawy
		With contributions by Robert Dovich
Chapter V:	Quality Audits	H. Fred Walker
Chapter VI:	Preventive and Corrective Action	H. Fred Walker

Preface

The quality technician is a person responsible for understanding and utilizing quality concepts and tools, statistical techniques, metrology and calibration procedures and protocols, inspection and test techniques, quality auditing, and preventive and corrective action in the context of product/process/service improvement or in correcting problems. Quality technicians frequently work in the quality function of organizations in the various measurement and inspection laboratories, as well as on the shop floor supporting and interacting with quality engineers, mechanical inspectors, and production/service delivery personnel. This book, the *Certified Quality Technician Handbook (CQTH),* was commissioned by the American Society for Quality (ASQ) to support individuals preparing for, or those already performing, this type of work.

The *CQTH* is intended to serve as a ready reference for quality technicians and quality technicians-in-training, as well as a comprehensive reference for those individuals preparing to take the ASQ Certified Quality Technician (CQT) examination. Examples and problems used throughout the handbook are thoroughly explained, are algebra-based, and are drawn from "real world" situations encountered in the quality profession.

To assist readers in using the book as a ready reference or as a study aid, most of the book has been organized so as to conform closely to the CQT Body of Knowledge (BOK). In some chapters, the flow of the material dictated a somewhat different organization. In those instances, the reader will find the index and glossary useful in finding discussion relating to specific points in the BOK.

I

Quality Concepts and Tools

A. QUALITY CONCEPTS

1. Customers and Suppliers

Organizations of all types and sizes have come to realize that their main focus must be to satisfy their customers. This applies to industrial firms, retail and wholesale businesses, governmental bodies, service companies, nonprofit organizations, and every subgroup within an organization. Two important questions arise:

1. Who are the customers?
2. What does it take to satisfy them?

Who Are the Customers?

Customers include anyone to whom the organization supplies products or services. Table I.1 illustrates some supplier–customer relationships. Note that many organizations are simultaneously customers and suppliers.

What Does It Take to Satisfy Customers?

It is important that a company not assume that it knows what the customer wants. There are many examples of errors in this area, such as "new Coke" and car models that didn't sell. Many organizations exert considerable effort determining the "voice" of the customer. Tools such as consumer surveys, focus groups, and polling are often used. Satisfying the customer includes providing what is needed when it is needed. In many situations, it is up to the customer to provide the supplier with requirements. For example, the payroll department as customer in Table I.1 should inform other departments as to the exact format for reporting number of hours worked. If the payroll department does not do this job properly, they must bear some responsibility for the variation in reporting that will occur.

There is some merit to more than merely meeting the specifications in the purchase order or contract, in order to "delight" the customer. An example might be a purchase order that specified 1.000 ± .005 being fulfilled with parts that were all within ± .002. Another example might be a report that is submitted earlier than the contracted due date.

Table I.1 Supplier–customer relationship examples.

Supplier	Customer	Product or Service
Automobile manufacturer	Individual consumers	Cars
Automobile manufacturer	Car dealer	Sales literature, and so on
Bank	Checking account holders	Secure check handling
High school	Students and parents	Education
County recorder	Residents of county	Maintenance of records
Hospital	Patients	Healthcare
Hospital	Insurance company	Data on patients
Insurance company	Hospital	Payment for services
Steel shear department	Punch press department	Steel sheets
Punch press department	Spot weld department	Shaped parts
All departments	Payroll department	Data on hours worked, and so on

2. Basic Quality Principles

All customers want their needs met consistently. Almost every product or service performs exactly right some of the time. The reason they don't perform exactly right all the time is because things change. What things change? The short answer is that almost everything involving the production and use of the product or service changes. A more elaborate answer might include: raw materials, worker morale, process parameters, customer expectations, conditions of use, employee abilities, machine wear, legal restrictions, the economy, the weather, and so on.

How does the quality professional cope with this vast amount of variation? Three approaches are:

1. Understand variation and its effect on performance.
2. Reduce variation where possible.
3. Design the product or service to perform consistently in the presence of variation.

Much of the content of this book relates in some way to these three activities.

Features, Fitness-for-Use, Freedom from Defects

The most successful companies are those that have developed a strong communication tie with their customers. For example, this would help a company know how a product will be assembled and how their component fits into the customer's product. This would permit the supplying company to do a better job of emphasizing the critical features and characteristics that make the product fit for the customer to use. It also helps when the supplier understands the effect of defective products on the customer's operations.

The ideal time to influence the performance of a product or service is the design stage. A system should be in place to assure that consideration is given to the variation that will be present in the production and use of the product or service. For example, if prototypes are built, some should be made from the full range of raw materials that will be specified. The prototypes should be exposed to the full range of temperature, humidity, acidity, vibration, operator usage, and so on, that the product will encounter in practice. If a service is being designed, consideration should be given to variation in the service provider, the service recipient, and the environment in which the service is performed.

A thorough study of the impact of all these sources of variation will not happen automatically unless the design phase is carefully planned and controlled. Therefore any quality policy should include provision for a system to do this. There are several tools available to aid in this effort, including design of experiments (DOE), failure mode and effects analysis (FMEA), and design for manufacture and assembly (DFMA).

Design changes present additional opportunities to ignore the effects of variation. Businesses are replete with examples of the law of unintended consequences. The automotive recalls that are later "re-recalled," the pharmaceuticals that are removed from the shelves, and the contract revisions that have to be revised are just a few examples. The design system should assure that proposed design changes be subjected to the same scrutiny with regard to variation as the original design.

If components or materials are purchased outside the organization, then the scrutiny regarding design should be pushed upstream to the supplier. It is the customer's responsibility to assure that the supplier employs a system to assure that this happens.

Processes

The processes that produce a product are also vulnerable to influence by many sources of variation. These sources are often grouped into categories such as:

- Machine (for example, speed variation, wear-related variation, lubrication schedule, and so on)
- Worker (for example, skills, training, health, attitudes, and so on)
- Methods (for example, procedures and practices for operating the process)
- Materials (for example, variations in raw materials, catalysts, and so on)
- Measurement (for example, since the information about the process often results from measurement activity, variation in the measurement system can be misleading)
- Environment (for example, temperature, humidity, and so on, some authorities include the psychological environment of the workplace)

For a visual scheme for portraying these sources of variation, see cause-and-effect diagrams in section I.D.

A good product design system considers these sources during the product design stage. Minor product design changes may result in significant reductions in process-related variation. For example, if maintaining cylindricity of deep holes is difficult, the product design should avoid deep holes where possible. In addition to product design, the system for process design should include steps for reducing variation and the impact of variation. These steps include understanding the capability of various processes and finding ways of increasing capability. Calculation of machine capability is discussed in section F of chapter II.

Once product and process designs have been finalized and the process is running, it may be advisable to monitor it through the use of statistical process control or other quality tools. This technique helps pinpoint the time when the process becomes unstable, increasing the probability that this source of variation can be reduced. Control charts are discussed in detail in section F of chapter II.

Every person in the organization must understand that continuous improvement is a significant part of his or her job. Envision a production line consisting of 40 people arranged along an overhead chain conveyor. Each of the 40 people has a red button that can be pushed when a problem is encountered. When a person pushes the button, the line stops and a response team made up of the group leaders and nearby workers help solve the problem. The clock on the wall at the end of the line is set at 12:00 at the start of each shift and only runs when the line is stopped. The number of minutes on the clock at the end of the shift is the number of minutes the line was stopped and also the number of minutes that problems were being solved. The company's philosophy is that the clock should have at least 30 minutes on it during each shift, because when the line is stopped problems are being solved and the process or product is a tiny bit better than it was the previous day. If everyone in an organization does something each day, that was better than the way it was done the previous day, then the organization will continuously improve.

Needless to say, continuous improvement requires resources and it may be necessary to consider several options in order to find one that is cost effective. Most authorities in the quality field feel that the typical organization could save dollars by investing more in continuous improvement. This will usually save money spent on costs of failure such as warranty, rework, lost customer goodwill, and so on. For example, a company may be unwilling to invest a lot of money in improving a 20¢ brake part until it realizes that the failure of the part can cause thousands of dollars of liability. In other words, the cost accountants may price a good part at 20¢, but a bad one can cost much more than that.

3. Quality Standards, Requirements, and Specifications

The quality of the product or service that an organization provides is dependent on the organization's suppliers. For example, the consumer's satisfaction with an appliance is impacted by the quality of the drive motor. If the appliance manufacturer purchases the drive motors from another company, the appliance manufacturer must have a method of assuring that the motor manufacturer provides a quality product.

Specifications

The first thing the appliance manufacturer would do in this situation is to produce specifications for the motor. These might include dimensions, horsepower, resistance to adverse environmental conditions, and so on. If the customer does not communicate appropriate requirements to the supplier, the customer must bear some of the responsibility for poor quality of the products.

Standards

Customer organizations realize that their suppliers need to prove that they can produce a good product and also show that they have some sort of system to assure that the product quality and consistency will continue in future orders. For this reason, customers sometimes audit their suppliers' quality management systems. Suppliers often find their quality systems being audited by various customers, sometimes with different and conflicting requirements. The International Organization for Standardization (ISO) attempts to reduce some of the confusion by publishing a series of documents called *standards*. One of these specifies the elements of a quality management system, for instance. Other organizations, such as the American National Standards Institute (ANSI) and the American Society for Quality (ASQ), have cooperated in producing and publishing the standards. Companies can be certified as having met these standards by third-party registrars. Many customers recognize this certification and do not require further audit of the certified function. Examples of some standards are shown in Table I.2. Copies of these and other standards are available through the American Society for Quality.

B. PLAN–DO–CHECK–ACT (PDCA) CYCLE

Dr. Walter Shewhart, the inventor of control charts, is credited with providing a roadmap for continuous improvement. Sometimes referred to as the Shewhart Cycle (or the Deming Cycle), PDCA has come to be recognized as a critical tool in the problem solver's toolbox. A brief discussion of each element follows, but it is important to recognize that the elements need to be incorporated into a cycle that is completed then repeated endlessly.

Plan

Once a problem has been clearly defined, the first steps in solving it are to collect and analyze data, consider and analyze alternative solutions, and choose the best solution. These steps, although easy to state, can be extremely difficult and time-consuming to execute. Jointly, these steps constitute the Plan phase in the PDCA cycle. One approach to this phase is to use a *force field analysis*, which lists the goals, the barriers to reaching those goals, and a strategy for coping with those barriers. This approach provides guidance for the next steps. In most situations, a cross-functional team representing everyone impacted by the problem and its solution should be formed and assigned the problem-solving task.

There is a great tendency to jump to the Do phase of the cycle rather than taking the time to adequately execute the Plan phase. Before moving to the Do phase, however, careful plans should be made regarding the collection of information during that phase.

Table I.2 Examples of standards.

Number	Contents
ANSI/ISO/ASQ Q9000-2000	Quality concepts and vocabulary
ANSI/ISO/ASQ Q9001-2000	Quality Management Standards—Requirements
ANSI/ISO/ASQ Q9004-2000	Guidelines for performance improvements
ANSI/ISO 14001-1996	Environmental Systems
ANSI/ASQC Z1.4-1993	Sampling Procedures and Tables—Attributes
ANSI/ISO/ASQC A3534-2-1993	Statistics—Vocabulary and Symbols—SQC

In some situations it may be useful to apply a "quick and dirty" (or "Band-Aid") solution to allow time to focus on the permanent solution. Of course, this approach risks the tendency to move on to the next problem because this one is "solved."

Do

Once a solution to the problem has been decided upon, and a data collection scheme has been determined, the next phase is to try it. If possible, this should be done on a small scale and/or off-line. Sometimes the proposed solution can be tried in a lab setting or outside the regular production process. During the Do phase, as much data as possible should be collected. In some situations, videotaping a process permits further data collection upon replay.

Check

The Check phase is used to analyze the information collected during the Do phase. The data must be studied carefully, using valid mathematical and statistical techniques. For this reason, some authors, including Dr. W. Edwards Deming, began calling this the Study phase and refer to the cycle as PDSA.

Act

In this phase, action is taken based on the conclusions reached in the Check phase. If the data show that the proposed solution is a good solution for the problem, the Act phase consists of integrating the solution into the standard way of doing things. If the data show that another proposed solution is needed, the Act phase consists of initiating the search for another solution. As the word "cycle" implies, the Act phase is followed by the Plan phase of the next cycle because quality improvement is a continuous journey.

Dale Gordon[1] observes that many organizations are pretty good at the Do and Check phases, but fall down on the Plan and Act phases. Perhaps this is partly due to the impulse to "Don't just stand there, do something." There is a tendency, for instance, to provide a service, process, or product to customers without adequate care in the design (Plan) phase. The strategy is that customers will provide feedback and a lot will be learned from the design mistakes. Automotive industries have attempted to combat this with such programs as advanced product quality planning (APQP), potential failure mode and effects analysis (FMEA), and production part approval process (PPAP).

C. EFFECTIVE TEAM FUNCTION

Many problems require the efforts of several people. It is common practice to assign such a problem to a task force or team. The team should be cross-functional, with representation from all areas impacted by the problem and its solution. During the investigation of a problem it may be desirable to recruit people with particular expertise to become temporary or permanent team members. The team is usually given defined goals and some sort of time line.

The team's first tasks often include clarification of the goals, including a definition of the measurement system to be used. The team should use PDCA as discussed in the previous section, or some variant of that cycle. It is usually necessary to go through the cycle several times.

1. Conflict Resolution

In the growth process the team will often find members in disagreement. Resolving these conflicts requires that:

- All team members must be heard (one at a time).
- Team members respect others' opinions and ideas.
- Everyone should rely on facts and data where possible. If the data aren't available, reach agreement on a method to obtain them.
- Outside expertise should be brought in if needed.
- It may be necessary to test more than one solution and collect data on each.

2. Consensus

Although it is sometimes necessary to put things to a team vote, it is usually advisable to reach agreement by continued discussion. Although this method, referred to as *consensus building,* takes more time than voting, it reduces the tendency for some team members to feel like losers. Reaching a consensus often means that people have to "give a little" in order for the team to make progress. The process is successful when everyone can "live with" the solution selected by the team.

3. Brainstorming

In the early stages of problem solving it is useful to get a large number of ideas. *Brainstorming* is a way to do that. There are several ways to conduct a brainstorming session. One approach starts with asking each person to express just one idea. This idea is written so all can see it and the next person expresses one thought. After all team members have had a turn, each is asked for a second idea, and so on. One of the rules of a brainstorming session is that no idea is to be criticized or judged. Often, members will "piggyback" on a previous idea and come up with a new or modified thought. The theory of brainstorming is that if all ideas are documented, it is likely that the best idea or solution is on the list somewhere. The next step is to compress the list somehow. It may be possible to combine two or more ideas into one. Sometimes the ideas can be grouped into categories such as machining problems, supplier problems, painting problems, and so on, an approach known as *affinity diagramming.* The team may elect to prioritize the items on the list, agreeing to study the highest priority items first. Individuals may be assigned the task of pursuing individual ideas further and reporting to the next team meeting.

4. Meeting Management

The hours spent in team meetings are a very valuable resource. Well-managed meetings help get the most out of the time spent together. Barriers to effective use of meeting time include:

- Lack of a clear agenda
- Tendency to digress from the subject

- Feeling on the part of team members that the meeting is a waste of time or has a lower priority than other responsibilities
- Strong disagreement among team members
- Tendency for some members to dominate the discussion and others to withdraw participation

It is the responsibility of the team leader to minimize these and other barriers that may impede the team. Techniques that have proven useful include:

- Publish an agenda in advance of the meeting.
- Begin the meeting by reviewing the agenda.
- Call the team back to the agenda when they stray too far or for too long.
- Keep the meeting moving. If an agenda item can't be adequately addressed, it may be best to postpone it for later consideration. Start and end on time. If the business of the meeting has been completed, end the meeting early.
- When conflicts among members arise, help them find a middle ground of agreement. Even an agreement on how to collect data is better than no agreement at all.
- Frequently go around the room asking for input from each member to maintain an even level of participation.

Experience and training in meeting management help the leader in using these techniques. When the team leader doesn't have the requisite skills, it may be useful to have a "team facilitator" assist with meeting management.

5. Stages of Team Development

Teams go through four growth stages:

1. Forming—Members struggle to understand the goal and its meaning for them individually.
2. Storming—Members express their own opinion and ideas, often in disagreement with others.
3. Norming—Members begin to understand the need to operate like a team rather than as a group of individuals.
4. Performing—The team works together to reach their common goal.

D. QUALITY CONTROL TOOLS

Some of the basic yet effective tools for quality improvement are discussed in this section. Often referred to as the "basic" quality improvement tools, they include cause-and-effect diagrams, flowcharts, check sheets, histograms, Pareto diagrams, scatter diagrams, run charts, and control charts. These tools are explained in the following sections.

1. Cause-and-Effect Diagrams

When a problem has been identified, the search for a root cause begins. A cause-and-effect diagram may be used to generate a list of possible root causes. This diagram, also known as an Ishikawa or fishbone diagram, divides root causes into broad categories that help stimulate thinking. The general structure of a cause-and-effect diagram, shown in Figure I.1, illustrates why this tool is also called a fishbone diagram. The choice of categories or names for the main "bones" depends on the situation. Some alternatives might include policies, technology, tradition, or others.

A team may use a cause-and-effect diagram to generate a number of potential causes in each category by going around the room asking each person to suggest one cause and its associated category. As each cause is selected, it is shown as a subtopic of the main category by attaching a smaller line to the main "bone" for that category. The result of such a session is illustrated in Figure I.2.

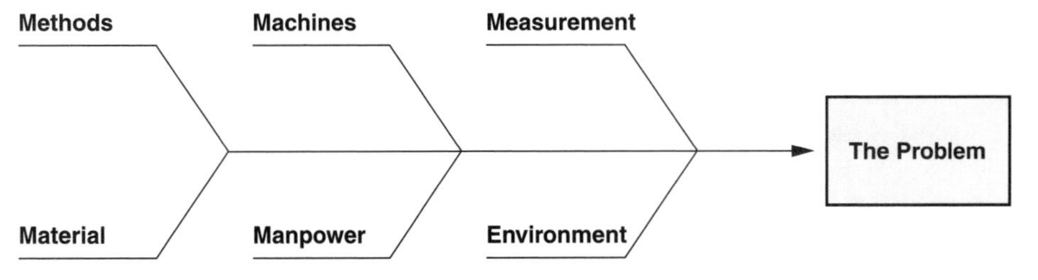

Figure I.1 Cause-and-effect diagram.

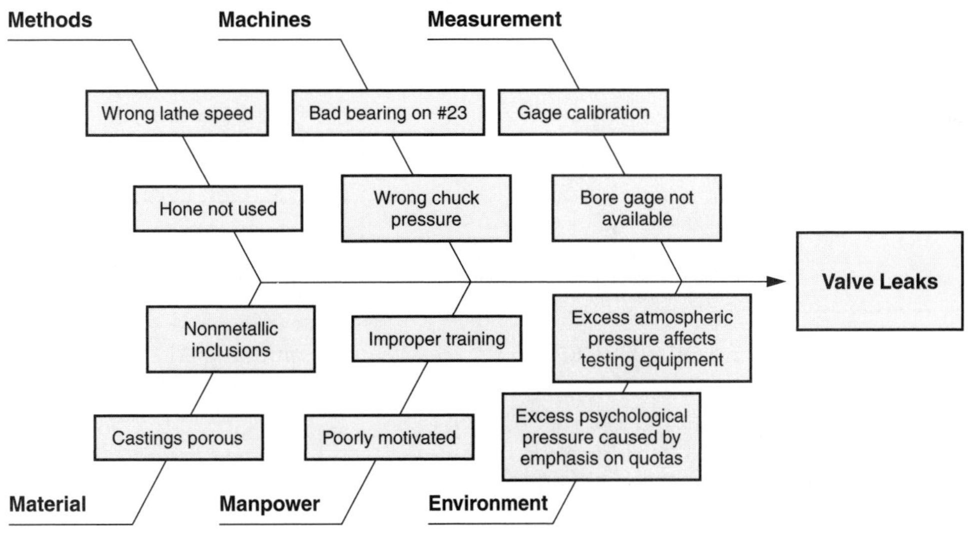

Figure I.2 Completed cause-and-effect diagram.

It is important to continue the session until all possible causes have been listed. The team may wish to identify subcauses. For example, "What are some reasons the hone is not being used?" A team session might produce several dozen potential causes and subcauses. The next step is to have individual team members obtain information on each of the suggested causes for discussion at the next meeting. Once data have been collected, the team may want to use a Pareto chart to prioritize their next efforts.

2. Process Mapping (Flowcharts)

When a group first begins the job of process improvement it is important that they have a good understanding of the various process steps and how they fit together. Various pictorial tools have been developed for this purpose and they are grouped under the general heading of *process maps.* One example of a process map is the flowchart. It may be designed to show the flow of material, information, documentation, custody, cash, or some other quantity. The quality professional will probably encounter flowcharts showing successive steps in a process or service. Two simple examples of flowcharts are shown in Figures I.3 and I.4.

There is no universal set of symbols for flowcharts, but decision points are usually designated with diamond-shaped boxes. An example is illustrated in Figure I.5.

The *value stream map* is another useful process map. It is somewhat more complex because it displays information such as inventory, personnel, cycle times, batch size, and so on, at each station. The value stream map has proven useful in highlighting waste in

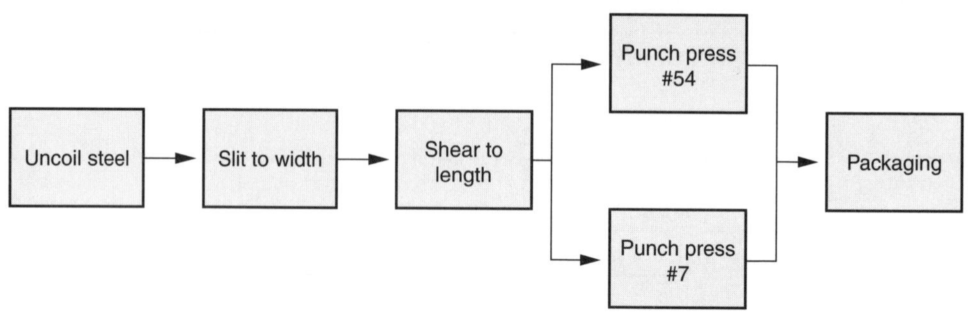

Figure I.3 Flowchart for a steel forming process.

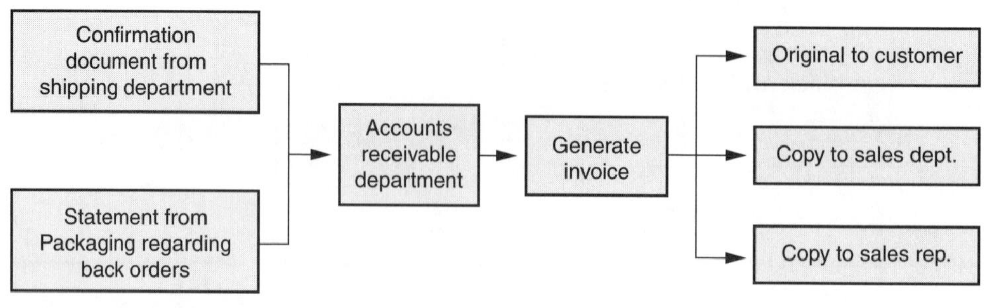

Figure I.4 Flowchart for an invoicing process.

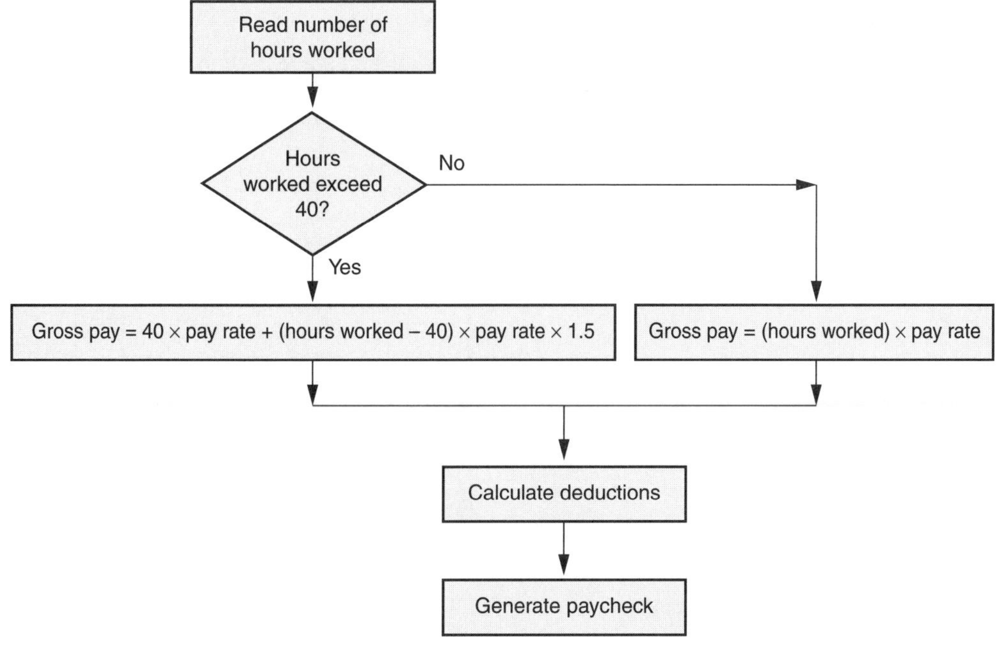

Figure I.5 Flowchart for calculating weekly paycheck.

processes. (For more information, see Rother.[2]) The advantage of process maps is that they provide overall process information and help maintain focus on process improvement.

3. Check Sheets

A *check sheet* is used to record the occurrence of defined events. The user is typically observing the events in real time but may be examining products or data produced earlier. As an event is observed, a tally mark is placed in the appropriate area on the sheet. An example of a tally sheet is shown in Figure I.6. Suppose a quality technician inspected a batch of finished products and recorded the observed defects as shown in Figure I.6. The advantages of the check sheet in this case are:

- It emphasizes facts, not opinion. (In this example, it would help dispel the opinion that incomplete lenses are a big problem.)
- It may show groupings to be investigated. (In this case, why are most cracked covers black and all fogged lenses green?)
- Rows and columns can be easily totaled to obtain useful subtotals.
- It requires a valid definition of the various defects. (Exactly what is a fogged lens? and so on)

Some check sheet categories are time related. An example is shown in Figure I.7. Time-related check sheets sometimes show trends to be investigated. In this example, an interesting trend occurs in the "TV Guide missing" category. Something worth studying appears to have happened on July 8, also.

Line 12 Dec. 4, 2001	Lens Color Red	 Green	 Black
Cracked cover	II	I	IIIIII
Fogged		IIII	
Pitted	IIII	III	IIIII
Incomplete	I		I

Figure I.6 Defects table.

Deficiencies notes July 5–11, 1999	5	6	7	8	9	10	11
Towels incorrectly stacked				IIIII			
Soap or shampoo missing	IIIIIIII	IIIIIII		IIIII			
TV Guide missing		II	III	IIIII	IIIIIII	IIIIIIIII	I
Mint missing from pillow	I		I	IIIII		I	
Toilet paper not folded into V			I	IIIII			

Figure I.7 A time-related check sheet.

4. Pareto Diagrams

Process improvement teams may need help in prioritizing activities. The *Pareto diagram* is a useful tool for this purpose. This diagram is based on the theory that the vast majority of problems are caused by a few sources. Suppose the following data have been collected on power outages:

Cause	Number of Occurrences	% of Occurrences
Human error	5	10
Capacitor failure	2	4
Animals	33	65
Transformer leaks	3	6
Weather	8	16
Total	**51**	**101**

A Pareto diagram of this data would list the causes on the horizontal axis and the percent of occurrences on the vertical axis. The causes are listed in order of decreasing number of occurrences. The Pareto diagram is shown in Figure I.8.

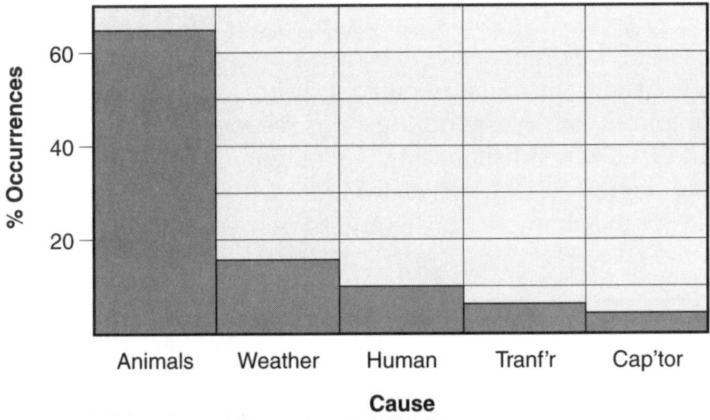

Figure I.8 Pareto diagram of power outage causes.

The Pareto diagram shows that the people working to reduce the number of occurrences should put their main efforts into preventing outages caused by animals. If they expended a lot of time and money preventing transformer leakage and were able to eliminate it completely as a cause of power outage, it would still solve only about six percent of the occurrences.

A Pareto diagram often shows one source as the overwhelming cause of defects. In some cases it may be necessary to do some creative grouping to obtain a single cause that accounts for the bulk of the problem. Suppose a team is seeking to reduce the number of defective valve stems from a multi-stage machining operation. They gather the following data on the type of defect observed:

Type	Percent
1. Scratched shaft	12%
2. ID undersize	4%
3. ID oversize	6%
4. Dented chamfer	7%
5. Length oversize	5%
6. Length undersize	8%
7. Nicks on shift	7%
8. OD oversize	3%
9. OD undersize	4%
10. Scratched face	7%
11. Surface finish	6%
12. Porosity	1%
13. Material hardness	2%
14. Gouges in knob area	5%
15. Nonconcentricity	3%
16. Bent shaft	5%
17. Tapered shaft	4%
18. Out of round	5%
19. Abrasion of head	6%
Total	**100%**

The resulting Pareto diagram is shown in Figure I.9. No single cause has an overwhelming percent of the occurrences. The team might look for grouping schemes that produce a single group with a large percent. In this case, suppose that, upon further study, the team found that "Mishandling" was responsible for all defects in categories 1, 4, 7, 10, 14, and 19. Then "Mishandling" accounts for 44 percent of the defects and the resulting Pareto diagram is illustrated in Figure I.10. It suggests that the team should give a high priority to solving the mishandling problems, labeled "M" in the figure.

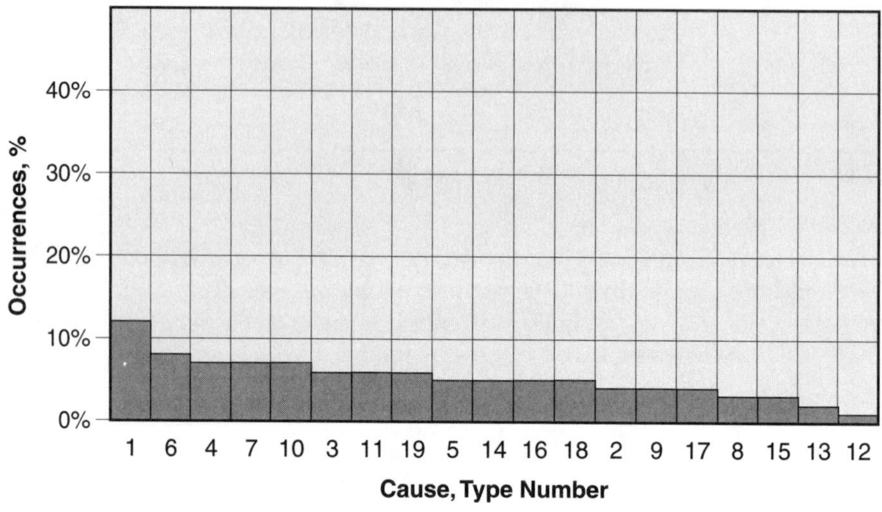

Figure I.9 Pareto diagram of valve stem defects.

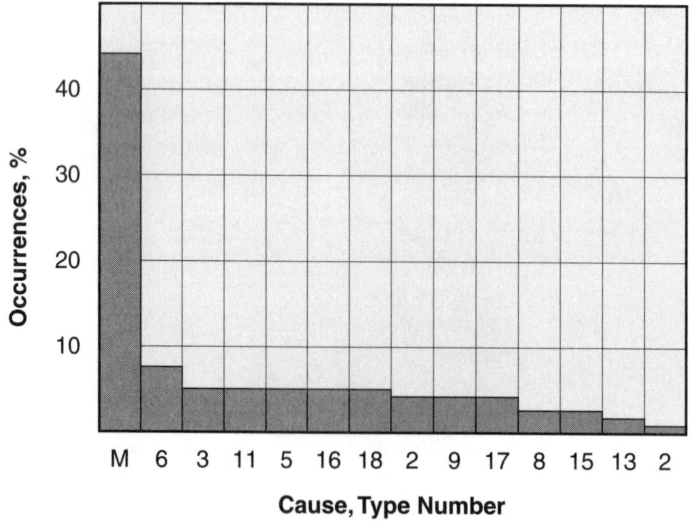

Figure I.10 Revised Pareto diagram.

5. Scatter Diagrams

When several causes for a problem have been proposed it may be necessary to collect some data to help determine which is the root cause. One way to analyze such data is with a *scatter diagram.* In this technique, measurements are taken for various levels of the variables suspected as being the cause. Then each variable is plotted against the measured value of the problem to get a rough idea of correlation or association. For example, suppose an injection molding machine is producing parts with pitted surfaces. The following causes have been suggested:

Mold pressure
Coolant temperature
Mold cool down time
Mold squeeze time

Values of each of these variables as well as the quality of the surface finish were collected on 10 batches. The data:

Batch No.	Mold Pres.	Coolant Temp.	Cooldown Time	Squeeze Time	Surface Finish
1	220	102.5	14.5	.72	37
2	200	100.8	16.0	.91	30
3	410	102.6	15.0	.90	40
4	350	101.5	16.2	.68	32
5	490	100.8	16.8	.85	27
6	360	101.4	14.8	.76	35
7	370	102.5	14.3	.94	43
8	330	99.8	16.5	.71	23
9	280	100.8	15.0	.65	32
10	400	101.2	16.6	.96	30

Four graphs have been plotted in Figure I.11. In each graph, Surface Finish is on the vertical axis. The first graph plots Mold Pressure against Surface Finish. Batch #1 has a Mold Pressure of 220 and a surface finish of 37. Therefore one dot is plotted at 220 in the horizontal direction and 37 in the vertical direction. One each graph, one point is plotted for each batch.

If the points tend to fall along a straight line, this indicates linear correlation or association between the two variables. If the points tend to closely follow a curve rather than a straight line, there may be a nonlinear correlation. Note that high correlation does not imply a cause-and-effect relationship. A low correlation, however, does provide evidence that there is no such relationship. What variables can be eliminated as probable causes based on the above analysis?

The closer the points are to forming a straight line, the greater the linear correlation coefficient, denoted by the letter r. A positive correlation means that the line tips up on its right end. A negative correlation means that the line tips down on its right end. If all the points fall exactly on a straight line that tips up on the right end, $r = +1$. If all the points fall on a straight line that tips down on the right end, $r = -1$. The value of r is always between –1 and +1 inclusive. This may be stated symbolically as $-1 \leq r \leq +1$.

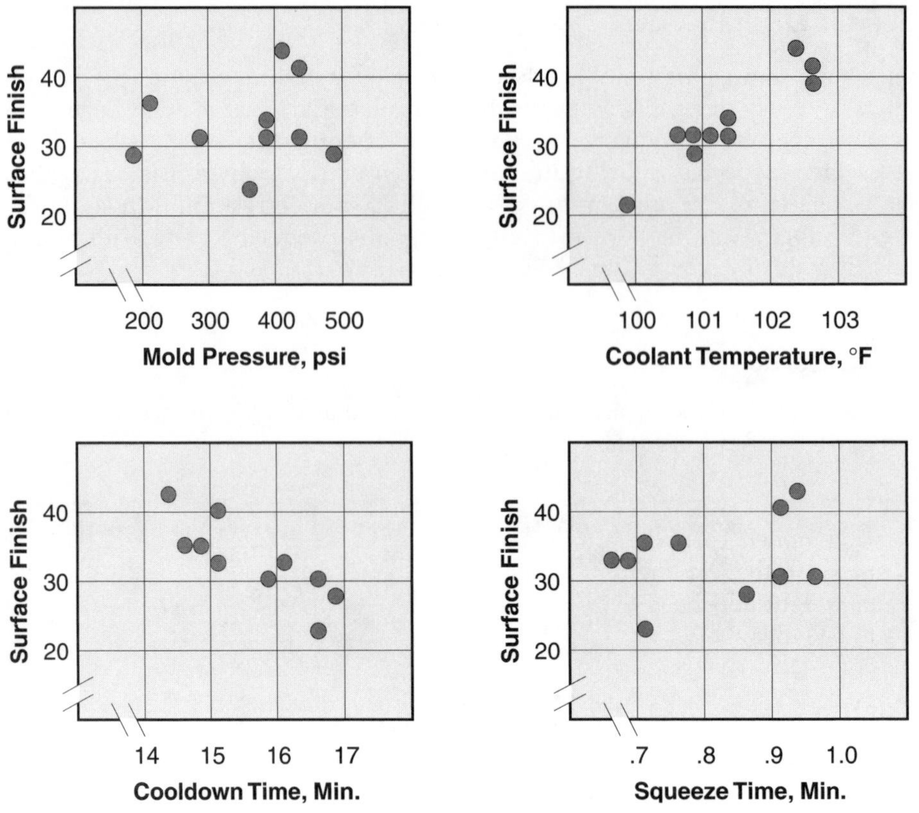

Figure I.11 Scatter diagrams.

Most authorities suggest that the first step in analyzing a set of data for correlation is to construct a scatter diagram. If the points on this diagram tend to form a straight line then it makes sense to calculate the value of *r*. For example, suppose a relationship is suspected between the ambient temperature of a paint booth and the paint viscosity. To check that suspicion, four readings are taken, although in an actual application much more data would be desirable.

Temperature, °C	10	15	20	15
Viscosity, centipoises/100	2	3	5	4

The first step is to plot the data as shown in Figure I.12 to see if it seems reasonable to approximate it with a straight line. Although a straight line can't be drawn through these four points, the trend looks linear. The next step would be to calculate the coefficient of linear correlation. This can be done using the statistical functions on a spreadsheet. Another alternative is to use the fairly complicated formula for *r*. (For a worked example, see Benbow, et al., chapter 14, page 354.)

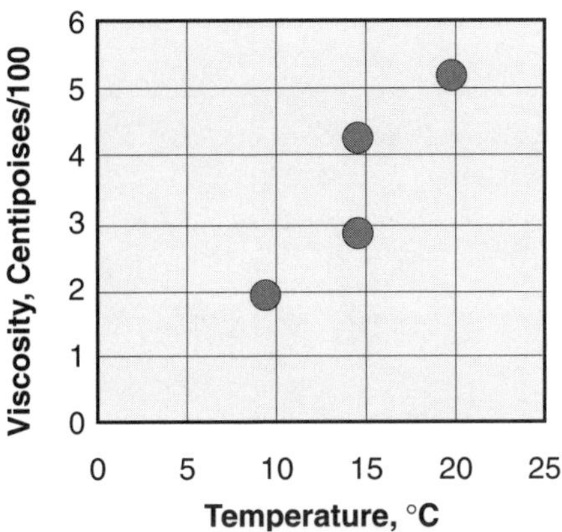

Figure I.12 Scatter plot.

As mentioned earlier, the existence of a high correlation between two variables does not mean that one causes the other. There is, for example, a positive correlation between weight and height for adult males. That does not mean that a person who wants to be taller should put on some weight to accomplish this goal.

6. Control Charts

One of the disadvantages of many of the tools discussed up to this point is that they have no time reference. The chart may clearly demonstrate that a process had a problem but gives no clue as to when the problem occurred. This section will illustrate a number of time-related techniques culminating in control charts.

The Run Chart

If a specific measurement is collected on a regular basis, say every 15 minutes, and plotted on a time scale, the resultant diagram is called a *run chart*. An example of a run chart is shown in Figure I.13.

One of the problems of the run chart is that the natural variation in the process and in the measurement system tend to cause the graph to go up and down when no real change is occurring. One way to smooth out some of this "noise" in the process is to take readings from several consecutive parts and plot the average of the readings. The result is called an *average chart*. An example is shown in Figure I.14.

One of the dangers of the average chart is that it can make the process look better than it really is. For example, note that the average of the five 3:00 readings is .790, which is well within the tolerance of .780–.795, even though every one of the five readings is outside the tolerance. Therefore, tolerance limits should never be drawn on an average chart. To help alert the chart user that the readings are widely dispersed, the average chart usually has a range chart included as part of the same document. The range for each set of points is found by subtracting the smallest number in the set from the largest number in the set. The data from Figure I.14 are used in the average and range chart illustrated in Figure I.15. Note that the sharp jump in the value of the range for the 3:00 readings would warn the user of this chart that the dispersion of the readings has drastically increased.

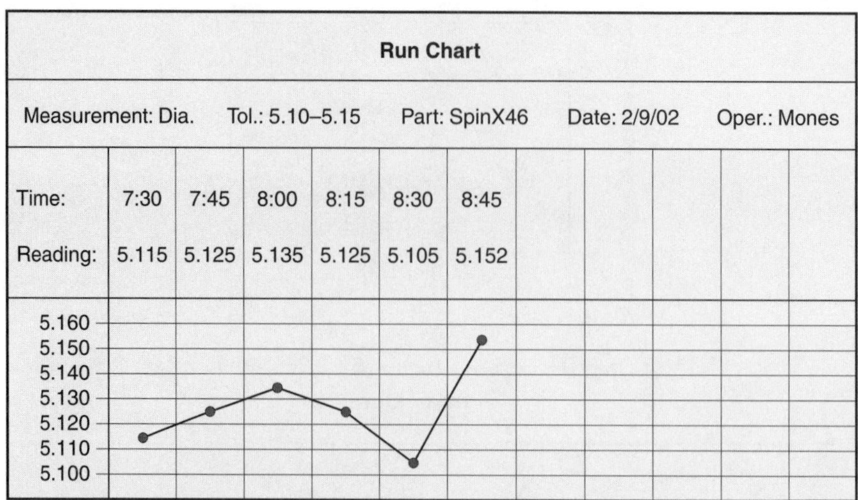

Figure I.13 Example of run chart with first six points plotted.

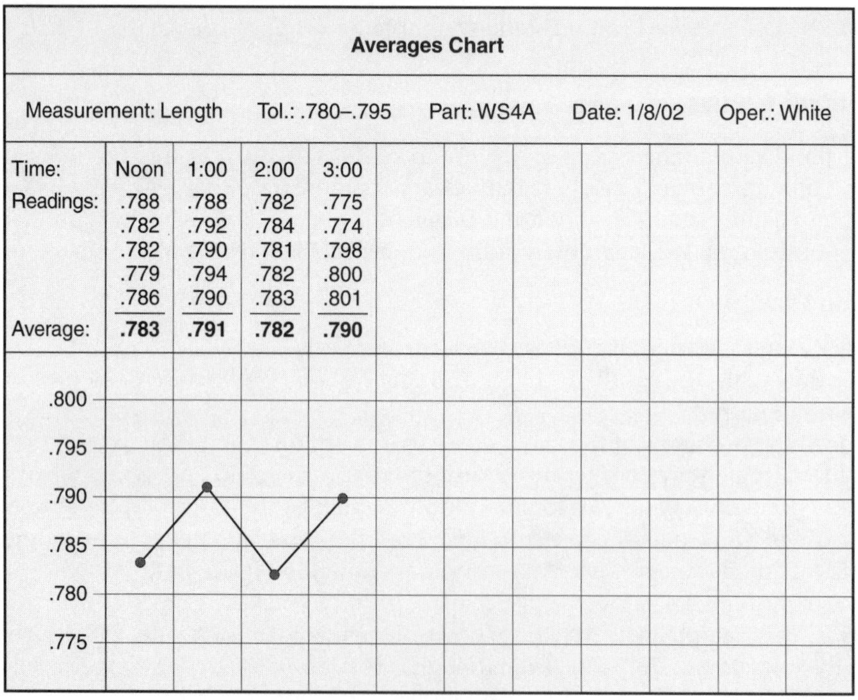

Averages Chart

Measurement: Length Tol.: .780–.795 Part: WS4A Date: 1/8/02 Oper.: White

Time:	Noon	1:00	2:00	3:00
Readings:	.788	.788	.782	.775
	.782	.792	.784	.774
	.782	.790	.781	.798
	.779	.794	.782	.800
	.786	.790	.783	.801
Average:	**.783**	**.791**	**.782**	**.790**

.800
.795
.790
.785
.780
.775

Figure I.14 Example of averages chart with first four points plotted.

None of the charts listed so far are "control charts." The averages and range chart requires the user to notice when the range is "too high." The control chart that uses averages and ranges differs from this chart in that it has control limits drawn on the chart. When a point falls outside these limits the user is alerted that the process has

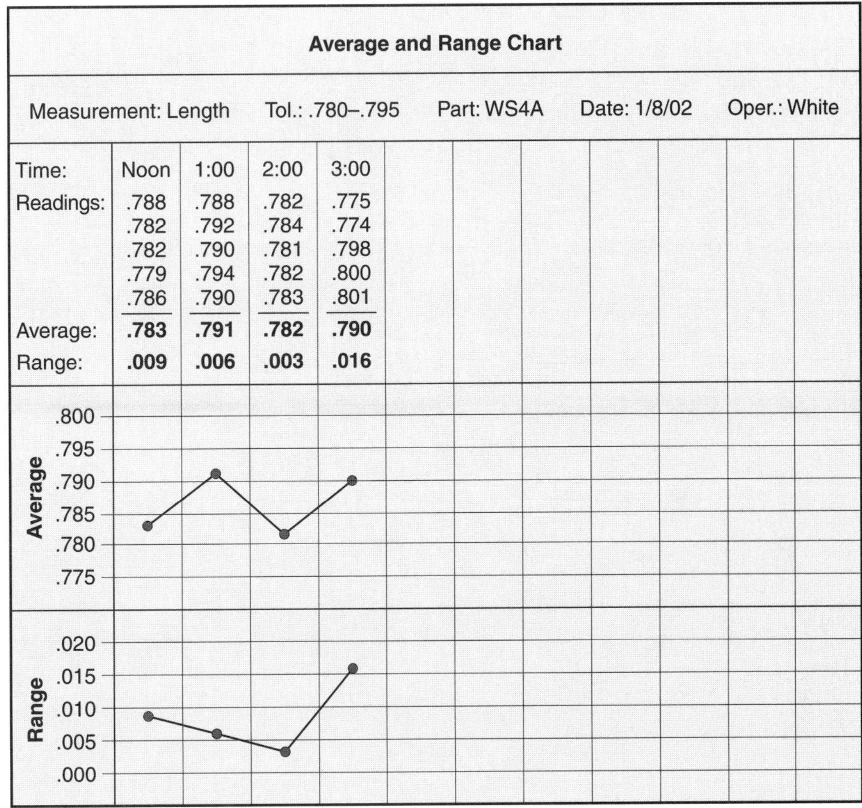

Figure I.15 Example of an average and range chart.

changed and appropriate action should be taken. The control chart using averages and ranges is called the X-bar and R ($\overline{X}$ and R) chart and is illustrated in Figure I.16. The data used in Figure I.16 are taken from Figure I.15. It is conventional to draw the control limits with dashed lines or in a contrasting color. The average value is usually drawn with a solid line. Control limits help the user of the chart make statistically sound decisions about the process. This is because the limits are drawn so that a very high percentage of the points should fall between them. In the case of the averages chart, about 99.7 percent of the points from a stable process should fall between the upper and lower control limits. This means that when a point falls outside the limits, there is approximately 0.3 percent probability that this could have happened if the process hasn't changed. Therefore, points outside the control limits are very strong indicators that the process has changed. Control charts, then, can be used by process operators as real-time monitoring tools.

There are a number of events that are very unlikely to occur unless the process has changed and thus serve as statistical indicators of process change. The lists vary somewhat from textbook to textbook but usually include something like those shown in Table I.3.

When one of these events occurs on a control chart, the process operator needs to take appropriate action. Sometimes this may entail a process adjustment. Sometimes

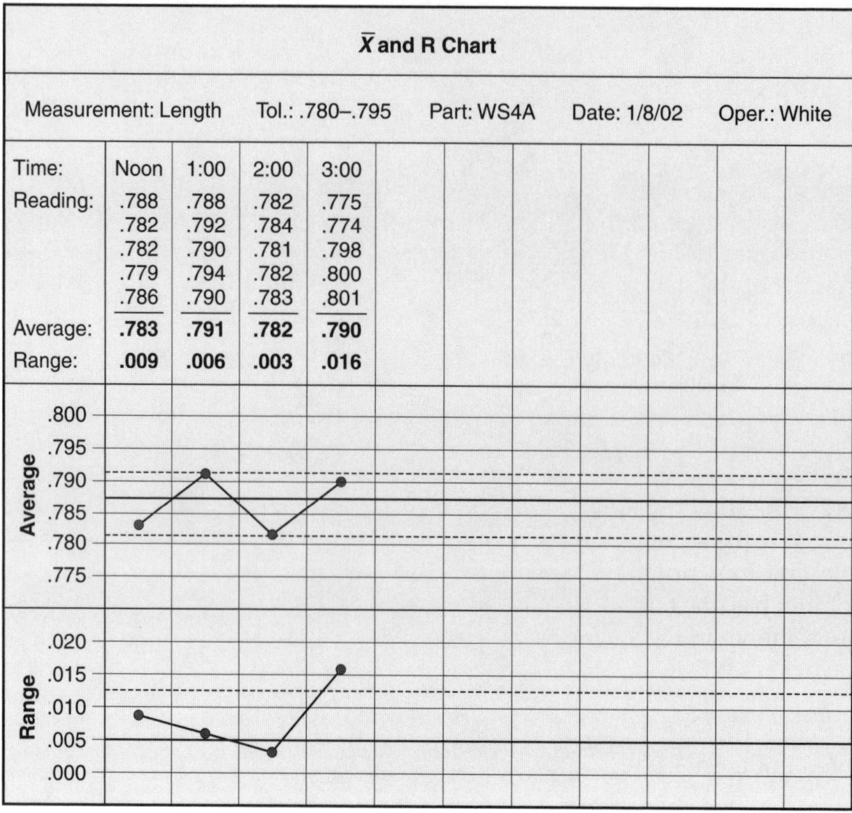

Figure I.16 $\overline{X}$ and R chart.

Table I.3 Control chart indicators of process change.

1. A point above the upper control limit or below the lower control limit
2. Seven successive points above (or below) the average line
3. Seven successive points trending up (or down)
4. Middle one-third of the chart includes more than 90% or fewer than 40% of the points after at least 25 points have been plotted
5. Nonrandom patterns

the appropriate action is to stop the process. In some situations the operator should increase watchfulness, perhaps taking readings every few minutes instead of every hour, for instance. The important issue is that the chart has provided a statistical signal that there is a high probability that the process has changed. Further details on the construction and use of various control charts is provided in section II.F.

7. Histograms

The following numbers were obtained by measuring the diameters of 27 drilled holes.

.127 .125 .123 .123 .120 .124 .126 .122 .123 .125 .121 .123 .122 .125

.124 .122 .123 .123 .126 .121 .124 .121 .124 .122 .126 .125 .123

What is known about the drilling process just by looking at the data? For one thing, the smallest diameter is .120 and the largest is .127. This gives an idea of the spread or "dispersion" of the data. The values seem to be centered around .123 or .124, which is related to the "central tendency" of the data. Sometimes it helps to make a diagram from the data. A good first step is to list the possible values from smallest to largest in a column. In the adjacent column a tally mark is made for each number in the original data set.

The first step is shown in Figure I.17a. The possible values of the hole diameter are listed in the first column and a tally mark is shown opposite the .127 because the first number in the data set is .127. The next step will be to put a tally mark opposite the .125 since it is the second number in the data set. Figure I.17b shows the tally column after the first four numbers have been tallied. This procedure is continued until the tally column has one tally mark for each number in the original set. The completed tally column is shown in Figure I.17c.

The next step is to count the number of tally marks in each row and put this number in the next column. This column is labeled "frequency" because it shows how frequently each number appears. The result is called a *frequency distribution* and is illustrated in Figure I.18a.

Value	Tally
.120	
.121	
.122	
.123	
.124	
.125	
.126	
.127	I

a) The first step

Value	Tally
.120	
.121	
.122	
.123	II
.124	
.125	I
.126	
.127	I

b) After tallying the first four numbers

Value	Tally
.120	I
.121	III
.122	IIII
.123	IIIIIII
.124	IIII
.125	IIII
.126	III
.127	I

c) Completed tally column

Figure I.17 Making a tally column.

If a bar graph such as that shown in Figure I.18b is drawn, the result is called a *histogram,* or more precisely a *frequency histogram.* In this text, the vertical axis of a histogram displays the frequency and the horizontal axis represents measured values.

Suppose this data is to be displayed on a frequency histogram:

46, 65, 55, 72, 108, 33, 70, 68, 51, 44, 110, 84, 52, 75, 106, 62, 90, 71, 86,

54, 98, 80, 73, 39, 101, 64, 59, 82, 87, 94, 57, 32, 61, 78, 38, 63, 49, 87, 63

If each bar represents just one value, most bars would have a frequency of zero or one and there would be a very large number of bars. An alternative approach would be to group the data. One grouping scheme would have 10 possible values in each group. The first group could be 30–39 and the following groups 40–49, 50–59, and so on. The tally sheet, frequency distribution, and histogram are shown in Figure I.19.

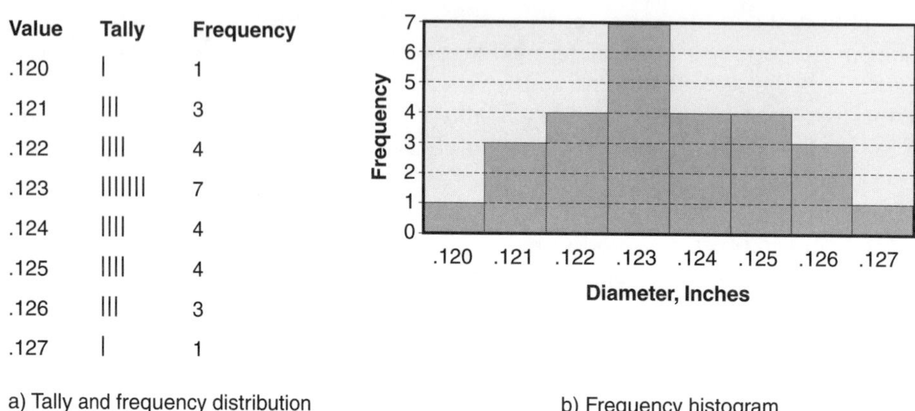

Value	Tally	Frequency
.120	I	1
.121	III	3
.122	IIII	4
.123	IIIIIII	7
.124	IIII	4
.125	IIII	4
.126	III	3
.127	I	1

a) Tally and frequency distribution

b) Frequency histogram

Figure I.18 Frequency distribution and frequency histogram.

Value	Tally	Frequency
30–39	IIII	4
40–49	III	3
50–59	IIIIII	6
60–69	IIIIIII	7
70–79	IIIIII	6
80–89	IIIII	5
90–99	IIII	4
100–109	III	3
110–119	I	1

Frequency
0
2
4
6
8
30s 40s 50s 60s 70s 80s 90s 100s 110s

Figure I.19 Frequency histogram using grouped data.

Endnotes

1. D. K. Gordon, "Where Does Quality Begin?" *ASQ Quality Progress* (March 2002).
2. M. Rother and J. Shook, *Learning to See* (Brookline, MA: The Lean Enterprise, 1998).

References

Benbow, D. W., et. al. *Certified Quality Engineer Handbook.* 2nd ed. Milwaukee: ASQ Quality Press, 2002.

Berger, R. W., and T. H. Hart. *Statistical Process Control: A Guide for Implementation*. Milwaukee: ASQC Quality Press, 1986.

Brassard, M., and D. Ritter. *The Memory Jogger II.* Methuen, MA: GOAL/QPC, 1994.

Montgomery, D. C. *Introduction to Statistical Quality Control*. 4th ed. New York: John Wiley & Sons, 2001.

Pitt, H. *SPC for the Rest of Us*. Reading, MA: Addison Wesley, 1994.

II

Statistical Techniques

A. BASIC STATISTICS

The frequency histograms illustrated in chapter I show information about the data set that is not immediately obvious from the raw numbers themselves. This is especially true if the data set has a large number of values. The frequency histogram in Figure I.18 shows that the *spread* of the data is from .120 to .127 and the data are *centered* around .123, with a *shape* something like a pyramid. These three attributes—spread, center, and shape—are key to understanding the data and the process that generated them.

1. Measures of Central Tendency

The values that represent the center of a data set are called, rather awkwardly, *measures of central tendency.* There are three measures of central tendency: mean, median, and mode.

Mean

Mean is statistical jargon for the more common word "average." It is calculated by finding the total of the values in the data set and dividing by the number of values. The symbol used for "total" is the Greek capital sigma, Σ. The values of the data set are symbolized by x's and the number of values is usually referred to as n. The symbol for mean is an x with a bar above it ($\bar{x}$). This symbol is pronounced "x bar." The formula for mean is:

$$\bar{x} = \frac{\Sigma x}{n}$$

This formula tells the user to obtain $\bar{x}$ by adding all the x's and dividing the sum by n, the number of values. In other words, what is commonly known as "finding the average."

Example: Find the mean of this data set: 4 7 8 2 3 3 2 1 6 7 4 3 9

There are 13 members in the data set so the mean is the total divided by 13:

$$\bar{x} = \frac{\Sigma x}{n} = \frac{4+7+8+2+3+3+2+1+6+7+4+3+9}{13} \approx 3.8$$

The ≈ symbol is used to indicate "approximately equal" because the value has been rounded to 3.8. It is common practice to calculate the mean to one more digit of accuracy than that of the original data.

Median

The *median* is the value that has approximately 50 percent of the values above it and 50 percent below. To find the median, first sort the data in ascending order. If there are an odd number of values, the median is the middle value of the sorted list. If there are an even number of values, the median is the mean of the two middle values.

Example: The list in the previous example is first sorted into ascending order: 1 2 2 3 3 3 4 4 6 7 7 8 9

Since there are 13 values, the median is the seventh value in the sorted set, in this case four.

Example: Find the median of the six element set: 12.7 12.9 13.5 15.0 15.0 17.2

Since the list is already sorted and has an even number of values, the median is the mean of the two middle values, in this case the mean of 13.5 and 15.0. The median of this set is 14.35.

Mode

The *mode* is the value that occurs most often in a data set. If no value occurs more than once, the set has no mode. If there is a tie for the value that occurs most often, the set will have more than one mode.

Example: For the data set 1 2 2 3 3 3 3 4 4 6 7 7 8 9, the mode is 3 because this value occurs most often, four times in this example.

Example: For the data set 1 2 2 3 3 4 4 6 7 7 8 9, there are four modes because four values each occur twice. The four modes are 2, 3, 4, and 7.

Modes appear as high points or peaks on histograms. If a histogram has two peaks, it is referred to as *bimodal* even if the peaks aren't exactly the same height. A bimodal histogram usually indicates that a process variable had two different values. For example, the data might include values collected when two different raw materials were used. A bimodal histogram often presents an opportunity to reduce variation by using more consistent raw materials, for instance.

2. Measures of Dispersion

The *spread,* also called the *dispersion* or the *variation,* may be measured using the *range,* which is defined as the largest value minus the smallest value.

Range = (largest value) – (smallest value)

Example: For the data set 15.7 12.9 13.5 15.0 15.0 13.2
the range = 15.7 – 12.9 = 2.8

The range is often plotted on control charts as discussed in chapter I.

One of the disadvantages of using the range as a measure of dispersion is that it uses only two of the values from the data set: the largest and the smallest. If the data set is large, the range does not make use of much of the information contained in the data. For this and other reasons, the *standard deviation* is frequently used to measure dispersion. The value of the standard deviation may be approximated using numbers from the control chart. This method is explained in part 6, "Process Capability," of section F of this chapter. The standard deviation can also be found by entering the values of the data set into a calculator that has a standard deviation key. See the calculator manual for appropriate steps.

Although the standard deviation is seldom calculated by hand, the following discussion provides some insight into its meaning.

Suppose it is necessary to estimate the standard deviation of a very large data set. One approach would be to randomly select a sample from that set. Suppose the randomly selected sample consists of the values 2, 7, 9, and 2. Naturally, it would be better to use a larger sample, but this will illustrate the steps involved. It is customary to refer to the sample values as "x-values" and list them in a column headed by the letter x. The first step, as illustrated in Figure II.1a, is to calculate the sum of that column Σx, and the mean of the column $\bar{x}$. Recall that $\bar{x} = \Sigma x/n$, where n is the sample size, four in this case. The next step as illustrated in Figure II.1b is to calculate the deviation of each of the sample values from the mean. This is done by subtracting $\bar{x}$ from each of the sample values. In this example, the value of $\bar{x}$ is five, so five is subtracted from each of the sample values. The values in this column are called the *deviations from the mean*. The total of the $x - \bar{x}$ column will typically be zero, so this total is not of much use. In Figure II.1c a third column, labeled $(x - \bar{x})^2$, has been added. The values in this column are obtained by squaring each of the four values in the previous column. Recall that the square of a negative number is positive. The values in this column are called the *squares of the deviations from the mean*, and the sum of this column is the *sum of the squares of the deviations from the mean*. The next step is to divide this sum by $n - 1$. Recall that $n = 4$ in this example, so the result is $38/3 \approx 12.7$. This quantity is called the *variance* and it's rather ugly formula is:

$$\text{Sample variance} = s^2 = \frac{\Sigma(x-\bar{x})^2}{n-1}$$

x
2
7
9
2
Σ 20

a) Step 1: Find Σx and $\bar{x}$

x	$x - \bar{x}$
2	2 − 5 = −3
7	7 − 5 = 2
9	9 − 5 = 4
2	2 − 5 = −3
Σ 20	0

b) Step 2: Form $x - \bar{x}$ column by subtracting $\bar{x}$ from each x-value

x	$x - \bar{x}$	$(x - \bar{x})^2$
2	−3	9
7	2	4
9	4	16
2	−3	9
Σ 20	0	38

c) Step 3: Form the $(x - \bar{x})^2$ column by squaring the values in the $(x - \bar{x})$ column

Figure II.1 Standard deviation calculation.

One disadvantage of the variance is that, as the formula indicates, it is measured in units that are the square of the units of the original data set. That is, if the x-values are in inches, the variance is in square inches. If the x-values are in degrees Celsius, the variance is in square degrees Celsius, whatever that may be. For many applications, quality professionals need to use a measure of dispersion that is in the same units as the original data. For this reason, the preferred measure of dispersion is the square root of the variance, which is called the *standard deviation.* Its formula is:

$$\text{Sample standard deviation} = s = \sqrt{\frac{\Sigma(x-\bar{x})^2}{n-1}}$$

As indicated at the beginning of this example, the sample standard deviation is used to estimate the standard deviation of a data set by using a sample from that data set. In some situations it may be possible to use the entire data set rather than a sample. Statisticians refer to the entire data set as the *population* and the standard deviation is called the population standard deviation, symbolized by the small case Greek sigma, σ. It is common to use capital N to refer to the number of values in the population. The only difference in the formula is that the divisor in the fraction is N rather than $n - 1$.

$$\text{Population standard deviation} = \sigma = \sqrt{\frac{\Sigma(x-\bar{x})^2}{N}}$$

When using the standard deviation function on a calculator, care should be taken to use the appropriate key. Unfortunately there is not a universal labeling agreement among calculator manufacturers. Some label the sample standard deviation key σ_{n-1} and the population standard deviation key σ_n, while others use S_x and σ_x. Consult the calculator manual for details. Try entering the values 2, 7, 9, 2 in a calculator and verify that the sample standard deviation rounds to 12.7 and the population standard deviation is 9.5.

Just what use is the standard deviation? One application is the comparison of two data sets. Suppose two machines can produce a certain shaft diameter. Sample parts from the two machines are collected and the diameters are measured and their sample standard deviations are calculated. Suppose the sample standard deviation of the parts from machine A is much smaller than the sample standard deviation of the parts from machine B. This means that the diameters from machine A have less variation, or smaller dispersion, that those produced by machine B and, other things being equal, machine A would be the preferred machine for these parts. The sample standard deviation is used rather than the population standard deviation because the population would be all the parts of this type that the machine would ever produce. In most practical applications the sample standard deviation is the appropriate choice. In fact, some calculators do not have a population standard deviation key.

Notice that as the sample size gets large, the difference between the values of the sample standard deviation and the population standard deviation becomes quite small. For instance, if the sample size is 300, the divisor in the sample standard deviation formula is 299, and in the population standard deviation formula it is 300.

The standard deviation also has applications to statistical inference, control charts, and process capability that will be discussed later in this chapter.

B. OBJECTIVES OF STATISTICAL QUALITY CONTROL

The goal of any quality activity is to meet the needs of the customer. Statistical quality control consists of a set of tools and activities that contributes to this goal through the following objectives:

- Reducing variation
- Improving understanding of products and processes
- Improving product and process design
- Monitoring processes in real time
- Making statistically valid decisions

The statistical quality control (SQC) tools achieve these objectives by collecting and analyzing data. Figure II.2 depicts SQC as a machine that uses data as an input and has information as its output. The SQC tools squeeze the information out of the raw data.

When setting out to improve a process, the first step is to form a data collection plan. The general rule is to collect as much data as possible, recognizing that data collection costs money. In some cases historical data may be available, but they should be used with caution unless information is available on the conditions under which they were collected. Once data have been collected, they are often placed on a histogram and the mean and standard deviation calculated. The histogram provides a visual picture of the variation and center of the process, while the mean and standard deviation provide numerical values for comparison. Other charts that are often used include scatter diagrams, run charts, and control charts. The use of these charts is discussed in section D of chapter I and section F of this chapter. In addition, process capability and gage repeatability and reproducibility (R&R) can be calculated using the SQC techniques discussed in section F of this chapter and section B of chapter III. The statistical inference techniques discussed in section E of this chapter can be used when more sophisticated analysis is needed.

These and other statistical quality control tools are available in various SQC software packages and in some spreadsheets such as Excel or Lotus. These spreadsheets can be used to find values of various statistical distributions, including the normal distribution.

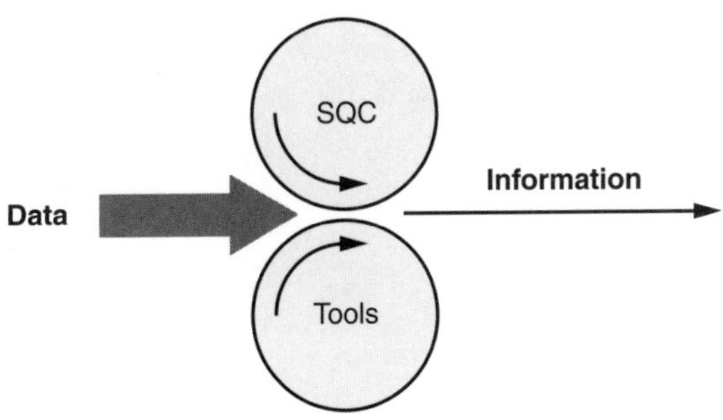

Figure II.2 Function of statistical quality control tools.

Another use of SQC is lot inspection, using the sampling techniques discussed in section H of chapter IV. These techniques determine whether to accept or reject an entire lot or batch by inspecting a sample from the lot.

C. ELEMENTARY CONCEPTS OF PROBABILITY

The probability that a particular event occurs is a number between 0 and 1 inclusive. For example, if a lot consisting of 100 parts has four defectives, we would say the probability of randomly drawing a defective is .04 or 4 percent. Symbolically this is written P(defective) = .04. The word "random" implies that each part has an equal chance of being drawn. If the lot had no defectives, the probability would be 0 or 0 percent. If the lot had 100 defectives, the probability would be 1 or 100 percent.

1. Basic Probability Rules

Complementation Rule: The probability that an event A will not occur is 1 – (the probability that A does occur). Stated symbolically, P(not A) = 1 – P(A). Some texts use symbols for "not A" including –A, ~A, and sometimes A with a bar over it.

Special Addition Rule: Suppose a card is randomly selected from a standard 52 card deck. What is the probability that the card is a club? Since there are 13 clubs, P(♣) = 13/52 = .25. What is the probability that the card is either a club or a spade? Since there are 26 cards that are either clubs or spades, P(♣ or ♠) = 26/52 = .5. Therefore it appears that P(♣ or ♠)= P(♣) + P(♠) which, generalized, becomes the special addition rule:

$$P(A \text{ or } B) = P(A) + P(B)$$

Warning: Use only if A and B cannot occur simultaneously.

The General Addition Rule: What is the probability of selecting either a king or a club? Using the special addition rule, P(K or ♣) = P(K) + P(♣) = 4/52 + 13/52 = 17/52. This is incorrect because there are only sixteen cards that are either kings or clubs (the thirteen clubs plus K♦, K♥, and K♠). The reason that the special addition rule doesn't work here is that the two events (drawing a king and drawing a club) can occur simultaneously. We'll denote the probability that A and B both occur as P(A&B). This leads to the General Addition Rule:

$$P(A \text{ or } B) = P(A) + P(B) - P(A\&B)$$

The Special Addition Rule has the advantage of being somewhat simpler but its disadvantage is that it is not valid when A and B can occur simultaneously. The General Addition Rule, although more complex, is always valid. For the above example:

$$P(K \,\&\, \clubsuit) = 1/52$$

since only one card is both a K and a club. To complete the example:

$$P(K \text{ or } \clubsuit) = P(K) + P(\clubsuit) - P(K \,\&\, \clubsuit) = 4/52 + 13/52 - 1/52 = 16/52$$

Two events that can't occur simultaneously are called *mutually exclusive*. So the warning for the special addition rule is sometimes stated as follows: "Use only if events A and B are mutually exclusive."

Contingency Tables

Suppose each part in a lot is one of four colors (red, yellow, green, blue) and one of three sizes (small, medium, large). A tool that displays these attributes is the contingency table:

	Red	Yellow	Green	Blue
Small	16	21	14	19
Medium	12	11	19	15
Large	18	12	21	14

Each part belongs in exactly one column and each part belongs in exactly one row. So each part belongs in exactly one of the 12 cells. When columns and rows are totaled, the table becomes:

	Red	Yellow	Green	Blue	Totals
Small	16	21	14	19	**70**
Medium	12	11	19	15	**57**
Large	18	12	21	14	**65**
Totals	**46**	**44**	**54**	**48**	**192**

Note that 192 can be computed in two ways. If one of the 192 parts is randomly selected, find the probability that the part is red.

Solution: P(red) = 46/192 ≈ .240

Find the probability that the part is small.

Solution: P(small) = 70/192 ≈ .365

Find the probability that the part is red and small.

Solution: Since there are 16 parts that are both red and small, P(red & small) = 16/192 ≈ .083

Find the probability that the part is red or small.

Solution: Since it is possible for a part to be both red and small simultaneously, the General Addition Rule must be used:

P(red or small) = P(red) + P(small) – P(red & small) = 46/192 + 70/192 – 16/192 ≈ .521

Find the probability that the part is red or yellow.

Solution: Since no part can be both red and yellow simultaneously, the Special Addition Rule can be used:

P(red or yellow) = P(red) + P(yellow) = 46/192 + 44/192 ≈ .469

Notice that the General Addition Rule also could have been used:

$$P(\text{red or yellow}) = P(\text{red}) + P(\text{yellow}) - P(\text{red \& yellow}) = 46/192 + 44/192 - 0 \approx .469$$

Conditional Probability: Continuing with the above example, suppose the selected part is known to be green. With this knowledge, what is the probability that the part is large?

Solution: Since the part is located in the green column of the table, it is one of the 54 green parts. So the lower number in the probability fraction is 54. Since 21 of those 54 parts are large, P(large, given that it is green) = 21/54 ≈ .389

This is referred to as *conditional probability*. It is denoted P(large | green) and pronounced "The probability that the part is large given that it is green." It is useful to remember that the category to the right of the | in the conditional probability symbol points to the lower number in the probability fraction. Find the following probabilities:

P(small | red) *Solution:* P(small | red) = 16/46 ≈ .348

P(red | small) *Solution:* P(red | small) = 16/70 ≈ .229

P(red | green) *Solution:* P(red | green) = 0/54 = 0

A formal definition for conditional probability is:

$$P(B \mid A) = P(A \,\&\, B) \div P(A)$$

Verifying that this formula is valid in each of the above examples will aid in understanding this concept.

General Multiplication Rule

Multiplying both sides of the conditional probability formula by P(A):

$$P(A \,\&\, B) = P(A) \times P(B \mid A)$$

This is called as the General Multiplication Rule. It is useful to verify that this formula is valid using examples from the contingency table.

Independence and the Special Multiplication Rule

Consider the contingency table:

	X	Y	Z	Totals
F	17	18	14	**49**
G	18	11	16	**45**
H	25	13	18	**56**
Totals	**60**	**42**	**48**	**150**

$$P(G \mid X) = 18/60 = .300 \text{ and } P(G) = 45/150 = .300 \text{ so } P(G \mid X) = P(G)$$

The events G and X are called *statistically independent* or just *independent*. Knowing that a part is of type X does not affect the probability that it is of type G. Intuitively, two events are called independent if the occurrence of one does not affect the probability that the other occurs. The formal definition of independence: $P(B \mid A) = P(B)$. Making this substitution in the General Multiplication Rule produces the Special Multiplication Rule:

$$P(A\&B) = P(A) \times P(B)$$

Caveat: Use only if A and B are independent.

Example: A box holds 129 parts, of which six are defective. A part is randomly drawn from the box and placed in a fixture. A second part is then drawn from the box. What is the probability that the second part is defective?

The probability can't be determined directly unless the outcome of the first draw is known. In other words, the probabilities associated with successive draws depend on the outcome of previous draws. Using the symbol D_1 to denote the event that the first part is defective and G_1 to denote the event that the first part is good, and so on, here is one way to solve the problem:

There are two mutually exclusive events that can result in a defective part for the second draw: good on first draw and defective on second, or else defective on first and defective on second. Symbolically these two events are (G_1 & D_2) or else (D_1 & D_2). The first step is to find the probability for each of these events.

By the general multiplication rule:

$$P(G_1 \& D_2) = P(G_1) \times P(D_2 \mid G_1) = 123/129 \times 6/128 = 0.045$$

Also by the general multiplication rule:

$$P(D_1 \& D_2) = P(D_1) \times P(D_2 \mid D_1) = 6/129 \times 5/128 \approx 0.002$$

Using the special addition rule:

$$P(D_2) = 0.045 + 0.002 = 0.047$$

When drawing two parts, what is the probability that one will be good and one defective? Drawing one good and one defective can occur in two mutually exclusive ways:

$$P(\text{one good and one defective}) = P(G_1 \& D_2 \text{ or } G_2 \& D_1) = P(G_1 \& D_2) + P(G_2 \& D_1)$$

$$P(G_1 \& D_2) = P(G_1) \times P(D_2 \mid G_1) = 123/129 \times 6/128 \approx 0.045$$

$$P(G_2 \& D_1) = P(D_1) \times P(G_2 \mid D_1) = 6/129 \times 123/128 \approx 0.045$$

$$\text{So } P(\text{one good and one defective}) = 0.045 + 0.045 \approx 0.090$$

2. Combinations

Example: A box of 20 parts has two defectives. The quality technician inspects the box by randomly selecting two parts. What is the probability that both parts selected are defective? The general formula for this type of problem is:

$$P = \frac{\text{number of ways an event can occur}}{\text{number of possible outcomes}}$$

The "event" in this case is selecting two defectives so "number of ways an event can occur" refers to the number of ways two defective parts could be selected. There is only one way to do this since there are only two defective parts. Therefore the top number in the fraction is 1. The lower number in the fraction is the "number of possible outcomes." This refers to the number of different ways of selecting two parts from the box. This is also called the "number of combinations of two objects from a collection of 20 objects." The formula is:

number of combinations r objects from a collection of n objects $= nCr = \dfrac{n!}{r!(m-r)!}$

Note: Another symbol for number of combinations is $\binom{n}{r}$.

In this formula the exclamation mark is pronounced "factorial," so n! is pronounced "n factorial." The value of 6! is $6 \times 5 \times 4 \times 3 \times 2 \times 1 = 720$. The value of n! is the result of multiplying the first n positive whole numbers. Most scientific calculators have a factorial key, typically labeled $x!$. To calculate 6! using this key, press 6 followed by the $x!$ key. Returning to the previous example, the lower number in the fraction is the number of possible combinations of two objects from a collection of 20 objects. Substituting into this formula:

$$\binom{20}{2} = \frac{20!}{2!(20-2)!} = \frac{20!}{2!(18!)}$$

This value would be calculated by using the following sequence of calculator keystrokes:

$20x! \div (2x! \times 18x!) =$ The correct answer is 190.

The answer to the example is probability is $\dfrac{1}{190} \approx .005$.

How might this be useful in the inspection process? Suppose a supplier has shipped this box with the specification that it have no more than two defective parts. What is the probability that the supplier has met this specification? Answer $\approx$ .005.

Example: A box of 20 parts has three defectives. The quality technician inspects the box by randomly selecting two parts. What is the probability that both parts selected are defective?

The bottom term of the fraction remains the same as in the previous example. The top term is the number of combinations of two objects from a collection of three objects:

$$\binom{n}{r} = \frac{n!}{(n-r)r!} = \binom{3}{2} = \frac{3!}{(3-2)!2!} = \frac{6}{1!2!} = \frac{6}{2} = 3$$

To see that this makes sense, name the three defectives A, B, and C. The number of different two-letter combinations of these three letters is AB, AC, BC. Note that AB is not a different combination from BA because it is the same two letters. If two defectives are selected, the order in which they are selected is not significant. The answer to the probability problem has a three as its top term: P = 3/190 $\approx$ .016.

An important thing to remember: *Combinations are used when order is not significant.*

Note: Calculators have an upper limit to the value that can use the $x!$ key. If a problem requires a higher factorial, use the statistical function on a spreadsheet program such as Excel. It is interesting to observe that a human can calculate the value of some factorial problems that a calculator can't.

Example: Find $\frac{1000!}{997!}$. Most calculators can't handle 1000!

But humans know that the terms of this fraction can be written:

$$\frac{1000!}{997!} = \frac{1000 \times 999 \times 998 \times 997 \times 996 \times 995 \times 994 \text{ and so on}}{997 \times 996 \times 995 \times 994 \text{ and so on}}$$

The factors in the bottom term cancel out all but the first three factors in the top term so the answer is $1000 \times 999 \times 998$ which, unfortunately, most of us need a calculator to calculate.

3. Permutations

With combinations, the order of the objects doesn't matter. Permutations are very similar except that the order does matter.

Example: A box has 20 parts labeled A through T. Two parts are randomly selected. What is the probability that the two parts are A and T in that order? The general formula applies:

$$P = \frac{\text{number of ways an event can occur}}{\text{number of possible outcomes}}$$

The bottom term of the fraction is the number of orderings or permutations of two objects from a collection of 20 objects. The general formula:

Number of permutations of r objects from a collection of n objects $= n\text{Pr} = \frac{n!}{(n-r)!}$

In this case, $n = 20$ and $r = 2$: ${}_{20}P_2 = \frac{20!}{(20-2)!} = \frac{20!}{18!}$

This fraction can be calculated on a calculator using the following keystrokes: $20x! \div 18x! =$. The correct answer is 380. Of these 380 possible permutations, only one is AT, so the top term in the fraction is one. The answer to the probability problem is $P = 1/380 \approx .003$.

Example: A team with seven members wants to select a task force of three people to collect data for the next team meeting. How many different three-person task forces could be formed? This is not a permutations problem because the order in which people are selected doesn't matter. In other words, the task force consisting of Barb, Bill, and Bob is the same task force as the one consisting of Bill, Barb, and Bob. Therefore the combinations formula will be used to calculate the number of combinations of three objects from a collection of seven objects:

$$_7C_3 = \frac{7!}{(7-3)!3!} = 35$$

Thirty-five different task forces could be formed.

Example: A team with seven members wants to select a cabinet consisting of a chairman, facilitator, and scribe. How many ways can the three-person cabinet be formed? Here the order is important because the cabinet consisting of Barb, Bill, and Bob will have Barb as chairman, Bill as facilitator, and Bob as scribe while the cabinet consisting of Bill, Barb, and Bob has Bill as chairman, Barb as facilitator, and Bob as scribe. The appropriate formula is the one for permutations of three objects from a collection of seven objects.

$$_7P_3 = \frac{7!}{(7-3)!} = 210$$

Two hundred ten different cabinets could be formed.

4. Area under Normal Curve

There are several applications in the quality field for the area under a normal curve. This section discusses the basic concepts so the individual applications will be simpler to understand when introduced later in the book.

Example: A 1.00000″ gage block is measured ten times with a micrometer and the readings are: 1.0008, 1.0000, 1.0000, 0.9996, 1.0005, 1.0001, 0.9990, 1.0003, 0.9999, and 1.0000.

The slightly different values were obtained due to variation in the micrometer, the technique used, and so on. The errors for these measurements can be found by subtracting 1.00000 from each. The errors are: 0.0008, 0, 0, -0.0004, 0.0005, 0.0001, -0.0010, 0.0003, -0.0001, and 0. These error values have been placed on a histogram in Figure II.3a. If 500 measurements had been made and their errors plotted on a histogram, it would look something like Figure II.3b.

The histogram in Figure II.3b approximates the normal distribution. This distribution occurs frequently in various applications in the quality sciences. The normal curve is illustrated in Figure II.4.

It has a fairly complex formula so locations on the normal curve are seldom calculated directly. Instead a "standard normal table," such as the one in appendix III, is used. Some properties of the "standard normal curve" are:

- The mean is zero and the curve is symmetric about zero.
- It has a standard deviation of one. The units on the horizontal axis are standard deviations.

- The total area under the curve is one square unit.
- The curve doesn't touch the horizontal axis; it extends infinitely far in each direction.

Example: Use the standard normal table (appendix C) to find the area under the standard normal curve to the right of 1. The values on the horizontal are often referred to as z-values, so this problem is sometimes stated as: Find the area under the standard normal curve to the right of $z = 1$.

In appendix C find 1 in the z-column. The associated area is 0.1587, which is the correct answer to this problem.

Example: Find the area under the standard normal curve to the right of $z = 0$.

Intuitively, since the curve is symmetric about 0, we would feel that the answer is 0.5. Verify this by finding 0 in the z-column in appendix C.

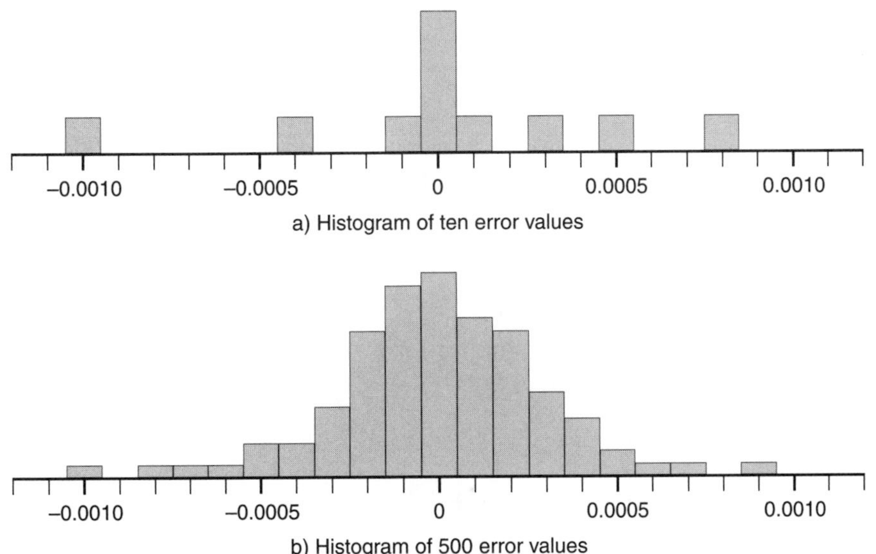

Figure II.3 Histograms of error values.

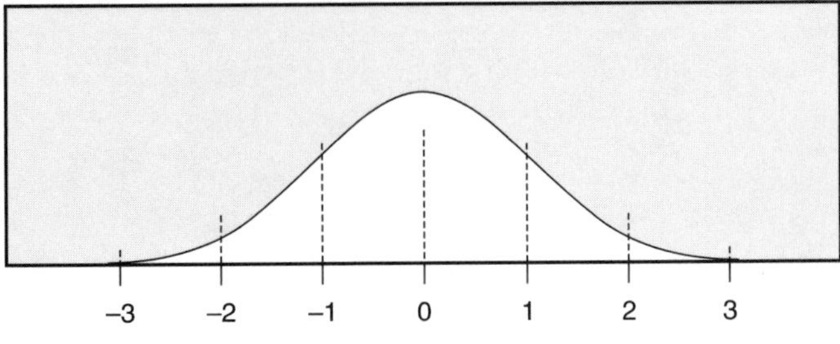

Figure II.4 Normal curve.

Example: Find the area under the standard normal curve to the right of $z = -1$. The area to the right of $z = 1$ is 0.1587, and because of the symmetry of the curve, the area to the *left* of $z = -1$ is also 0.1587. Since the total area under the curve is 1, the area to the right of $z = -1$ is $1 - .1587 = 0.8413$.

Example: Find the area under the standard normal curve between $z = 0$ and $z = 1$. This is the shaded area in Figure II.5. The entire area to the right of $z = 0$ is 0.5 and the area to the right of $z = 1$ is 0.1587. The shaded area is $0.5 - 0.1587 = 0.3413$

Example: Find the area under the standard normal curve between $z = -2$ and $z = 1$. This is the shaded area in Figure II.6. From the table in appendix C, the area to the right of $z = 2$ is 0.0228, so the area to the *left* of $z = -2$ is also 0.0228. Consequently, the area to the right of $z = -2$ is $1 - 0.0228 = 0.9772$, and the area to the right of $z = 1$ is 0.1587. The shaded area is $0.9772 - 0.1587 = 0.8185$

Some normal distributions are not the standard normal distribution. The next example shows how the standard normal table in appendix C can be used to find areas for these cases.

Example: An automatic bar machine produces parts whose diameters are normally distributed with a mean of 0.750 and standard deviation of 0.004. What percentage of the parts have diameters between 0.750 and 0.754?

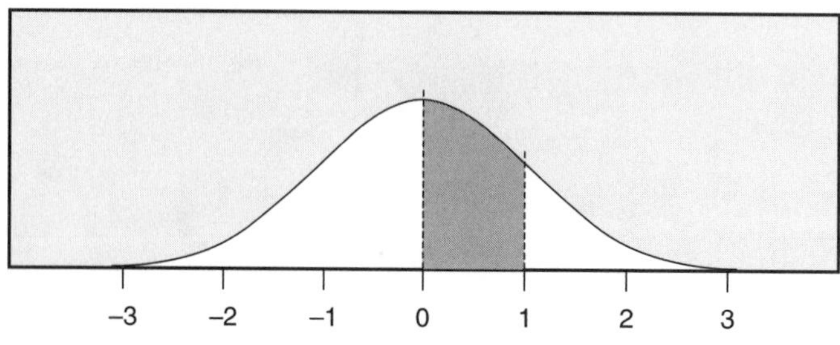

Figure II.5 Area under the standard normal curve between $z = 0$ and $z = 1$.

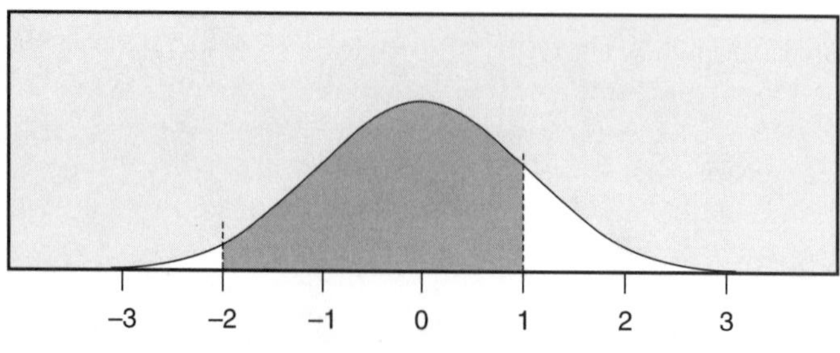

Figure II.6 Area under the standard normal curve between $z = -2$ and $z = 1$.

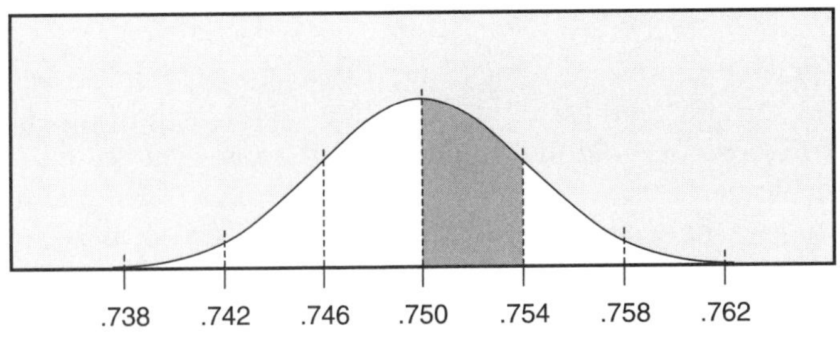

Figure II.7 Area under a normal curve between 0.750 and 0.754.

Figure II.7 illustrates the problem. This is not the standard normal distribution, because the mean is not zero and the standard deviation is not one. Figure II.7 shows vertical dashed lines at standard deviations from –3 to 3. The horizontal axis has the mean scaled at the given value of 0.750, and the distance between standard deviation markers is the given value of 0.004. The problem asks what percentage of the total area is shaded. From the diagram, this is the area between $z = 0$ and $z = 1$ on the standard normal curve, so the area is $0.5 - 0.1587 = 0.3413$. Since the total area under the standard normal curve is 1, this represents 34.13 percent of the area and is the answer to the problem. Further examples of this type are given in the Process Capability discussion, part 6 of section F of this chapter.

The standard normal curve can be related to probability in the previous example by asking the question, "If a part is selected at random from the output of the automatic bar machine, what is the probability that it will have a diameter between .750 and .754?" Since 34.13 percent of the parts have diameters in this range, the probability is .3413.

How accurate are the answers to the above examples? Suppose that 10,000 parts are produced. If the distribution is exactly normal and the population mean and standard deviation are exactly .750 and .004, then the number with diameters between .750 and .754 would be 3413. But since exactly normal distributions exist only in theory and sample data are typically used to estimate the population mean and standard deviation, the actual number will vary somewhat.

D. FREQUENCY DISTRIBUTIONS

1. Normal Distribution

The normal distribution discussed in the previous section results from "continuous" data, that is, data that come from measurement on a continuous scale such as length, weight, temperature, and so on. Between any two values on a continuous scale there are infinitely many other values. For example, on an inch scale, between 1.256 and 1.257 there are values such as 1.2562, 1.2568, 1.25683, and so on.

The other two distributions discussed here, the binomial distribution and the Poisson distribution, are called "discrete" distributions. In quality applications these distributions typically are based on count data rather than data measured on a continuous scale. The items being counted are often defective products or products that have defects. The word *defective* is used when all products are divided into two categories such as good and bad. The word *defect* is used when a particular product may have several defects or flaws, none of which may cause the product to be defective. The word defective would be used for light bulbs that failed to light up. The word defect would be used to describe minor scratches, paint runs, and so on, that would not cause the product to be rejected. To add to the confusion, a defective product is sometimes referred to as a nonconforming product while a defect is sometimes called a nonconformity.

2. Binomial Distribution

The prefix "bi-" implies the number two, as in *bi*cycle (two wheels) and *bi*partisan (two political parties). The binomial distribution is used when every object fits in one of two categories. The most frequent application in the quality field is when every part is classified as either good or defective, such as valve leak tests or circuit continuity tests. In these cases there are two possibilities: the valve either leaks or it doesn't, the circuit either passes current or it doesn't. If data on the amount of leakage or the amount of resistance were collected, the binomial distribution would not be appropriate. The word defective is often used in binomial distribution applications. A typical example might consider the number of defectives in a random sample of size 10. Notice that the number of defectives is not a continuous variable because, for instance, between two defectives and three defectives there are not an infinite number of other values, that is, there can't be 2.3 defectives. That is why this distribution is called *discrete.*

Example: Suppose 20 percent of the parts in a batch of 100,000 are defective and a sample of 10 parts is randomly selected. What is the probability that exactly one of the 10 is defective? The correct answer, stated in the usual notation, is $P(X = 1) \approx .27$. This reads: "The probability that the number of defectives equals 1 is approximately .27." The formula for finding this answer will be given later. It can be used to find the probability that exactly two of the 10 are defective, exactly three are defective, and so on. The results of applying the formula 11 times for the 11 possible answers are shown in Figure II.8. Figure II.8 also displays a histogram of the 11 results.

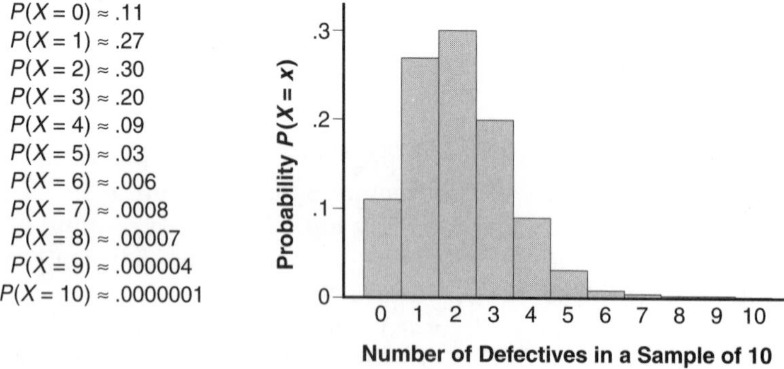

Figure II.8 Binomial distribution with $n = 10$ and $p = .20$.

As the title line of Figure II.8 indicates, the histogram depicts the binomial distribution for sample size = 10 when the rate of defectives is 20 percent. Statistics books sometime refer to this as "ten trials with probability of success = .20 on each trial." *Success* in this example refers to selection of a defective part.

The formula for calculating the binomial probabilities is called the binomial formula:

$$P(X=x)=\binom{n}{x}p^x(1-p)^{n-x}$$

where

n = number of trials or sample size
x = number of successes (or defectives in this example)
p = probability of success in each trial (the probability of a part being defective)
and $\binom{n}{x}$ = number of combinations of x objects from a collection of n objects

(Refer to section C of this chapter for a formula.)

To calculate $P(X = 3)$ in the example shown in Figure II.7:

$$P(X=3)=\binom{10}{3}.2^3\times.8^7\approx\frac{10!}{3!\times7!}.008\times.21\approx.2016$$

The probability of finding at most three defectives, $P(X \le 3)$, can be found by calculating four probabilities and adding them:

$$P(X \le 3) = P(X = 0) + P(X = 1) + P(X = 2) + P(X = 3)$$

Example: A large batch of parts is 3.5 percent defective. A random sample of five is selected. What is the probability that this sample has at least four defective parts?

Calculate two probabilities and add them together:

$$P(X\ge4)=P(X=4)+P(X=5)$$

$$P(X=4)=\binom{5}{4}.035^4\times.965^1=\frac{5!}{4!\times1!}.0000015\times.965\approx.00000724$$

$$P(X=5)=\binom{5}{5}.035^5\times.965^0=.00000005$$

$$P(X\ge4)=P(X=4)+P(X=5)\approx.00000724+.00000005=.00000729$$

The mean and standard deviation of a binomial distribution are given by the formulas:

$$\mu=np \qquad \sigma=\sqrt{p(1-p)}$$

In this example,

$$\mu = 5 \times .035 = .175 \qquad \sigma = \sqrt{.035 \times .965} \approx .184$$

3. Poisson Distribution

When counting defects rather than defectives, the Poisson distribution is used rather than the binomial distribution. For example, a process for making sheet goods has an upper specification of eight bubbles per square foot. Every 30 minutes, the number of bubbles in a sample square foot are counted and recorded. If the average of these values is $\bar{c}$, the Poisson distribution is:

$$P(X = x) = \frac{e^{-\bar{c}}\bar{c}^{x}}{x!}$$

where

x = number of defects

$\bar{c}$ = mean number of defects

e = natural log base (use the e^x key on the calculator)

In the example, if the average number of defects (bubbles) per square foot is 2.53, the probability of finding exactly four bubbles is:

$$P(X = 4) = \frac{e^{-2.53}2.53^{4}}{4!} \approx \frac{.0797 \times 40.972}{24} \approx 0.136$$

Consult calculator instruction manual to evaluate $e^{-2.53}$

The symbol in the position of the $\bar{c}$ in the above formula varies from book to book; some authors use the Greek letter λ (lambda). The use of $\bar{c}$ in this formula is more consistent with the control limit formulas for the c-chart to be discussed later in this chapter.

The formulas for the mean and standard deviation of the Poisson distribution are:

$$\mu = \bar{c} \qquad \sigma = \sqrt{\bar{c}}$$

E. STATISTICAL INFERENCE

1. Universe versus Sample

Kennett and Zacks[1] define a sample as "a subset of the elements of a given population." A *population,* also referred to as a universe, is generally defined as that set of all possible elements of an item, grouping, or category of data of interest. For purposes of the quality technician, samples may be drawn from populations in the form of measurements such as length, width, height, weight, volume, flow, and so on, or as any other measure of interest as it relates to quality. Figure II.9 describes the relationship between a sample and a given population.

As can be seen in Figure II.9, a sample represents a much smaller portion of the data available in the larger population. As quality technicians, we are interested in

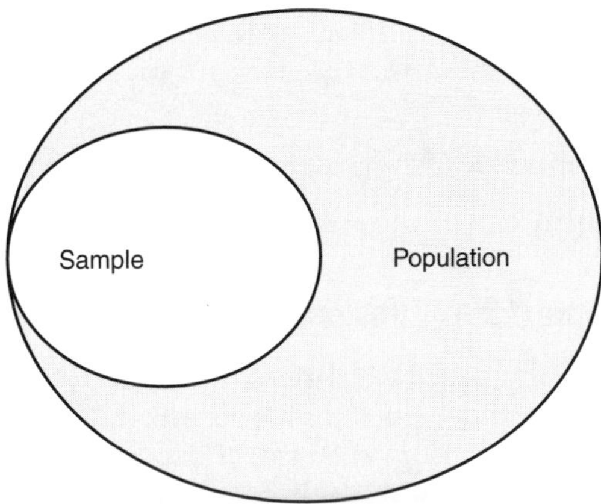

Figure II.9 Sample versus population.

samples of data from certain populations (that is, smaller sets of data) to describe current conditions or the status of a larger population. The primary issue with our interest in samples, as opposed to populations, is one of economics, wherein we don't have the time or financial resources to physically check, inspect, or verify each piece of data in a given population. Hence, as quality technicians, we want to be able to look at a sample of data and describe, or generalize, about the condition of the population as a whole.

In relation to statistical inference, samples are an extremely important quantity. Since we generalize about a population from sample data, the sample data are summarized and mathematically manipulated into statistics that describe the population. From these sample statistics quality technicians, and other quality professionals, make inferences about the population. From these inferences come a variety of actions based on a quantitative-based decision-making process.

2. Parameter versus Statistic

In many cases, whether data are drawn from a sample or a population determines when, where, and how in the quality function the data are used as input to decision-making processes. Accordingly, anyone using or referring to the data must be acutely aware of the origin of the data (that is, a sample or a population). The reasons for needing to know the origin of data are many, however two extremely important reasons for knowing if data were drawn from a sample or a population are as follows:

1. Since data drawn from samples do not represent a definitive look at, or verification of, the characteristic of interest in relation to the population, it is standard practice to assume there is some error in the sample data—this error in sample data is called *bias*.

2. To eliminate or compensate for the error or bias requires, in many cases, that different mathematical tools and techniques be applied to sample data than to population data.

To ensure that anyone using or referring to sample or population data correctly communicates the origin of the data, it is standard practice to make that distinction as follows:

- *Parameter*—A quantity describing a given population.
- *Statistic*—A quantity describing a given sample.

3. Standard Deviation (Computation)

Standard deviation was thoroughly described and computed in section II.A (Basic Statistics). However, standard deviation, as a measure of dispersion, is one example of a commonly calculated quantity of interest that is dependant upon its origin as a sample or a population. In fact, the formulae for standard deviation based on a sample rather than a population are different, and the difference between the formulae resides in a bias correction factor found in the sample standard deviation formula.

4. Confidence Level

When making inferences based on statistical data, it is common practice to quantify the level of confidence one has with respect to the inferences. By specifying the level of a term called a *confidence coefficient*, it is possible to identify a probability that describes the risk associated with making any given inference. This probability also describes the area in one or both tails of a normal distribution, wherein we would expect to see data or observations that fall outside a selected confidence coefficient.

In normal use, the confidence coefficient (which is stated as a decimal value indicating a probability) is converted to a percent. When a confidence coefficient is converted to a percent, it is referred to as a *confidence level.* Confidence levels are normally set as one of the follows: 90 percent, 95 percent, or 99 percent.

Table II.1 indicates the relationship between confidence levels and confidence coefficients at the most commonly used levels.

5. Confidence Limits

A *confidence limit,* also commonly referred to as a *confidence interval,* is a quantity used when making inferences about a sample statistic. When using sample data, a true

Table II.1 Relationship between confidence levels and confidence coefficients.

Confidence Level 100(1 – a)	**One-Tailed: Confidence Coefficient (a)**	**Two-Tailed: Confidence Coefficient (a/2)**	**Normalized: ($Z_{a/2}$)**
99%	.01	.005	2.575
95%	.05	.025	1.96
90%	.10	.05	1.645

measure such as a point estimate (that is, a statistical measure of location such as a mean or proportion) is not known with certainty, so it is necessary to specify at some level of confidence the upper and lower boundaries of where a true population parameter would be located if the population parameter were known.

A confidence limit has three components as follows:

Point estimate ± Margin of error

As mentioned above, a *point estimate* is obtained from a sample statistic and generally involves a measure of location, such as a mean or a proportion. The *margin of error* involves a simple calculation and is the component of the formula that determines the width of the limit or interval. As the level of confidence decreases, the width of the limit or interval increases to reflect the uncertainty for making inferences.

The margin of error is calculated for a given level of confidence using the following formula:

$$\text{Margin of error} = Z_{a/2} \times \frac{s}{\sqrt{n}}$$

Where

$Z_{a/2}$ = Confidence level (normalized)

s = Sample standard deviation

n = Sample size

The following example is provided to illustrate application of the concept:

Let u = the average particulate count as the byproduct of a production process that was monitored for 30 days. In this case, u = 5250 with s (sample standard deviation) = 1445.

Wanted: A confidence limit or interval at a confidence level of 95 percent.

Confidence Limit	**=**	**Point Estimate**	**±**	**Margin of Error**	
	=	u	±	$Z_{a/2} \times \frac{s}{\sqrt{n}}$	
	=	5250	±	$1.96 \times \frac{1445}{\sqrt{30}}$	
	=	5250	±	517	
	=				4733, 5767

Interpretation: Based on our 30 days of observations, we are confident that the limit or interval specified by 4733 and 5767 will contain the true population value for mean particulate count 95 percent of the time.

F. CONTROL CHARTS

Control charts were introduced briefly in section D of chapter I. This section provides more detail on the theory and application of these charts.

1. Control Limits versus Specification Limits

The discussion in chapter I indicated that control limits are used to detect when a process changes. These limits are calculated using statistical formulas which guarantee that, for a stable process, a high percentage of the points will fall between the upper and lower control limits. In other words, the probability that a point from a stable process falls outside the control limits is very small and the user of the chart is almost certainly correct to assume that such a point indicates that the process has changed. When the chart is correctly used, the user will take appropriate action when a point occurs outside the control limits. The action that is appropriate varies with the situation. In some cases it may be that the wisest course is to increase vigilance through more frequent sampling. Sometimes an immediate process adjustment is called for. In other cases, the process must be stopped immediately.

One of the most common mistakes in using control charts is to use the specification limits as control limits. Since the specification limits have no statistical basis, the user of the chart has no statistical basis for assuming that the process has changed when a point occurs outside them. The statement, "I just plotted a point outside the control limits but it is well within specification limits, so I don't have to worry about it," represents a misunderstanding of the chart. The main purpose of the control chart is to signal the user that the process has changed. If the signal is ignored, the control chart loses much of its value as an early warning tool. This misunderstanding of the significance of the control limits is especially dangerous in the case of the averages portion of the $\bar{x}$ and R or $\bar{x}$ and s chart. Recall that the points on this portion of the chart are calculated by averaging several measurements. It is possible for the average (or mean) to fall within the specification limits even though none of the actual measurements are within these limits. For example, suppose the specification limits for a dimension are 7.350 to 7.360 and a sample of five parts yields the following measurements: 7.346, 7.344, 7.362, 7.365, 7.366. The mean of these values is 7.357, well within the specification limits. In this case the range chart would likely have shown the point above its upper control limit. Should the user take comfort in the fact that the plotted point, located at the mean, is well inside the specification limits?

2. Techniques and Applications of Control Charts

Variables Charts

In section D of chapter I, the $\overline{X}$ and R chart was introduced. It is called a *variables chart* because the data to be plotted result from measurement on a variables or continuous scale. The $\bar{x}$ and s chart is another variables control chart. With this chart the sample standard deviation s is used instead of the range to indicate dispersion. The standard deviation is a better measure of spread than the range, so this chart provides a somewhat more precise statistical signal than the $\bar{x}$ and R chart. The $\bar{x}$ and s chart should be used when calculation of the standard deviation is feasible. Users who are comfortable with the standard deviation function on a handheld calculator will be able to calculate s almost as easily as R. The $\bar{x}$ and s chart is often the preferred chart when the chart is constructed using software.

Construction and use of these charts is discussed in chapter I.

Attribute Charts

Attribute charts are used for count data. As discussed in section D, if every item is in one of two categories such as good or bad, "defectives" are counted. If each part may have several flaws, "defects" are counted.

Charting Defectives

If defectives are being counted, the p-chart can be used. For example, a test for the presence of the "Rh-" factor in 13 samples of donated blood has the following results:

	Test number												
	1	**2**	**3**	**4**	**5**	**6**	**7**	**8**	**9**	**10**	**11**	**12**	**13**
No. of units of blood	125	111	133	120	118	137	108	110	124	128	144	138	132
No. of Rh– units	14	18	13	17	15	15	16	11	14	13	14	17	16

These data are plotted on a p-chart in Figure II.10.

Note that the p-chart in Figure II.10 has two points that are outside the control limits. These points indicate that the process was "out of statistical control," which is sometimes

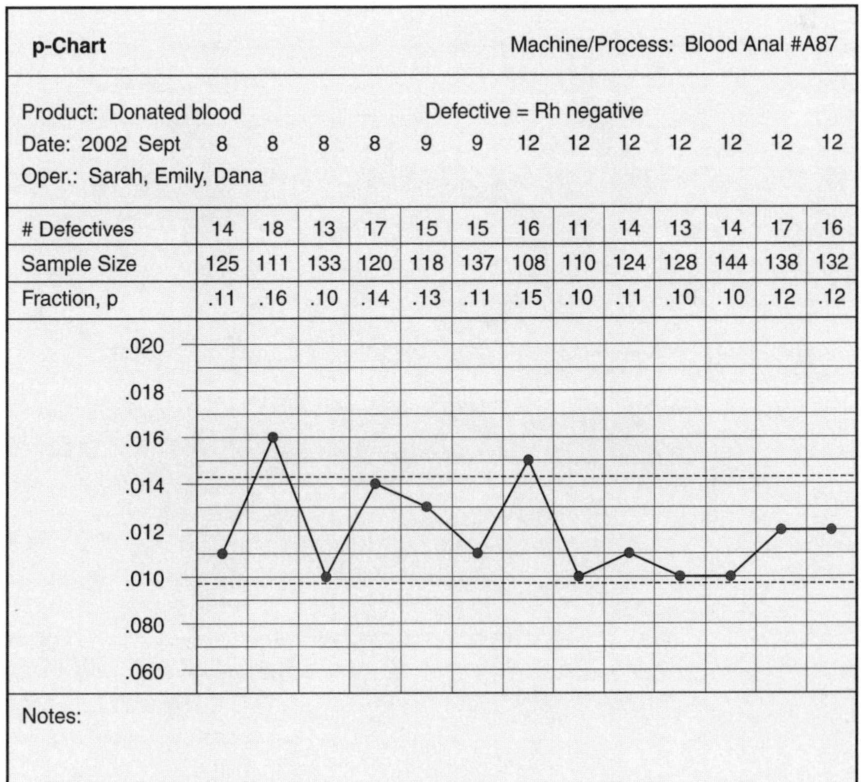

Figure II.10 P-chart example.

referred to as "out of control." It means that there is a very low probability that these points came from the same distribution as the one used to calculate the control limits. It is therefore very probable that the distribution has changed. These "out of control" points are a statistical signal that the process needs attention of some type. People familiar with the process need to decide how to react to various points that are outside the control limits. In the situation in this example an unusually high number of units of blood test Rh–. This could indicate a different population of donors or possibly a malfunction of the testing equipment or procedure. The calculation of control limit is explained in part 4 of this section beginning on page 54.

If defectives are being counted and the sample size remains constant, the np chart can be used.

Example: Packages containing 1000 light bulbs are randomly selected and all 1000 bulbs are light-tested. The np chart is shown in Figure II.11. Note that on March 25 the point is outside the control limits. This means there is a high probability that the process was different on that day than on the days that were used to construct the control limits. In this case the process was different in a good way. It would be advisable to pay attention to the process to see what went right and to see if the conditions could be incorporated into the standard way of running the process. Notice the operator note at the bottom of the chart.

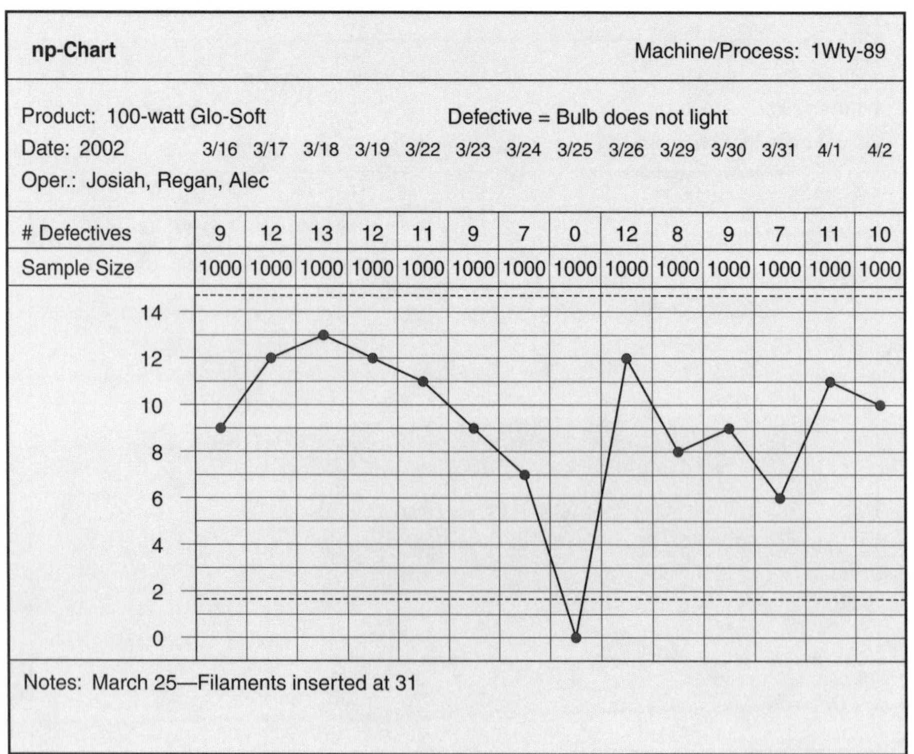

Figure II.11 Example of np chart.

The u- and c-charts are used when defects rather than defectives are being counted. If the sample size varies, the u-chart is used. If the sample size is constant, the c-chart may be used. An example of a u-chart is shown in Figure II.12. A c-chart would look much like the np-chart illustrated in Figure II.11 and is not shown here.

To decide which attribute chart to use:

- For defectives, use *p* or *np*:
  - Use *p* for varying sample size.
  - Use *np* for constant sample size.
- For defects, use *u* or *c*:
  - Use *u* for varying sample size.
  - Use *c* for constant sample size.

3. State of Statistical Control

This section summarizes and reviews some of the ideas previously mentioned. As explained in the following section, the control limits for each control chart are calculated

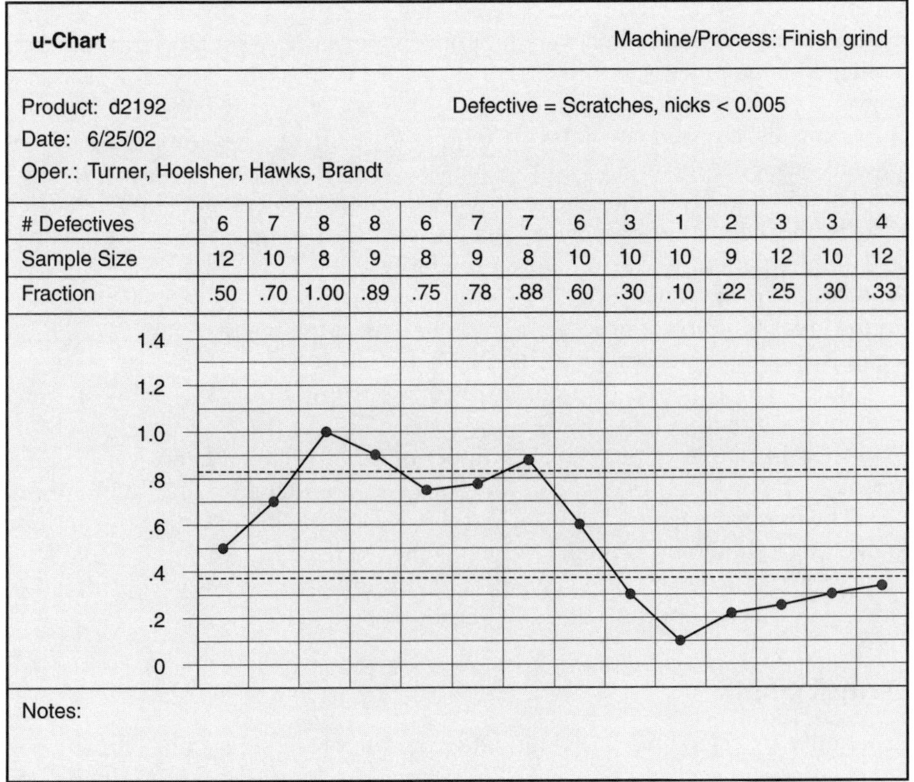

Figure II.12 Example of a u-chart.

based on data from the process. The control chart compares each new point with the distribution that was used as the basis for the control limits. The control limits enclose the vast majority of the points from the distribution, 99.72 percent if it is a normal distribution. Therefore, for the normal distribution, if the point is outside the control limits it is common to state that there is a 99.72 percent probability that the point didn't come from the distribution that was used to calculate the control limits. The percentages vary somewhat from chart to chart, but the control limits are constructed so that this probability will be quite high. It should be noted that these probabilities are somewhat theoretical because no process runs as if its output were randomly selected numbers from some historical distribution. It is enough to say that when a point falls outside the control limits, the probability is quite high that the process has changed.

When the probability is very high that a point did not come from the distribution used to calculate the control limits, the process is said to be "out of statistical control." Unfortunately, this is often abbreviated to "out of control," which implies some wild action on the part of the process. In reality the "out of statistical control" condition is often very subtle and would perhaps not be detected without the control chart. This, in fact, is one of the main values of the control chart: it detects changes in a process that would not otherwise be noticed. This may permit adjustment or other action on the process before serious damage is done.

On the other side of the coin, one of the hazards of using a control chart without proper training is the tendency to react to a point that is not right on target by adjusting the process, even though the chart does not indicate that the process has changed. If an adjustment is made whenever the point is not exactly on target, it may tend to destabilize a stable process. For instance, suppose a new student nurse wakes a patient for morning vitals at 4:00 AM and finds the body temperature to be 98.64°. The student nurse, having just covered normal body temperature the previous day in class, sees that the patient has a .04° fever and administers a Tylenol. At the 5:00 AM vitals, the temperature is down to 98.4°, the Tylenol having done its job. The nurse realizes the temperature is now below target and administers one ounce of brandy to warm the patient. By 6:00 AM the patient is warm enough to justify three Tylenol and by 7:00 AM needs four ounces of brandy, and so on.

In the ideal situation, a process should not need adjustment except when the chart indicates it is out of statistical control. Dr. W. E. Deming, one of the authorities in the field, stated, "The function of a control chart is to minimize the net economic loss from . . . over-adjustment and under-adjustment."[2]

As stated in chapter I, there are a number of other events that are very unlikely to occur unless the process has changed and thus serve as statistical indicators of process change. The lists vary somewhat from textbook to textbook, but usually include something like those shown in Table II.2 (which is the list used by the Automotive Industry Action Group). Whenever one of these events occurs, the process is considered out of statistical control and appropriate action needs to be taken.

4. Control Limits

Control limits are calculated based on data from the process. Formulas for control limits and examples of each are given in this section. The formulas are repeated in appendix IV. Several constants are needed in the formulas. These appear as subscripted

Table II.2 Indicators of process change as used by the Automotive Industry Action Group.

1. A point above the upper control limit or below the lower control limit
2. Seven successive points above (or below) the average line
3. Seven successive points trending up (or down)
4. Nonrandom patterns

capital letters such as A_2. The values of these constants are given in appendix V. When calculating control limits, it is prudent to collect as much data as practical. Many authorities specify at least 25 samples.

Control Limits for $\overline{X}$ and R Control Charts

Upper control limit for the averages chart: $UCL_{\overline{x}} = \overline{\overline{x}} + A_2\overline{R}$

Lower control limit for the averages chart: $LCL_{\overline{x}} = \overline{\overline{x}} - A_2\overline{R}$

Upper control limit for the range chart: $UCL_R = D_4\overline{R}$

Lower control limit for the range chart: $LCL_R = D_3\overline{R}$

Example: Data are collected in a face-and-plunge operation done on a lathe. The dimension being measured is the groove inside diameter (ID), which has a tolerance of 7.125 ± .010. Four parts are measured every hour. The data are shown in Table II.3. Since the formulas use the values of $\overline{\overline{x}}$ and $\overline{R}$, the next step is to calculate the average ($\overline{x}$) and range (R) for each time and then calculate the average of the averages ($\overline{\overline{x}}$) and the average range. These calculations have been completed in Table II.4. The values of $\overline{\overline{x}}$ and $\overline{R}$ appear in the last two values in the last row of Table II.4. Notice that the average of the average column is 7.125, which happens to be at the center of the tolerance in this example. This means that the process is centered in the tolerance. The averages of the measurement columns need not be calculated but these four values should be close to each other. If they are not, there may be some error in the data collection or the measurement system.

$$UCL_{\overline{x}} = \overline{\overline{x}} + A_2\overline{R} = 7.125 + 0.729 \times .004 \approx 7.128$$

$$LCL_{\overline{x}} = \overline{\overline{x}} + A_2\overline{R} = 7.125 - 0.729 \times .004 \approx 7.122$$

$$UCL_R = D_4\overline{R} = 2.282 \times .004 \approx 0.009$$

$$LCL_R = D_4\overline{R} = 0 \times .004 = 0$$

In these calculations the values of A_2, D_3, and D_4 are found in appendix E. The row for subgroup size four is used because each hourly sample has four readings.

Table II.3 Data for $\overline{X}$ and R chart.

Time	1st Meas.	2nd Meas.	3rd Meas.	4th Meas.
4 PM	7.124	7.122	7.125	7.125
5	7.123	7.125	7.125	7.128
6	7.126	7.128	7.128	7.125
7	7.127	7.123	7.123	7.126
8	7.125	7.126	7.121	7.122
9	7.123	7.129	7.129	7.124
10	7.122	7.122	7.124	7.125
11	7.128	7.125	7.126	7.123
12 AM	7.125	7.125	7.121	7.122
1	7.126	7.123	7.123	7.125
2	7.126	7.126	7.127	7.128
3	7.127	7.129	7.128	7.129
4	7.128	7.123	7.122	7.124
5	7.124	7.125	7.129	7.127
6	7.127	7.127	7.123	7.125
7	7.128	7.122	7.124	7.126
8	7.123	7.124	7.125	7.122
9	7.122	7.121	7.126	7.123
10	7.128	7.129	7.122	7.129
11	7.125	7.125	7.124	7.122
12 PM	7.125	7.121	7.125	7.128
1	7.121	7.126	7.12	7.123
2	7.123	7.123	7.123	7.123
3	7.128	7.121	7.126	7.127
4	7.129	7.127	7.127	7.124

Table II.4 Data for $\overline{X}$ and R chart control limit calculations.

Time	1st Meas.	2nd Meas.	3rd Meas.	4th Meas.	Average	Range
4 PM	7.124	7.122	7.125	7.125	7.124	0.003
5	7.123	7.125	7.125	7.128	7.125	0.005
6	7.126	7.128	7.128	7.125	7.127	0.003
7	7.127	7.123	7.123	7.126	7.125	0.004
8	7.125	7.126	7.121	7.122	7.124	0.005
9	7.123	7.129	7.129	7.124	7.126	0.006
10	7.122	7.122	7.124	7.125	7.123	0.003
11	7.128	7.125	7.126	7.123	7.126	0.005
12 AM	7.125	7.125	7.121	7.122	7.123	0.004
1	7.126	7.123	7.123	7.125	7.124	0.003
2	7.126	7.126	7.127	7.128	7.127	0.002
3	7.127	7.129	7.128	7.129	7.128	0.002
4	7.128	7.123	7.122	7.124	7.124	0.006
5	7.124	7.125	7.129	7.127	7.126	0.005
6	7.127	7.127	7.123	7.125	7.126	0.004
7	7.128	7.122	7.124	7.126	7.125	0.006
8	7.123	7.124	7.125	7.122	7.124	0.003
9	7.122	7.121	7.126	7.123	7.123	0.005
10	7.128	7.129	7.122	7.129	7.127	0.007
11	7.125	7.125	7.124	7.122	7.124	0.003
12 PM	7.125	7.121	7.125	7.128	7.125	0.007
1	7.121	7.126	7.12	7.123	7.123	0.006
2	7.123	7.123	7.123	7.123	7.123	0
3	7.128	7.121	7.126	7.127	7.126	0.007
4	7.129	7.127	7.127	7.124	7.127	0.005
Average	7.125	7.125	7.125	7.125	7.125	0.004

Control Limits for $\overline{X}$ and s Control Charts

Calculation of control limits for the $\bar{x}$ and s control chart is the same except that the range column is replaced by the sample standard deviation s. Instead of using $\overline{R}$, these formulas use $\bar{s}$, and the constants from appendix E are changed as follows:

Upper control limit for the averages chart: $UCL_{\bar{x}} = \bar{\bar{x}} + A_3\bar{s}$

Lower control limit for the averages chart: $LCL_{\bar{x}} = \bar{\bar{x}} - A_3\bar{s}$

Upper control limit for the standard deviation chart: $UCL_s = B_4\bar{s}$

Lower control limit for the standard deviation chart: $LCL_s = B_3\bar{s}$

Table II.5 shows the calculated values using the data from Table II.2. The formula calculations:

$$UCL_{\bar{x}} = \bar{\bar{x}} + A_3\bar{s} = 7.125 + 1.628 \times .0020 \approx 7128$$

$$LCL_{\bar{x}} = \bar{\bar{x}} - A_3\bar{s} = 7.125 - 1.628 \times .0020 \approx 7.122$$

Upper control limit for the standard deviation chart:

$$UCL_s = B_4\bar{s} = 2.266 \times .0020 \approx .005$$

Lower control limit for the standard deviation chart:

$$LCL_s = B_3\bar{s} = 0 \times .0020 = 0$$

Control Limits for p-Charts

As indicated earlier, p-charts are used when the data indicate the number of defective units in each sample. An example of this type of data is shown in Table II.6, where the column labeled "number of discrepancies" shows the number of defective units.

The formulas for the control limits for the p-chart are:

$$UCL = \bar{p} + 3\sqrt{\frac{\bar{p}(1-\bar{p})}{\bar{n}}}$$

$$LCL = \bar{p} - 3\sqrt{\frac{\bar{p}(1-\bar{p})}{\bar{n}}}$$

Where

$$\bar{n} = \frac{\text{Sum of the sample sizes}}{\text{Number of samples}}$$

$$\bar{p} = \frac{\text{Sum of the discrepencies}}{\text{Sum of the sample sizes}} = \frac{\Sigma\, discrepancies}{\Sigma n}$$

The first step in calculating these control limits is to find $\bar{n}$ and $\bar{p}$. The totals needed for these values are calculated in Table II.7.

Table II.5 Data for calculation of control limits of an $\bar{x}$ and s chart.

Time	1st Meas.	2nd Meas.	3rd Meas.	4th Meas.	Average	Std. Dev.
4 PM	7.124	7.122	7.125	7.125	7.124	0.0014
5	7.123	7.125	7.125	7.128	7.125	0.0021
6	7.126	7.128	7.128	7.125	7.127	0.0015
7	7.127	7.123	7.123	7.126	7.125	0.0021
8	7.125	7.126	7.121	7.122	7.124	0.0024
9	7.123	7.129	7.129	7.124	7.126	0.0032
10	7.122	7.122	7.124	7.125	7.123	0.0015
11	7.128	7.125	7.126	7.123	7.126	0.0021
12 AM	7.125	7.125	7.121	7.122	7.123	0.0021
1	7.126	7.123	7.123	7.125	7.124	0.0015
2	7.126	7.126	7.127	7.128	7.127	0.0010
3	7.127	7.129	7.128	7.129	7.128	0.0010
4	7.128	7.123	7.122	7.124	7.124	0.0026
5	7.124	7.125	7.129	7.127	7.126	0.0022
6	7.127	7.127	7.123	7.125	7.126	0.0019
7	7.128	7.122	7.124	7.126	7.125	0.0026
8	7.123	7.124	7.125	7.122	7.124	0.0013
9	7.122	7.121	7.126	7.123	7.123	0.0022
10	7.128	7.129	7.122	7.129	7.127	0.0034
11	7.125	7.125	7.124	7.122	7.124	0.0014
12 PM	7.125	7.121	7.125	7.128	7.125	0.0029
1	7.121	7.126	7.12	7.123	7.123	0.0026
2	7.123	7.123	7.123	7.123	7.123	0.0000
3	7.128	7.121	7.126	7.127	7.126	0.0031
4	7.129	7.127	7.127	7.124	7.127	0.0021
Average	7.125	7.125	7.125	7.125	7.125	0.0020

Table II.6 Attribute data.

Time	Sample size n	No. Discrepancies D
8 AM	48	3
8:30	45	6
9	47	2
9:30	51	3
10	48	5
10:30	47	4
11	48	1
11:30	50	0
12 PM	46	1
12:30	45	0
1	47	2
1:30	48	5
2	50	3
2:30	50	6
3	49	2
3:30	46	4
4	50	1
4:30	52	1
5	48	6
5:30	47	5
6	49	6
6:30	49	4
7	51	3
7:30	50	4
8	48	1
8:30	47	2
9	47	5
9:30	49	0
10	49	0

Table II.7 Attribute data with totals.

Time	Sample size n	No. Discrepancies d
8 AM	48	3
8:30	45	6
9	47	2
9:30	51	3
10	48	5
10:30	47	4
11	48	1
11:30	50	0
12 PM	46	1
12:30	45	0
1	47	2
1:30	48	5
2	50	3
2:30	50	6
3	49	2
3:30	46	4
4	50	1
4:30	52	1
5	48	6
5:30	47	5
6	49	6
6:30	49	4
7	51	3
7:30	50	4
8	48	1
8:30	47	2
9	47	5
9:30	49	0
10	49	0
Totals	**1401**	**85**

$$\bar{n} = \frac{\Sigma n}{\text{number of samples}} = \frac{1401}{29} \approx 48.3$$

$$\bar{p} = \frac{\Sigma d}{\Sigma n} = \frac{85}{1401} \approx 0.061$$

Using these values in the formula for the upper control limit:

$$UCL = 0.061 + 3\sqrt{\frac{0.061(1-0.061)}{48.3}} \approx 0.061 + 3\sqrt{0.1186} \approx 0.061 + 0.103 = 0.164$$

Using the formula for the lower control limit and taking advantage of some of the values just calculated:

$$LCL = 0.061 - 0.103 = -0.042$$

Since this value is negative there is no lower control limit.

It is important to note that zero is commonly used as the lower control limit. It is equally important to note that using zero as the lower control limit ignores the statistical significance of a grouping of points near zero, wherein such a grouping does not mean the same thing statistically as a grouping of points near an LCL.

Control Limits for u-Charts

If the values in the "D" column of Table II.7 represent number of defects rather than number of defectives, then the u-chart is appropriate. The formulas for control limits for the u-chart are:

$$UCL_u = \bar{u} + 3\sqrt{\frac{\bar{u}}{\bar{n}}}$$

$$LCL_u = \bar{u} - 3\sqrt{\frac{\bar{u}}{\bar{n}}}$$

where

$$\bar{u} = \frac{\Sigma d}{\Sigma n}$$

$$\text{and } \bar{n} = \frac{\Sigma n}{\text{number of samples}}$$

Using the data from Table II.6:

$$\bar{u} = \frac{85}{1401} \approx 0.062$$

$$\text{and } \bar{n} = \frac{1401}{29} \approx 48.3$$

$$UCL_u = 0.061 + 3\sqrt{\frac{0.061}{48.3}} \approx 0.061 + .107 = 0.168$$

$$LCL_u = 0.061 - 3\sqrt{\frac{0.061}{48.3}} \approx 0.061 - .107 = -0.046$$

Again, since the lower control limit formula returns a negative value, there is no lower control limit. (Some authors use zero as the lower control limit.)

5. Pre-Control

Pre-control is sometimes used in place of control charts or until sufficient data is collected to construct a control chart. Upper and lower pre-control limits, called *PC limits,* are calculated based on the tolerance limits. The value of the tolerance (upper specification limit – lower specification limit) is multiplied by .25. The resulting value is subtracted from the upper specification limit forming the upper PC limit and added to the lower specification limit, forming the lower PC limit. As parts are measured, their values are compared to the PC limits and appropriate action is taken based on rules such as these:

1. If the first part is outside the specification limits, adjust the process.
2. If a part is inside the specification limits but outside PC limits, measure the next part.
3. If two successive parts are outside PC limits, adjust the process.
4. If five successive parts are inside PC limits, switch to less frequent measuring.

Various authors provide additional rules. The principle advantage of pre-control is that it is simpler. The main disadvantage is that it is not statistically based. When the pre-control rules indicate the process should be adjusted, there is not necessarily a high probability that the process has changed. This may lead to over adjustment and decreased stability of the process. For this reason, there is some controversy over the use of pre-control, with Montgomery stating that, "This author believes that pre-control is a poor substitute for standard control charts and would never recommend it in practice."[3]

6. Process Capability

The data in Table II.3 were used to calculate the control limits for the $\bar{x}$ and R control chart. If the control chart does not exhibit any of the indicators of instability as discussed in part 3 (State of Statistical Control), it is assumed that the process is stable. If the process is stable, it is appropriate to do a process capability analysis. The purpose of a capability analysis is to estimate the percent of the population that meets specifications. If the process continues to run exactly the same way, this estimate can be used as a prediction for future production. Note that such a study is not valid if the process is not stable (that is, "out of control") because the analysis produces a prediction of the ability of the process to meet specifications. If the process is unstable, then it is unpredictable.

The following discussion shows how to calculate three different capability indices: C_{pk}, C_p, and CR. These indices were developed to provide a single number to quantify process capability.

Calculating C_{pk}

Probably the most useful capability index is C_{pk}. The first step in calculating C_{pk} is to find the values of Z_U and Z_L using the following formulas:

$$Z_U = \frac{USL - \bar{\bar{x}}}{\sigma}$$

$$\text{and } Z_L = \frac{\bar{\bar{x}} - LSL}{\sigma}$$

where USL and LSL are the upper and lower specification limits and σ is the process standard deviation which may be approximated by

$$\hat{\sigma} = \frac{\bar{R}}{d_2} \text{ (values of } d_2 \text{ are given in appendix E)}$$

For example, suppose the tolerance on a dimension is 1.000 ± .005 and a control chart shows the process is stable with $\bar{\bar{x}} = 1.001$ and $\bar{R} = .003$ with sample size $n = 3$.

For this example $USL = 1.005$, $LSL = 0.995$, $\bar{\bar{x}} = 1.001$, $\bar{R} = 0.003$ and the estimated value of σ is

$$\frac{0.003}{1.693} \approx .0018$$

Substituting these values into the Z formulas:

$$Z_U = \frac{1.005 - 1.001}{0.0018} \approx 2.22 \quad \text{and} \quad Z_L \frac{1.001 - 0.995}{0.0018} \approx 3.33$$

The formula for C_{pk}:

$$C_{pk} = \frac{Min(Z_U, Z_L)}{3}$$

where Min means select the smallest of the values in the parenthesis.
In this example,

$$C_{pk} = \frac{Min(2.22, 3.33)}{3} = \frac{2.22}{3} \approx 0.74$$

The higher the value of C_{pk}, the more capable the process. A few years ago, a C_{pk} value of one or more was considered satisfactory. This would imply that there is at least 3σ between the process mean ($\bar{\bar{x}}$) and the nearest specification limit. More recently, many industries require four, five, or even six standard deviations between the process mean and the nearest specification limit. This would correspond to a C_{pk} of 1.33, 1.67, and 2, respectively. The push for six standard deviations was the origin of the "Six Sigma" programs.

If the process data are normally distributed, the Z-values may be used in a Standard Normal Table (appendix C) to find approximate values for the percent of production that lies outside the specification. In this example, the upper Z of 2.22 corresponds to 0.0132 in appendix C. This means that approximately 1.32 percent of the production of this process violates the upper specification limit. Similarly, the lower Z of 3.33 corresponds to 0.0004 in appendix C. This means that approximately 0.04 percent of the production of this process violates the lower specification limit. Note that the use of the Standard Normal Table in appendix C is only appropriate if the process data are normally distributed. Since no real-world process data are exactly normally distributed, it is best to state these percentages as estimates. The percentages can be useful in estimating return on investment for quality improvement projects.

When the two Z-values are not equal, this means that the process average is not centered within the specification limits and some improvement to the percentages can be made by centering. Suppose, in the above example, that a process adjustment can be made that would move $\bar{\bar{x}}$ to a value of 1.000. Then Z_U and Z_L would each be 2.77, and from the table in appendix III, the two percentages would be 0.28 percent.

Calculating C_p

The formula for the capability index C_p is:

$$C_p = \frac{USL - LSL}{6\sigma}$$

Using the values from the previous example:

$$C_p = \frac{1.005 - 0.995}{6(0.0018)} \approx 0.93$$

Note that the formula for this index does not make use of the process average, $\bar{\bar{x}}$. Therefore this index does not consider whether the process average is centered within the specification limits or, indeed, whether it is even between the two limits. In reality, C_p tells what the process could potentially do if it were centered. For centered processes, C_p and C_{pk} have the same value. For processes that aren't centered, C_p is larger than C_{pk}.

Calculating CR

This index is also referred to as the *capability ratio.* It is the reciprocal of C_p. The formula:

$$CR = \frac{6\sigma}{USL - LSL}$$

Using the data from the previous example,

$$CR = \frac{6(0.00180)}{1.005 - 0.995} \approx 1.08 \text{ which, not surprisingly, is approximately } \frac{1}{0.93}.$$

Of course, *lower* values of CR imply more capable processes.

7. Rational Subgroups

The method used to select samples for a control chart must be logical or "rational." In the case of the $\bar{x}$ and R chart, it is desirable that any process shift be detected by the $\bar{x}$ chart while the R chart should capture only common cause variation. That means that there should be a high probability of variation between successive samples while the

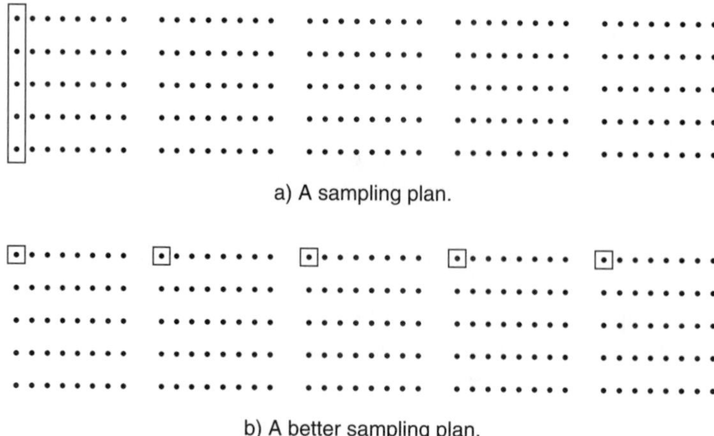

Figure II.13 Conveyor belt in chocolate making process. Possible sampling plans.

variation within the sample is kept small. Therefore samples frequently consist of parts that are produced successively by the same process to minimize the within-sample variation. The next sample is chosen somewhat later so that any process shifts that have occurred will be displayed on the chart. Choosing the rational subgroup requires care to make sure the same process is producing each item. For example, suppose a candy-making process uses 40 pistons to deposit 40 gobs of chocolate on a moving sheet of waxed paper in a 5×8 array as shown in Figure II.13. How should rational subgroups of size five be selected? The choice consisting of the first five chocolates in each row (as indicated in Figure II.13a) would have the five elements of the sample produced by five different processes (the five different pistons). A better choice would be to select the upper left-hand chocolate in five consecutive arrays as shown in Figure II.13b because they are all formed by the same piston. If the original sampling plan had been used and one piston were functioning improperly, the data might look like this:

Piston 1	.25	.24	.26	.24	.24	.25	.26	.26	.23	.24
Piston 2	.36	.38	.33	.34	.36	.35	.38	.35	.34	.34
Piston 3	.24	.26	.25	.25	.24	.23	.24	.25	.26	.24
Piston 4	.24	.21	.25	.24	.23	.21	.22	.22	.24	.21
Piston 5	.25	.26	.29	.24	.23	.25	.26	.26	.24	.29
Average	.248	.270	.276	.262	.260	.258	.272	.268	.262	.264
Range	.12	.17	.08	.10	.13	.14	.16	.13	.11	.13

If the upper and lower control limits for the averages chart are based on these data, they would be:

$$UCL \approx 0.34 \text{ and } LCL \approx 0.19$$

and the averages would all fall ridiculously near the centerline of the chart, 0.264. The chart would be worthless as a tool to signal process change. The reason this happened is that the errant piston, #2, caused the ranges to be very high which in turn caused the control limit values to be spread too far apart.

Another mistake sometimes made in selecting a rational subgroup is to measure what is essentially the same thing multiple times and use those values to make up a sample. One example of this might be to check the hardness of a heat-treated shaft at three different points or to measure the temperature of a well-stirred vat at three different points. Data such as these might result:

	7AM	8AM	9AM	10AM	11AM	Noon	1PM	2PM	3PM	4PM	5PM
	21	33	19	30	22	25	31	31	22	29	28
	22	30	19	29	20	26	33	32	22	28	29
	23	31	17	29	22	28	29	33	19	30	28
Average	22	31.3	18.3	29.3	21.3	26.3	31.0	32.0	31.7	29	28.3
Range	2	3	2	1	2	3	4	2	3	2	1

For the averages chart, the control limits are 29.6 and 25.6. In this situation the readings in each sample are so close to each other that the range is very small, which places the UCL and LCL so close together that only two points on the chart will be within the control limits. Again, the chart is worthless as a tool for signaling process change.

8. Variables Charts

In part 4 of this section, control limits were calculated for the data in Table II.3. The goal now is to construct the chart and use it to monitor future process activity. The first step is to choose scales for the $\bar{x}$ and R sections of the chart in such a way that the area between the control limits cover most of the chart area. One such choice is shown in Figure II.14. Figure II.14 also shows the chart with several points plotted. As each point is plotted, the user should check to determine whether any of the indicators of process change listed in Table II.2 have occurred. Those indicators are repeated here for convenience:

1. A point above the upper control limit or below the lower control limit
2. Seven successive points above (or below) the average line
3. Seven successive points trending up (or down)
4. Nonrandom patterns

If none have occurred, continue with the process. If one of the indicators has occurred, appropriate action should be taken as spelled out in the process operating instructions.

In part 4 of this section, $\bar{x}$ and s control limits were also calculated. Construction and use of a chart with these limits is quite similar to that for the $\bar{x}$ and R chart and is not shown here.

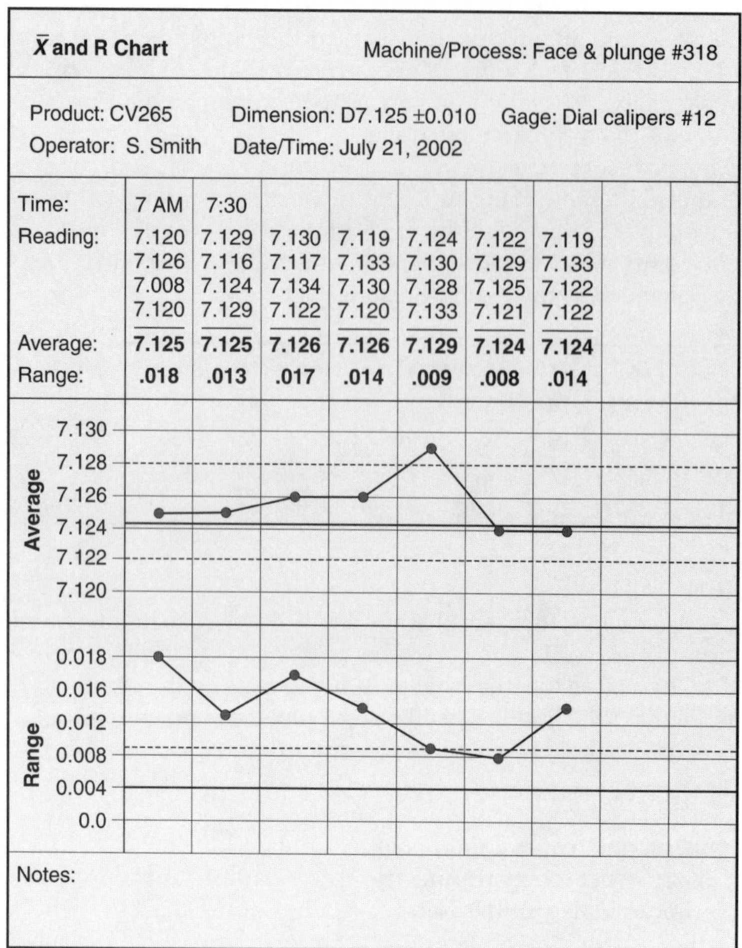

Figure II.14 $\overline{X}$ and R chart example.

9. Attribute Charts

In Part 4 of this section, control limits for four attribute charts (p-chart, np chart, u-chart and c-chart) were calculated. Figures II.15 and II.16 illustrate the u and np charts. The other charts are similar and are not shown. Analysis of attribute charts follows the same procedures as the $\bar{x}$ and R charts as outlined in part 8 of this section.

10. Machine Capability

Process capability analysis was discussed in part 6 of this section. Machine capability analysis is calculated in the same way mathematically; that is, the same formulas are used. The difference is that machine capability analysis attempts to isolate and analyze the variation due to an individual machine rather than the entire process. If a process has several machines linked together either in series or parallel, a machine capability

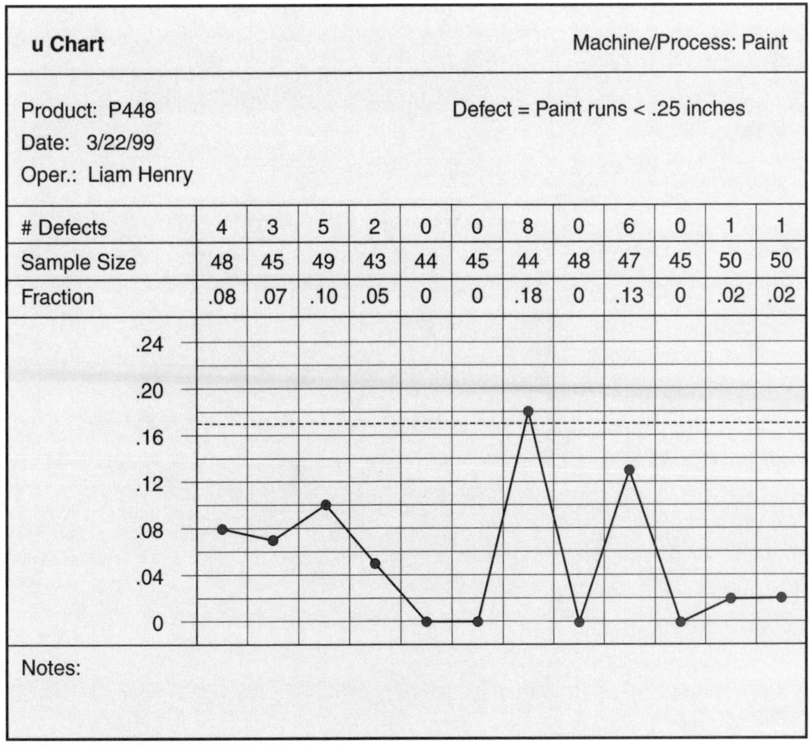

u Chart
Machine/Process: Paint
Product: P448
Date: 3/22/99
Oper.: Liam Henry
Defect = Paint runs < .25 inches
# Defects
4 3 5 2 0 0 8 0 6 0 1 1
Sample Size
48 45 49 43 44 45 44 48 47 45 50 50
Fraction
.08 .07 .10 .05 0 0 .18 0 .13 0 .02 .02
.24
.20
.16
.12
.08
.04
0
Notes:

Figure II.15 u-chart example.

analysis should be conducted on each machine. It is usually best to provide a very consistent input to the machine, and very precise and accurate measurement of the output. This helps assure that the analysis doesn't consider variation from other sources or from the measurement system. Machine capability analyses can be very useful in efforts to reduce process variation by identifying points in the process where excess variation is caused.

11. Analysis of Charts

The variation of a process that is in statistical control is called *common cause variation*. This variation is inherent in the process and can only be reduced through changes in the process itself. Therefore, it is important that process operators not respond to changes attributed to common cause variation.

When additional variation occurs, it is referred to as *special cause variation*. This variation can be assigned to some outside change that affects the process output. It is important that the process operator respond to this variation.

The purpose of a control chart is to distinguish between these two types of variation. It does this by providing a statistical signal that a special cause is impacting the process. This permits the operator to have immediate process feedback and to take timely and appropriate action.

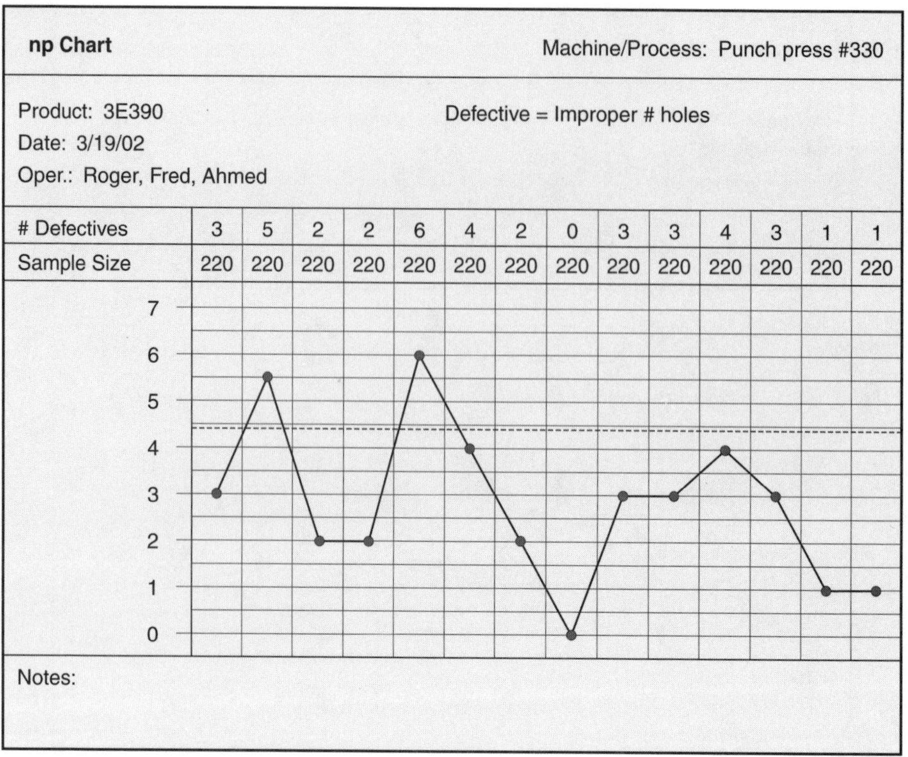

Figure II.16 Example of an np control chart.

The statistical signal consists of the occurrence of an event that is on the list of indicators of process change. That list is repeated here again for convenience:

1. A point above the upper control limit or below the lower control limit
2. Seven successive points above (or below) the average line
3. Seven successive points trending up (or down)
4. Nonrandom patterns

The action that is appropriate for the operator to take depends on the event and process. The action that is needed should be spelled out in the operating instructions for the process. These instructions should provide for logging of the event and actions taken.

Figures II.17 through II.21 illustrate the use of the indicators of process change to distinguish between special cause and common cause variation. The caption for each figure explains the indicator involved.

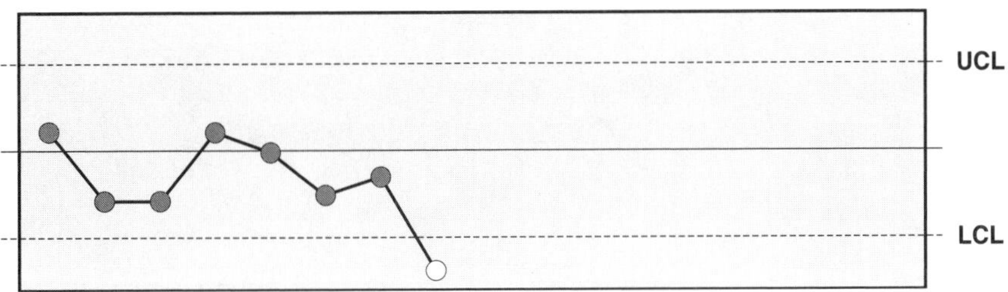

Figure II.17 Point outside control limit. When the open dot is plotted, the operator is signaled that there is a very high probability that the process has changed.

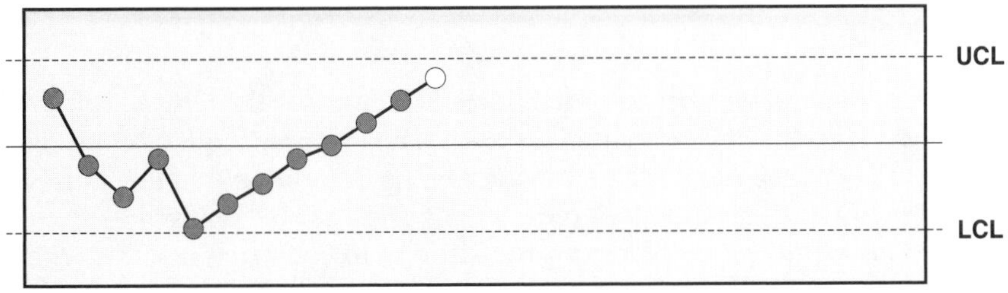

Figure II.18 Seven successive points trending upward. When the open dot is plotted, the operator is signaled that there is a very high probability that the process has changed.

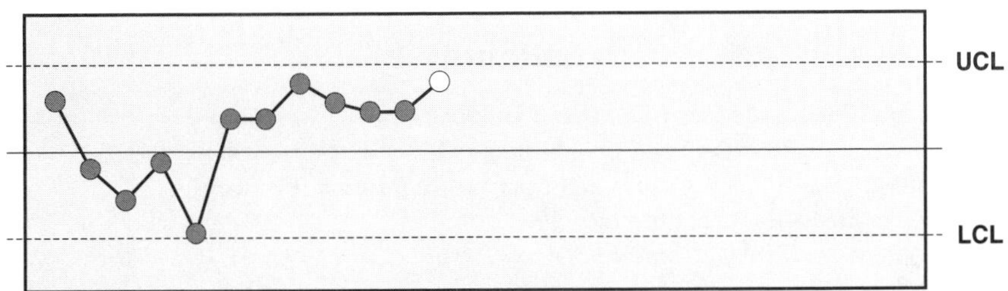

Figure II.19 Seven successive points on one side of the average. When the open dot is plotted, the operator is signaled that there is a very high probability that the process has changed.

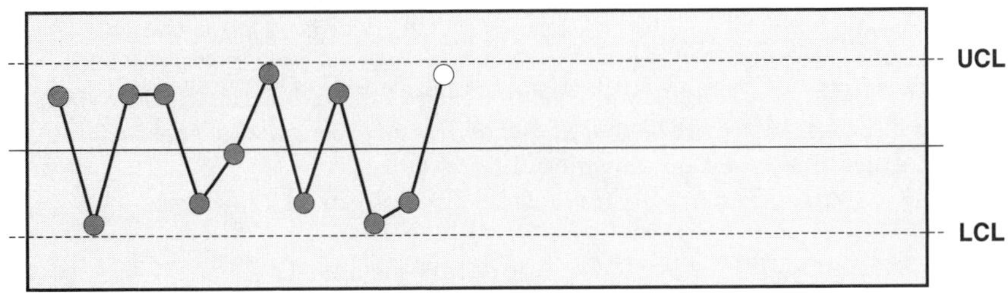

Figure II.20 Nonrandom pattern. This rule is not very well defined. In this case, the dots are jumping all over the place rather than being clustered around the average. Operator judgment is required here.

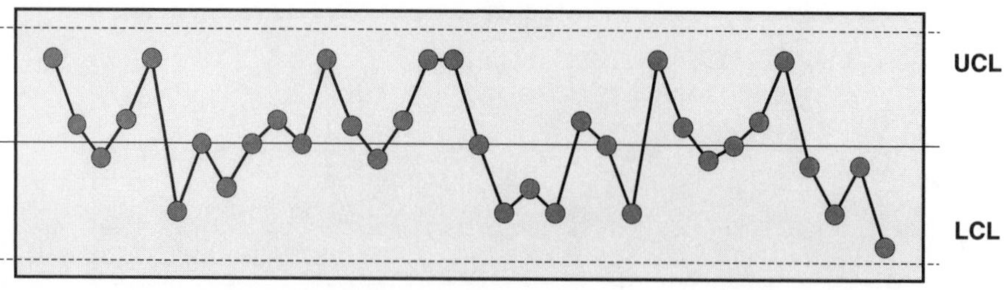

Figure II.21 Nonrandom patterns. The V-shape seems to occur at three different times. This could be meaningless or it could be a symptom of some special cause. Operator judgment is required.

12. Data Plotting

One of the hazards of using software for statistical analysis is the temptation to perform analysis on data without first "looking" at them. One example would be the calculation of linear correlation coefficients. This number helps determine whether two variables have a relationship that permits the prediction of one variable using the other variable in a straight line formula. The correct procedure is to construct a scatter diagram of the data as shown in chapter I. If the points seem to be grouped around a straight line in the scatter diagram it would be appropriate to calculate the coefficient. Otherwise the calculation may be misleading. In some cases (especially with small data sets), a fairly high correlation coefficient may result from data that, when plotted, are clearly not related.

Endnotes

1. R. Kennet and S. Zacks, *Modern Industrial Statistics: Design and Control of Quality Reliability* (Pacific Grove, CA: Brooks-Cole Publishing, 1998).
2. W. E. Deming, *Quality, Productivity, and Competitive Position* (Cambridge, MA: Massachusetts Institute of Technology, 1982).
3. D. C. Montgomery, *Introduction to Statistical Quality Control*, 4th ed. (New York: John Wiley & Sons, 2001).

References

Benbow, D. W. et. al. *Certified Quality Engineer Handbook,* 2nd ed. Milwaukee: ASQ Quality Press, 2002.

Berger, R. W., and T. H. Hart. *Statistical Process Control: A Guide for Implementation*. Milwaukee: ASQC Quality Press, 1986.

Grant, E., and R. Leavenworth. *Statistical Quality Control,* 7th ed. Boston: McGraw-Hill, 1996.

Kenett, R., and S. Zacks. *Modern Industrial Statistics: Design and Control of Quality and Reliability*. Pacific Grove, CA: Brooks-Cole Publishing, 1998.

Montgomery, D. C. *Introduction to Statistical Quality Control*. 4th ed. New York: John Wiley & Sons, 2001.

Pitt, H. *SPC for the Rest of Us*. Reading, MA: Addison Wesley, 1994.

III

Metrology and Calibration

INTRODUCTION

Metrology, the science of weights and measures that is also defined as the science of precision measurements, has many applications and requires a wide variety of instruments in just about every facet of science and industry. In the competitive manufacture of precision-engineered products where a high degree of quality is required, it is particularly important that the proper measuring and gaging instruments be employed to provide accurate, reliable, and cost-effective inspection results. Some industry studies have indicated that the dimensional tolerances on state-of-the-art manufactured products are shrinking by a factor of three every 10 years. Thus, the selection of appropriate measuring and gaging instruments will become even more critical and demanding in the future.

DIMENSIONAL METROLOGY

Dimensional metrology is concerned with the measurement or gauging of a variety of work piece characteristics, including: length, diameter, thickness, angle, taper, roughness, concentricity, and profile. Different sensing technologies may be employed to measure or gauge those characteristics, depending on the requirements for accuracy and other considerations. There are basically five different technologies that may be used individually or in combination to perform these inspection functions:

1. *Mechanical*: Small displacements are amplified by a mechanical system.
2. *Electronic*: Utilize an electric or electronic phenomenon, such as electrical resistance.
3. *Air* or *pneumatic:* Small variations made in the dimension are measured with respect to a reference dimension, and are shown by a variation in air pressure or the velocity of air flow.
4. *Light waves*: Use of the phenomenon of the interference of light waves to provide a standard. Such standard is the wavelength of a monochromatic light, expressed in terms of the meter.
5. *Electron beam*: Stabilized lasers are used as working standards for dimensional measurements, providing precise and stable frequencies for the standard.

In general, the mechanical and electronic types of measuring and gauging instruments have sensing devices or probes that come in contact with the work piece and are referred to as contact instruments. Air instruments, while employing contacting elements, rely on air pressure difference to effect measurement. Thus, they are basically noncontact instruments. Although different technologies are involved in the light-wave and electron-beam instruments, they both utilize a variety of optical systems. Thus, they are often grouped together as optical noncontact instruments.

A. MEASUREMENT TOOLS

There are many factors to consider in the selection of a measuring or gauging instrument or system for a particular manufacturing inspection operation. In general, a reference to the *Rule of Ten* will serve as a baseline or beginning of that selection process. The Rule of Ten, often referred to as the *Gage Maker's Rule*, states that inspection measurements should be better than the tolerance of a dimension by a factor of 10, and calibration standards should be better than inspections measurements by a factor of 10. If, for example, the tolerance on a shaft diameter is ±0.025 mm (±.0010 in.), then the increment of measurement on the inspection instrument should be as small as 0.025/10 = 0.0025 mm (.00010 in.). Similarly, the increment of measurement for the calibration standard for that inspection instrument should be as small as 0.025/10 = 0.0025 mm (.00010 in.).

Once the smallest increment of measurement for an instrument has been determined, the candidate instruments then need to be evaluated in terms of the degree of satisfaction they offer relative to the following performance criteria:

1. *Accuracy*: The ability to measure the true magnitude of a dimension.
2. *Linearity*: The accuracy of the measurements of an instrument throughout its operating range.
3. *Magnification*: The amplification of the output reading on an instrument over the actual input dimension.
4. *Repeatability*: The ability of the instrument to achieve the same degree of accuracy on repeated applications (often referred to as *precision*).
5. *Resolution*: The smallest increment of measurement that can be read on an instrument.
6. *Sensitivity*: The smallest increment of difference in dimension that can be detected by an instrument.
7. *Stability* or *drift*: The ability of an instrument to maintain its calibration over a period of time.

Other selection criteria may include other factors such as the shape and size of the measured part or work piece, work piece material, and capabilities of the metrology laboratory.

Consideration of these factors, along with cost and operation convenience, should help in selecting an appropriate measurement or gauging device for a particular inspection operation. For operating convenience, most instruments are or can be equipped with discrete digital readout devices. Most of these can be connected to microprocessors or computers for data recording and analysis.

Basic Linear Measuring Instruments

The standard environmental conditions for length measurements include a temperature of 68°F (20°C) and a barometric pressure of 760 mm Hg. Because these conditions are assumed for all precision dimensional measurements, dimensional metrology laboratories are temperature controlled as nearly as is practical to 68°F, and thermal expansion corrections are made for any deviations that may occur. It is seldom necessary to correct for thermal expansion to achieve the accuracy required in industrial movement. Since the majority of precision parts, like the masters against which they are measured, are made of steel, it is generally safe to assume that their thermal expansion coefficients are identical and that no temperature correction need be made. Temperature corrections are also unnecessary when angles alone are measured, since a uniform temperature change cannot change the size of an angle. This will definitely change with the introduction of new materials.[1]

Measuring instruments may be *direct reading* or of the *transfer type*. An ordinary steel rule, such as the one shown in Figure III.1, items A–D, contains a graduated scale from which the size of a dimension being measured can be determined directly. The spring caliper in Figure III.1, item F, contains no scale graduations. It is adjusted to fit the size of a dimension being measured and then is compared to a direct reading scale to obtain the size of the dimension.

Most of the available measuring instruments may be grouped according to certain basic principles of operation. Many simple instruments use only a graduated scale as a measurement basis, while others may have two related scales and use the vernier principle of measurement. In a number of instruments, the movement of a precision screw is related to two or three graduated scales to form a basis for measurement. Many other instruments utilize some sort of mechanical, electrical, or optical linkage between the measuring element and the graduated scale so that a small movement of the measuring element produces an enlarged indication on the scale. Air pressure or metered airflow is used in a few instruments as a means of measurement. These operating principles will be more fully explained later in the descriptions of a few of the instruments in which they are applied.

Direct-Reading Instruments

Most of the basic or general-purpose linear measuring instruments are typified by the steel rule, the vernier caliper, or the micrometer caliper.

Steel Rules. *Steel rules* are used effectively as line measuring devices, which means that the ends of a dimension being measured are aligned with the graduations of the scale from which the length is read directly. A depth rule (Figure III.1, item I) for measuring the depth of slots, holes, and so on, is a type of steel rule. Steel rules are also incorporated in vernier calipers, as shown in Figure III.1 (item K), where they are adapted to end measuring operations. These are often more accurate and easier to apply than in-line measuring devices.

Verniers. The *vernier caliper* shown in Figure III.2 typifies the type of instrument using the vernier principle of measurement. The main or beam scale on a typical metric vernier caliper is numbered in increments of 10 mm, with the smallest scale division being equivalent to 1 mm. The vernier scale slides along the edge of the main scale and is

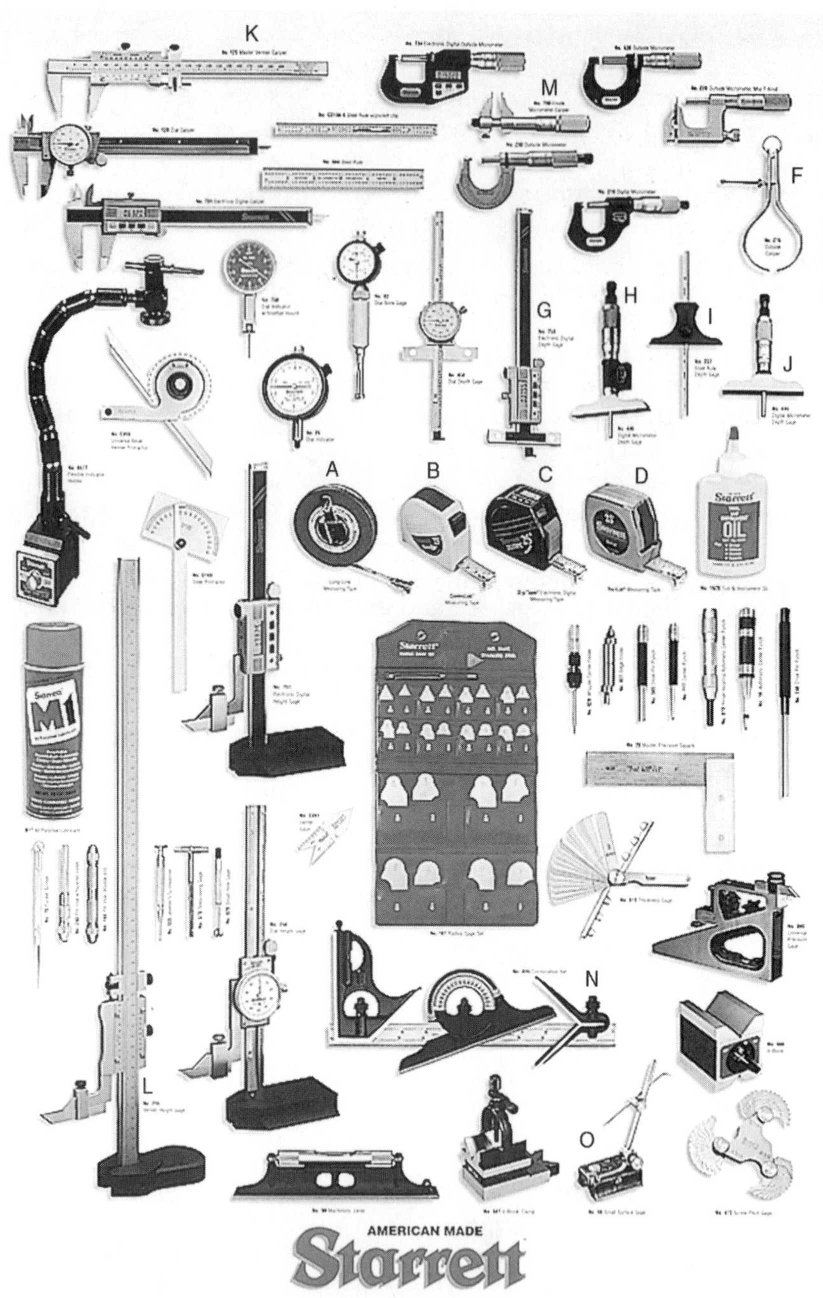

Figure III.1 Standard measuring instruments including: steel rules (A–D), spring caliper (F), micrometer depth gages (G, H, J), depth rule (I), vernier caliper (K), vernier height gage (L), inside micrometer (M), combination set (N), and surface gage (O). (Courtesy the L. S. Starrett Company.)

divided into 50 divisions, and these 50 divisions are the same in total length as 49 divisions on the main scale. Each division on the vernier scale is then equal to 1/50 of (49 × 1) or 0.98 mm, which is 0.02 mm less than each division on the main scale. Aligning the zero lines of both scales would cause the first lines on each scale to be 0.02 mm apart, the second lines 0.04 mm apart, and so on. A measurement on a vernier is designated by the positions of its zero line and the line that coincides with a line on the main scale. For example, the metric scale in Figure III.2a shows a reading of 12.42 mm. The zero index of the vernier is located just beyond the line at 12 mm on the main scale, and line 21 (after 0) coincides with a line on the main scale, indicating the zero index is 0.42 mm beyond the line at 12 mm. Thus 12.00 + 0.42 = 12.42 mm.

The vernier caliper illustrated in Figure III.2 also has an inch scale so that it can be used interchangeably for either inch or millimeter measurements. The smallest division on the main scale represents 0.25 in., and the vernier is divided into .001 in. increments. Thus the measurement illustrated is .475 away from the main scale, plus .014 from the vernier scale, for a total of .489 in.

The vernier caliper shown in Figure III.2b consists of a steel rule with a pair of fixed jaws at one end and a pair of sliding jaws affixed to a vernier. Outside dimensions are measured between the lower jaws; inside dimensions over the tips of the upper jaws. It costs about $40.

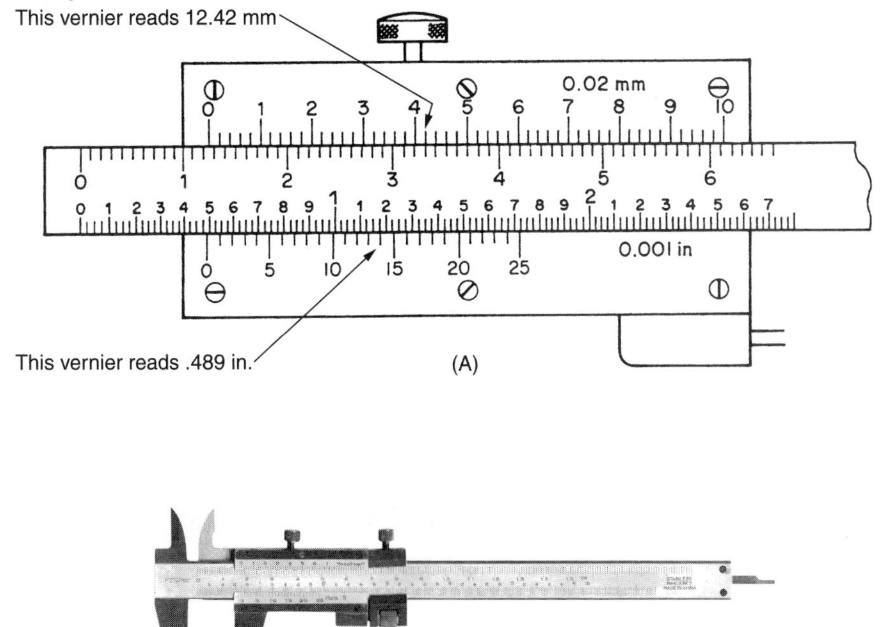

Figure III.2 Fine-adjustment style vernier caliper. (Courtesy Fred V. Fowler Company, Inc.)

Digital Calipers. The *digital reading caliper* shown in Figure III.3 provides LCD readouts in either millimeters or inches and operates by a microprocessor-based system. The caliper has a measuring range of 0–152 mm (0–6 in.) with readings in increments of 0.013 mm (.0005 in.). The unit is capable of retaining a reading in the display when the tool is used in an area where visibility is restricted. It is powered by long-life disposable batteries and costs about $175.

The *vernier height gage* of Figure III.1, item L, is similar to a vernier caliper except the fixed jaw has been replaced by a fixed base, and the sliding jaw may have a scriber attached to it for layout work or a dial indicator for measuring or comparing operations. A more sophisticated version of the vernier height gage is represented by the microprocessor-based digital height gage shown in Figure III.4. This instrument can easily measure in two dimensions in either angular or polar coordinates. It can measure external, internal, and distance dimensions, as well as perpendicularity, flatness, straightness, centers, and diameters.

Vertical measurements are made on the gage shown in Figure III.4 in either metric or inch units to a resolution of 0.0005 mm (.00002 in.) by an optoelectronic sensor moving over a high-accuracy glass scale. The gage head moves on a cushion of air generated by a completely self-contained pneumatic system. Dedicated function programs, along with a keypad and interactive LCD display, are designed to guide operators smoothly and efficiently through a variety of measurement operations. The gage can be equipped with an RS 232-C interface for direct data transfer to other data collection devices. Instruments of this type cost between $8000 and $14,000, depending on size and the type of control panel required.

Micrometers. The *micrometer caliper* illustrated in Figure III.5 is representative of the type of instruments that use a precision screw as a basis for measuring. The measuring elements consist of a fixed anvil and a spindle that moves lengthwise as it is turned.

The thread on the spindle of a typical metric micrometer has a lead of ½ or 0.5 mm, so that one complete revolution of the thimble produces a spindle movement of this amount. The graduated scale on the sleeve of the instrument has major divisions of 1.0

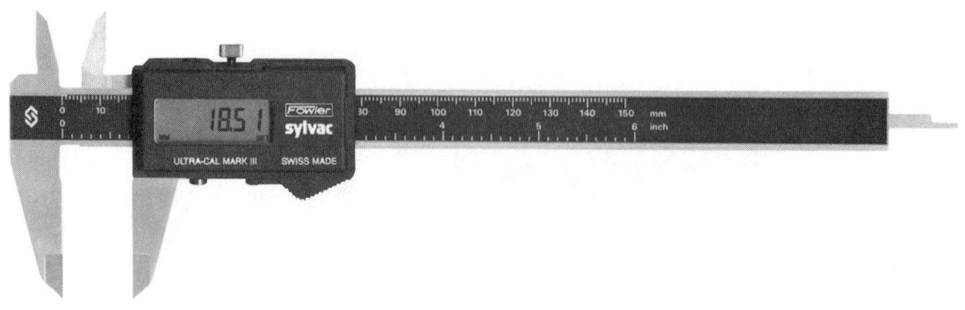

Figure III.3 LCD digital-reading caliper with 0-152 mm (0-6 in.) range. (Courtesy Fred V. Fowler Company, Inc.)

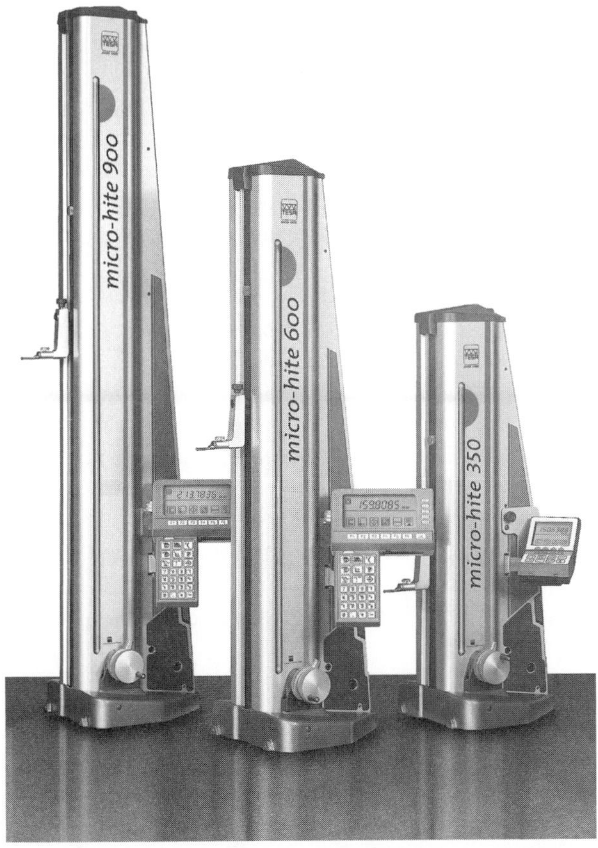

Figure III.4 Digital-reading, single-axis height gage for two-dimensional measurements. (Courtesy Brown and Sharpe Manufacturing Company.)

Figure III.5 A 0–25 mm micrometer caliper. (Courtesy Fred V. Fowler Company, Inc.)

mm and minor divisions of 0.5 mm. Thus, one revolution of the spindle causes the beveled edge of the thimble to move through one small division on the sleeve scale. The periphery of the beveled edge of the thimble is graduated into 50 equal divisions, each space representing 1/50 of a complete rotation of the thimble, or a 0.01 mm movement of the spindle. Micrometers with scales in inch units operate in a similar fashion. Typically, the spindle thread has a lead of .025 in. and the smallest division on the sleeve represents .025 in. The periphery of the beveled edge of the thimble is graduated into 25 equal divisions, each space representing 1/25 of a complete rotation of the thimble or a spindle movement of .001 in.

A reading on a micrometer is made by adding the thimble division that is aligned with the longitudinal sleeve line to the largest reading exposed on the sleeve scale. For example, in Figure III.6 the thimble has exposed the number 10, representing 10.00 mm, and one small division worth 0.50 mm. The thimble division 16 is aligned with the longitudinal sleeve line, indicating that the thimble has moved 0.16 mm beyond the last small division on the sleeve. Thus the final reading is obtained by summing the three components: 10.00 + 0.50 + 0.16 = 10.66 mm.

A *vernier micrometer caliper*, such as that represented by the scales shown in Figure III.7, has a vernier scale on the sleeve permitting measurement to 0.001 mm. The vernier scale shown has 10 divisions over a length equivalent to 19 divisions around the periphery of the thimble. Thus the difference in length of a division on the vernier scale and two divisions on the thimble is $0.02 - (1/10)(19 \times 0.01) = 0.001$ mm. Consequently, the reading illustrated in Figure III.7 is 10.00 + 0.50 + 0.16 + 0.006 = 10.666 mm.

Digital Micrometers. Micrometers with digital readouts are also available to make readings faster and easier for inspection personnel regardless of their degree of experience. The digital micrometer shown in Figure III.5 represents one instrument of this type for use in measuring to a resolution of 0.01 mm. The instrument shown in Figure III.8 has a digital readout with a resolution to .0001 in. When equipped with vernier scales, the resolution may be increased to 0.001 mm (commonly .0001 in. in the case of an inch-reading device).

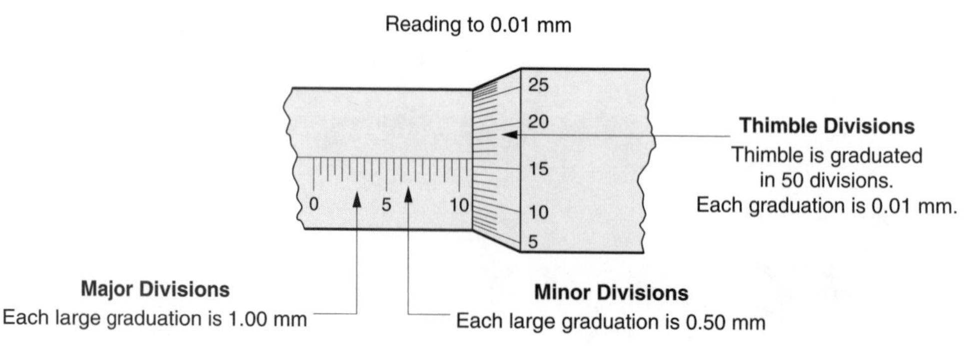

Figure III.6 Micrometer reading of 10.66 mm.

Reprinted with permission of the Society of Manufacturing Engineers, *Manufacturing Processes and Materials,* 4th Edition, Copyright 2000.

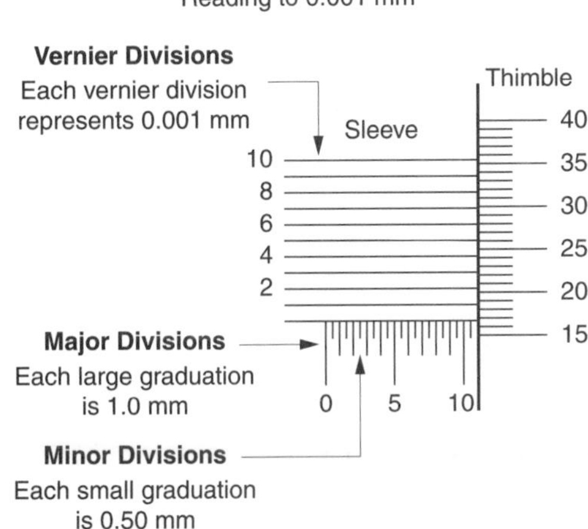

Figure III.7 Scales of a vernier micrometer showing a reading of 10.666 mm.
Reprinted with permission of the Society of Manufacturing Engineers, Manufacturing Processes and Materials, 4th Edition, Copyright 2000.

Figure III.8 A digital micrometer. (Courtesy Fred V. Fowler Company, Inc.)

Micrometer Calipers. The *micrometer caliper*, or mike as it is often called, is an end-measuring instrument for use in measuring outside dimensions. Although the mike is fairly easy to apply, the accuracy it gives depends upon the application of the proper amount of torque to the thimble. Too much torque is likely to spring the frame and cause error. Thus it is important that personnel using these instruments be trained in their use, and also that they be periodically required to check their measurements against a standard to minimize errors. The indicating micrometer of Figure III.9 has a built-in dial indicator to provide a positive indication of measuring pressure applied. The instrument can be used like an indicating snap gage.

Figure III.9 An indicating micrometer. (Courtesy Fred V. Fowler Company, Inc.)

A standard metric micrometer is limited to a range of 25 mm (1 in. for a micrometer reading in inch units). Thus different micrometers are needed to measure a wide range of dimensions. The precision screw principle is applied directly in other measuring instruments, such as the type of inside micrometer shown in Figure III.1, item M; the micrometer depth gage, in Figure III.1, items H and J; and the internal micrometer plug. It is also used as a device to provide precise calibrated linear movement to staging devices and other moving components of toolmakers' microscopes and optical projecting comparators.

Transfer-Type Linear Measuring Devices

Transfer-type linear measuring devices are typified by the spring caliper, spring divider, firm joint caliper, telescoping gage, and small hole gage. Examples of each of these are shown in Figure III.1.

The outside caliper is used as an end measure to measure or compare outside dimensions, while the inside caliper is used for inside diameters, slot and groove widths, and other internal dimensions. They are quite versatile but, due to the construction and method of application, their accuracy is somewhat limited.

Angular Measuring Devices

The unit standard of angular measurement is the degree. The measurement and inspection of angular dimensions are somewhat more difficult than linear measures and may require instruments of some complexity if a great deal of angular precision is required.

Simple Tools. The *combination set* consists of a center head, protractor, and square with a 45° surface, all of which are used individually in conjunction with a steel rule. The heads are mounted on the rule and clamped in any position along its length by means of a lock screw. The parts of such a set are shown in Figure III.1, item N. The center head is used to scribe bisecting diameters of the end of a cylindrical piece to locate the center of the piece. The protractor reads directly in degrees. Both the square head and the protractor may contain a small spirit level. A *bevel protractor* utilizes a vernier scale to show angles as small as five minutes.

The Sine Bar. The sine bar is a relatively simple device for precision measuring and checking of angles. It consists of an accurately ground, flat-steel straight-edge with precisely affixed round buttons a definite distance apart and of identical diameters.

Figure III.10 illustrates one method of applying a sine bar in the determination of the angle α on the conical surface of the part located on the surface plate. For precise results, a sine bar must be used on true surfaces. In Figure III.10, the center-to-center distance of the sine bar buttons is 127 mm (5 in.) and the distances A and B are determined by means of gage blocks, or a vernier height gage to be 25.400 mm (1.0000 in.) and 89.794 mm (3.5352 in.), respectively. Thus the sine α equals (89.794 – 25.400)/127.00 = 0.50704, and from trigonometric tables the angle α is 30°28'.

Dividing Heads. Mechanical and optical dividing heads are often employed for the circular measurement of angular spacing. The optical dividing head performs the same function but more precisely.

Layout Instruments and Locating Devices

Considerable metalworking and woodworking, particularly in job shops, for pattern building, and tool and die work, is done to lay out lines, circles, center locations, and so on, scribed on the work piece itself. Chalk or dye is often applied to the work surface before scribing so that the lines can be readily seen.

The Surface Plate. A *surface plate* provides a true reference plane from which measurement can be made. A cast-iron surface plate is a heavy ribbed, box-like casting that stands on three points (establishing a plane) and has a thick and well-supported flat top plate. New plates generally have an average of 18 bearing spots on an area of 6.5 cm^2 ($\approx$ 1 $in.^2$) that do not vary from a true plane by more than 0.005 mm (.0002 in.). The use

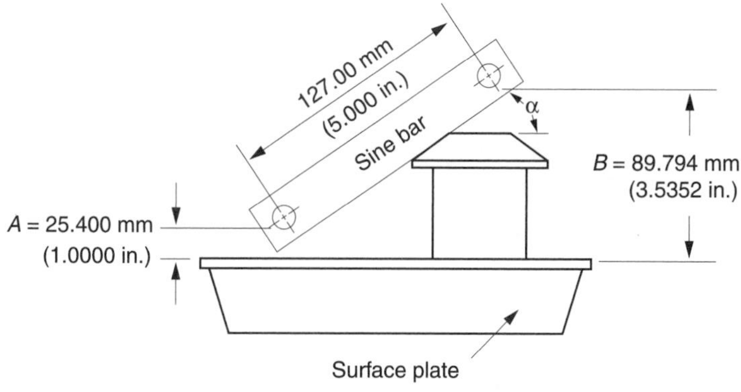

Figure III.10 Application of a sine bar.

Reprinted with permission of the Society of Manufacturing Engineers, *Manufacturing Processes and Materials,* 4th Edition, Copyright 2000.

of natural stones for surface plates is becoming increasingly popular because of their hardness, resistance to corrosion, minimum response to temperature change, and non-magnetic qualities. Figure III.11 shows a granite surface plate used in inspection work. Reference surfaces also may be obtained by the use of bar parallels, angle irons, V-blocks, and toolmakers' flats.

A variety of hand marking tools such as the scribe, spring divider, and center punch are employed by the layout person. These tools are shown in Figure III.1. The *surface gage*, Figure III.1, item O, consists of a base, an adjustable spindle, and a scriber, and may be used as a layout instrument. The scriber is first adjusted to the desired height by reference to a steel rule of gage blocks, and then the gage is moved to the work piece and a line is scratched on it at the desired location. The vernier height gage may be employed in a similar manner.

Gages

Classes. In mass-manufacturing operations it is often uneconomical to attempt to obtain absolute sizes during each inspection operation. In many cases, it is only necessary to determine whether one or more dimensions of a mass-produced part are within specified limits. For this purpose, a variety of inspection instruments referred to as *gages* are employed. However, the distinction between gauging and measuring devices is not

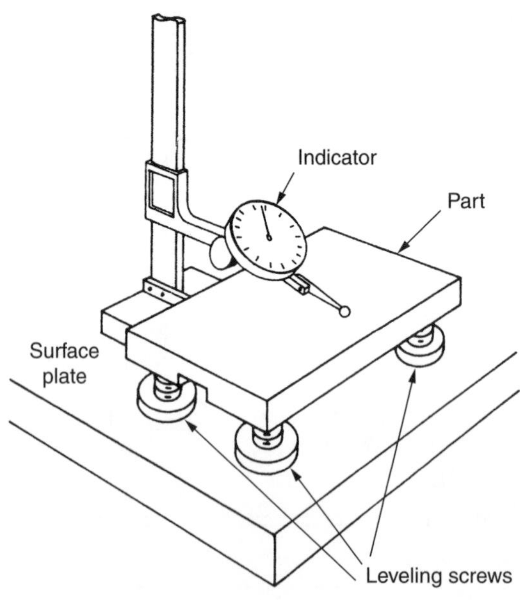

Figure III.11 Application of a granite surface plate for checking the flatness of a part with a dial indicator and leveling screws.

Reprinted with permission of the Society of Manufacturing Engineers, *Manufacturing Processes and Materials*, 4th Edition, Copyright 2000.

always clear, as there are some instruments referred to as gages that do not give definite measurements.

To promote consistency in manufacturing and inspection, gages may be classified as working, inspection, and reference or master gages. *Working gages* are used by the machine operator or shop inspector to check the dimensions of parts as they are being produced. They usually have limits based on the piece being inspected. *Inspection gages* are used by personnel to inspect purchased parts when received or manufactured parts when finished. These gages are designed and made so as not to reject any product previously accepted by a properly designed and functioning working gage. *Reference* or *master gages* are used only for checking the size or condition of other gages, and represent as exactly as possible the physical dimensions of the product.

A gage may have a single size and be referred to as a *nonlimit gage*, or it may have two sizes and be referred to as a *limit gage*. A limit gage, often called a "go" and "no go" gage, establishes the high and low limits prescribed by the tolerance on a dimension. A limit gage may be either double-end or progressive. A *double-end gage* has the "go" member at one end and the "no go" member at the other. Each end of the gage is applied to the work piece to determine its acceptability. The "go" member must pass into or over an acceptable piece, but the "no go" member should not. A *progressive gage* has both the "go" and "no go" members at the same end so that a part may be gauged with one movement.

Some gages are fixed in size while others are adjustable over certain size ranges. *Fixed gages* are usually less expensive initially, but they have the disadvantage of not permitting adjustment to compensate for wear.

Most gages are subjected to considerable abrasion during their application and therefore must be made of materials resistant to wear. High-carbon and alloy steels have been used as gage materials for many years because of their relatively high hardenability and abrasion resistance. Further increased surface hardness and abrasion resistance may be obtained from the use of chrome plating or cemented carbides as surface material on gages. Some gages are made entirely of cemented carbides, or they have cemented carbide inserts at certain wear points. Chrome plating is also used as a means of rebuilding and salvaging worn gages.

Common Gages. Typical common functional gages can be classified on the basis of whether they are used to check outside dimensions, inside dimensions, or special features. Some examples of typical gages are shown in Figure III.12. They include *ring* and *snap gages* for checking outside dimensions, *plug gages* for checking inside dimensions, and other gages for checking other geometrical shapes such as tapers, threads, and splines. Typical *plug gages*, such as the ones shown in Figure III.12a, consist of a hardened and accurately ground steel pin with two gage members: one is the "go" gage member and the other the "no go" gage member (top view of Figure III.12a). *Progressive plug gages* (bottom view of Figure III.12a) combine both "go" and "no go" members into one. The design of the gage member and the method used to attach it to the handle depends on its size as shown in Figure III.12b. The gage members are usually held in the handle by a threaded collet and bushing (view 1), a taper lock where gage members have a taper shank on one end that fits into the end of the handle (view 2), or a trilock where the gage members have a hole drilled through the center and are counter-bored on both ends to receive a standard socket-head screw (view 3). One way of checking a

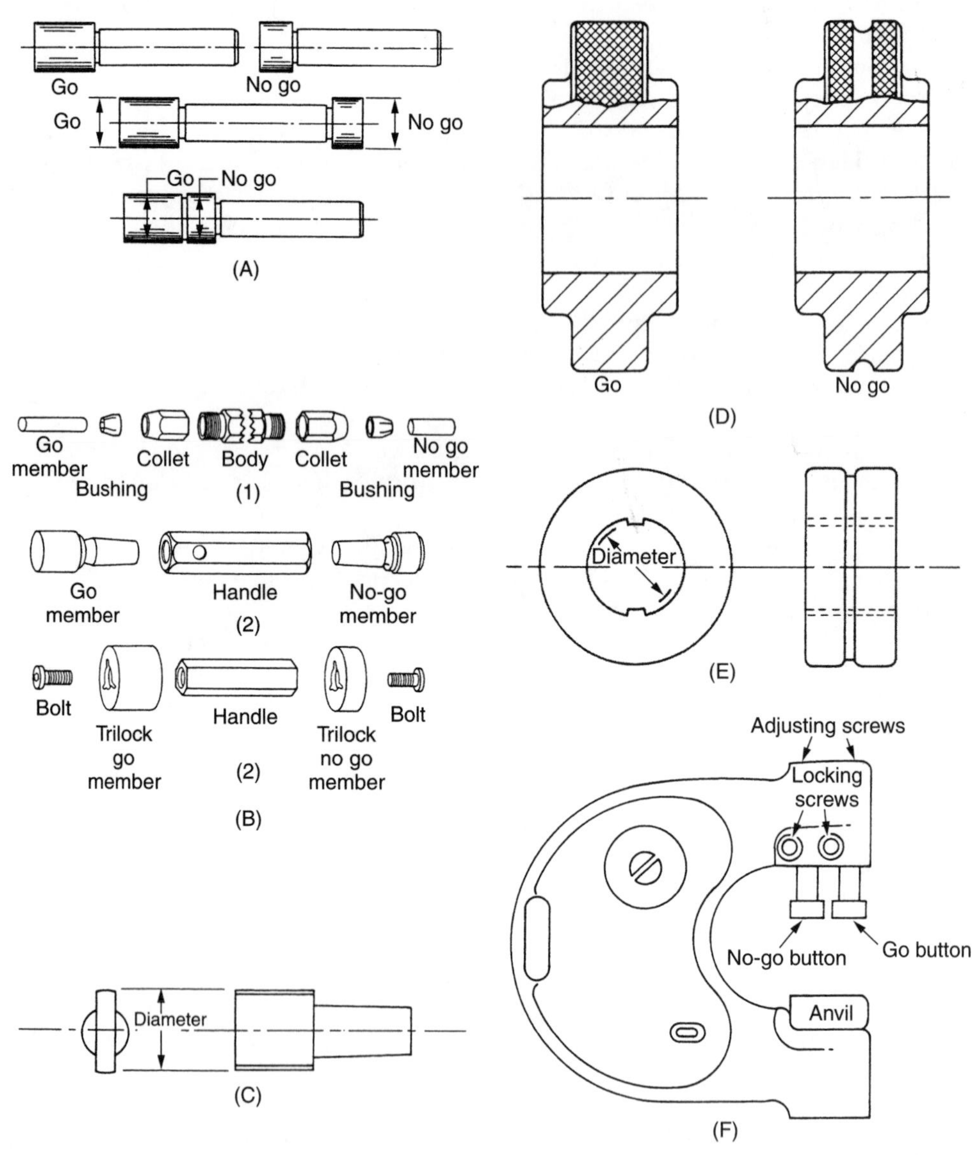

Figure III.12 Examples of typical gages.

Reprinted with permission of the Society of Manufacturing Engineers, *Manufacturing Processes and Materials*, 4th Edition, Copyright 2000.

hole for out-of-roundness is to have flats ground on the side of the gage member as shown in Figure III.12c.

Ring Gages. *Ring gages*, such as those shown in Figure III.12d, are used for checking the limit sizes of a round shaft. They are generally used in pairs: the "go" gage for checking the upper limit of the part tolerance and "no go" gage for checking the lower limit.

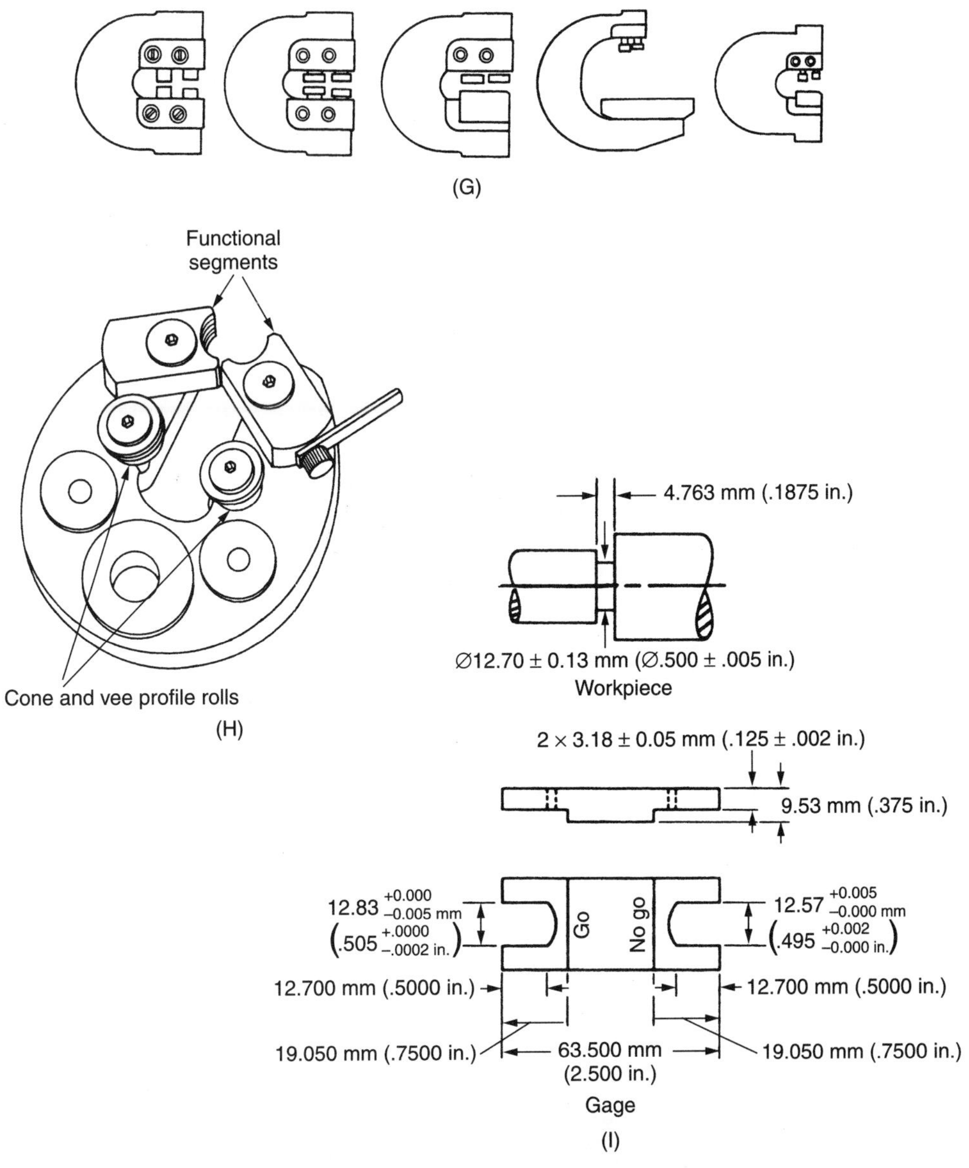

Figure III.12 *Continued.*

The "no go" ring has a groove in the outside diameter of the gage to distinguish it from the "go" ring. It is possible that a shaft's ends are larger than the middle or it could suffer an out-of-roundness condition. This situation cannot be detected with a standard cylindrical ring gage. Such an out-of-roundness condition can be checked by a ring gage that has the inside diameter relieved, such as the one shown in Figure III.12e.

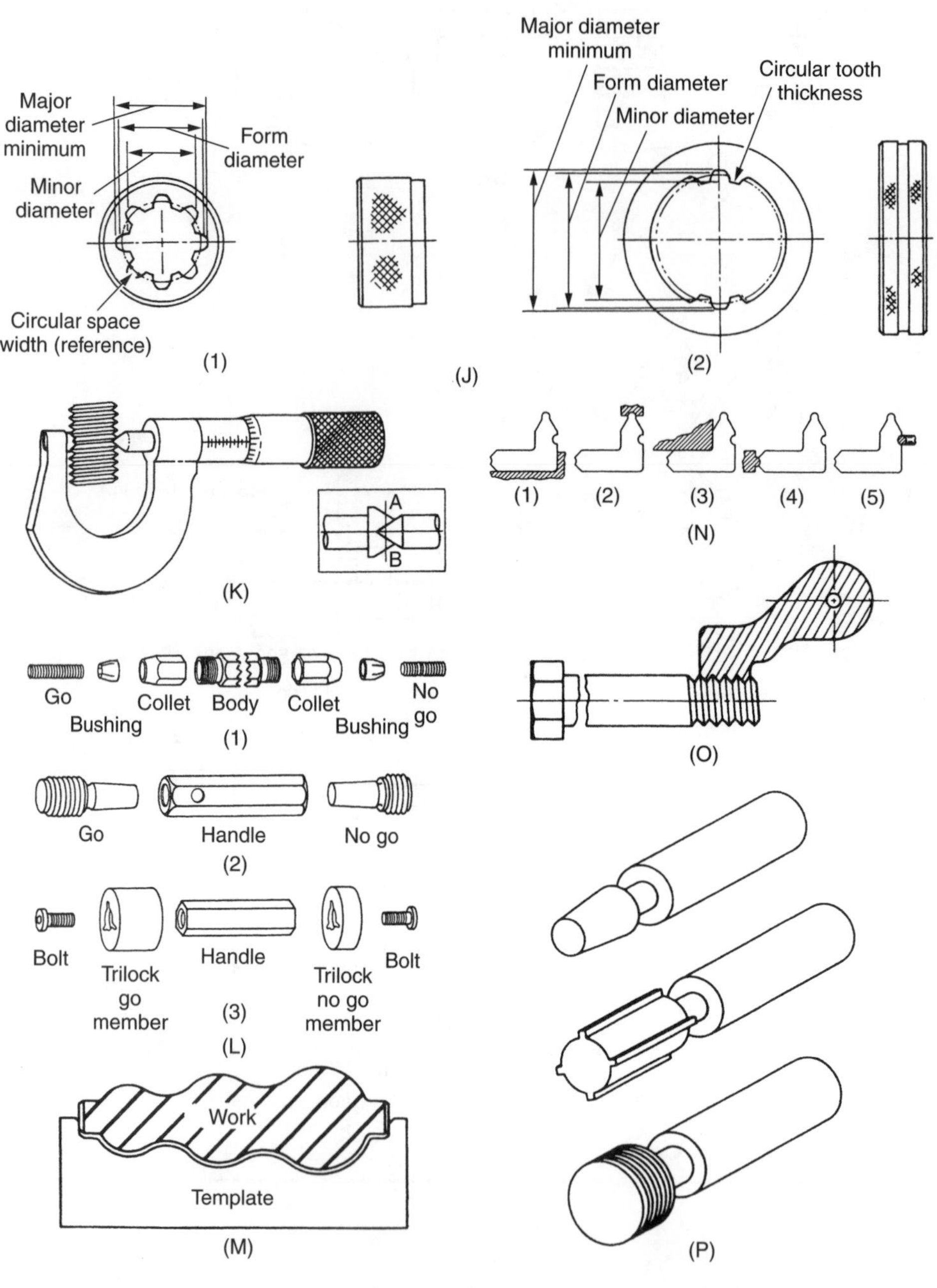

Figure III.12 *Continued.*

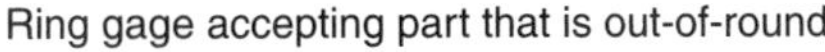

Ring gage accepting part that is out-of-round

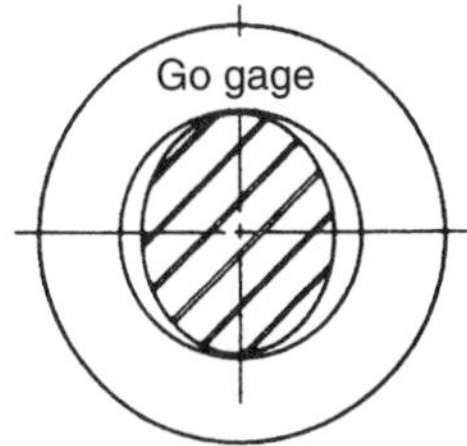

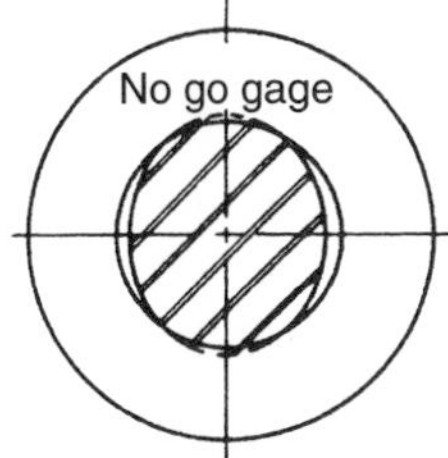

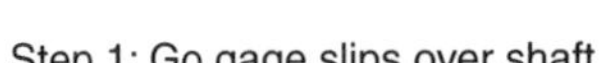

Step 1: Go gage slips over shaft

Step 2: No go gage will not slip over shaft

Snap gage rejecting part that is out-of-round

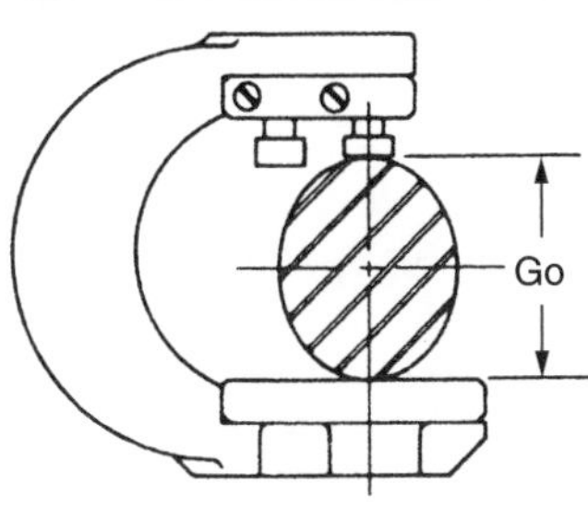

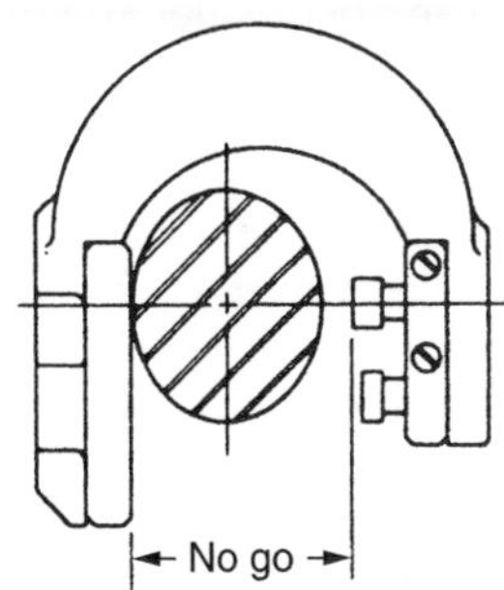

Step 1: Part enters go gage and does not enter no go

Step 2: Same part when inspected 90° from first position will enter no go gage

(Q)

Figure III.12 *Continued.*

Snap Gages. A *snap gage* is another fixed gage with the gauging members specially arranged for measuring diameters, thickness, and lengths. A typical (may also be called adjustable) *external measuring snap gage* is shown in Figure III.12f. It consists of a C-frame with gauging members in the jaw of the frame. Figure III.12g shows other types of snap gages. Threads can be checked with thread plug gages, thread ring gages, thread snap gages, or a screw thread micrometer. *Thread snap gages* have two pairs of gauging elements combined in one gage. With appropriate gauging elements, these gages may be used to check the maximum and minimum material limit of external screw threads in one path. An example of a thread snap gage is shown in Figure III.12h. In some cases, special snap gages may be desired. The example in Figure III.12i illustrated the use of a special double-end snap gage for inspecting the outside diameter of a narrow groove.

Spline Gages. The use of a *spline gage* is a common way of inspecting splined work pieces prior to assembly. External splines are checked with internal-toothed rings, whereas internal splines are checked with external-toothed plugs. Figure III.12j shows the two basic types of fixed-limit spline gages: composite and sector gages. *Composite gages* have the same number of teeth as that of the part. *Sector gages* have only two sectors of teeth 180° apart. These gages are further subdivided into "go" and "no go" gages. View 1 of Figure III.12j shows a "go" composite ring gage, and a "no go" sector ring gage is illustrated in view 2.

A *screw thread micrometer*, such as the one shown in Figure III.12k, has a specially designed spindle and anvil so that externally threaded parts can be measured. Screw thread micrometers are generally designed to measure threads within a narrow range of pitches. *Thread plug gages* are similar in design to cylindrical lug gages except that they are threaded. They are designed to check internal threads. Typical thread plug gages, such as those shown in Figure III.12l, consist of a handle and one or two thread gage members. Depending on the size of the gauging member, the member can be held in the handle using a threaded collet and bushing design (view 1), a taper lock design (view 2), or a trilock design (view 3).

Templates. To check a specified profile, *templates* may be used. They may also be used to control or gauge special shapes or contours in manufactured parts. These templates are normally made from thin, easy-to-machine materials. An example of a contour template for inspecting a turned part is shown in Figure III.12m. To visually inspect or gauge radii or fillets, special templates, such as those shown in Figure III.12n, may be used. The five basic uses of such templates are: inspection of an inside radius tangent of two perpendicular planes (view 1), inspection of a groove (view 2), inspection of an outside radius tangent to two perpendicular planes (view 3), inspection of a ridge segment (view 4), and inspection of roundness and diameter of a shaft (view 5).

Screw Pitch Gages. The pitch of a screw may be checked with a *screw pitch gage*. To determine the pitch, the gage is placed on the threaded part as shown in Figure III.12o. A drawback of using screw pitch gages is their inability to give an adequate check on thread form for precision parts.

Special Gages. It is sometimes necessary to design special gages for checking special part features such as square, hexagonal, or octagonal holes. Figure III.12p shows some special plug gages for checking the profile or taper of holes.

As an inspection tool, a snap gage is sometimes a better choice to use than a ring gage. Figure III.12q illustrates how a ring gage may accept an out-of roundness condition that would otherwise be rejected by a snap gage.

Functional Gages. A *functional gage* checks the fit of a work piece with a mating part. It normally just simulates the pertinent features of the mating part. An example of a functional gage would be a plate with four plugs, each located in true position as nearly as possible. Any part that would fit on that gage would pass inspection for hole positions.

Flush Pin Gages. A *flush pin gage* checks the limits of dimension between two surfaces in the manner illustrated in Figure III.13. The step on pin *B* is the same size as the tolerance on the depth of the hole being checked. Thus, the step on pin *B* must straddle the top of collar *A* for the depth of the hole to be within limits. An inspector can compare the surface quickly and reliably by feeling them with a fingernail.

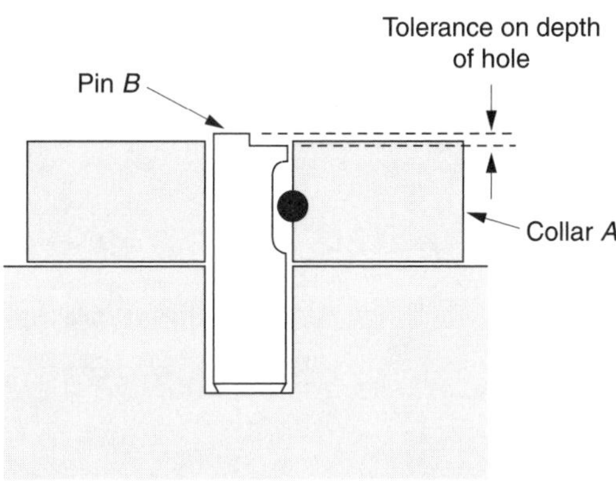

Figure III.13 Typical flush-pin gage for gauging the depth of a hole.
Reprinted with permission of the Society of Manufacturing Engineers, *Manufacturing Processes and Materials,* 4th Edition, Copyright 2000.

Sizes. In gage making, as in any other manufacturing process, it is economically impractical to attempt to make gages to an exact size. Thus it is necessary that some tolerance be applied to gages. It is desirable, however, that some tolerance still be available for the manufacturing process. Obviously, though, the smaller the *gage tolerance*, the more the gage will cost. Along with the gage makers' tolerance, it is usually necessary to provide a *wear allowance*.

Tolerances. There are three methods of applying tolerances to gages, each of which affects the outcome of the inspection operation differently. These three methods are illustrated in Figure III.14. The first is to use a unilateral gage tolerance and make the gage within the work tolerance as shown at *A*. This will result in some acceptable products being rejected. The second method is to use a bilateral gage tolerance about the limiting specifications on the part as shown at *B*. This might allow some acceptable parts to be rejected or some rejectable parts to be accepted. The third method is to use a unilateral tolerance and make the gage outside the work tolerance, as in *C*. Gages made according to this method will permit defective parts to be accepted at the start and continue to be accepted as long as the gage is in use, but it does provide the most manufacturing tolerance.

There is no universally accepted policy for the amount of gage tolerance. A number of industries where part tolerances are relatively large use 20 percent of the part tolerance for working gages and 10 percent for inspection gages. For each of these gages, one-half of the amount is used for wear on the "go" member and one-half for the gage makers' tolerance on both the "go" and "no go" members. This method has been used to determine the tolerances for the plug gages shown in Figure III.15 to check a hole with a diameter of 40.010 +0.10/–0.00 mm (1.5752 +.004/–.000 in.). The total part tolerance is 0.10 mm (.004 in.). Thus 20 percent of 0.10 mm (.004 in.) gives 0.020 mm (.0008

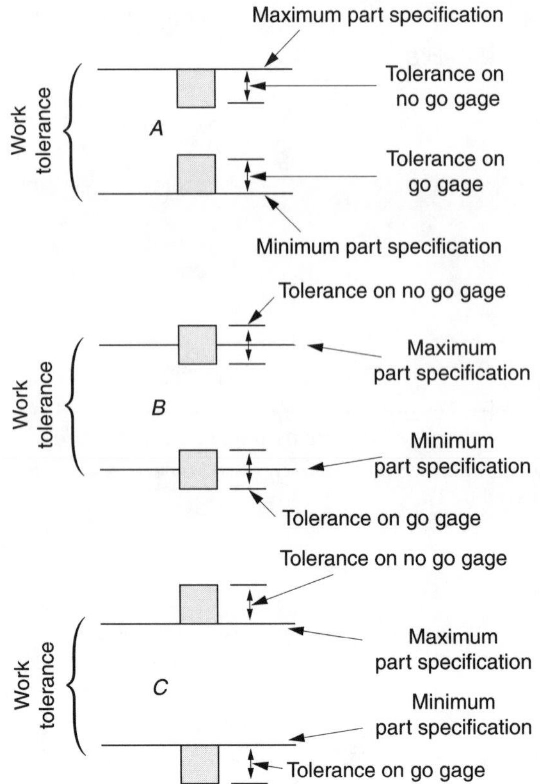

Figure III.14 Methods of assigning gage tolerances.

Reprinted with permission of the Society of Manufacturing Engineers, *Manufacturing Processes and Materials,* 4th Edition, Copyright 2000.

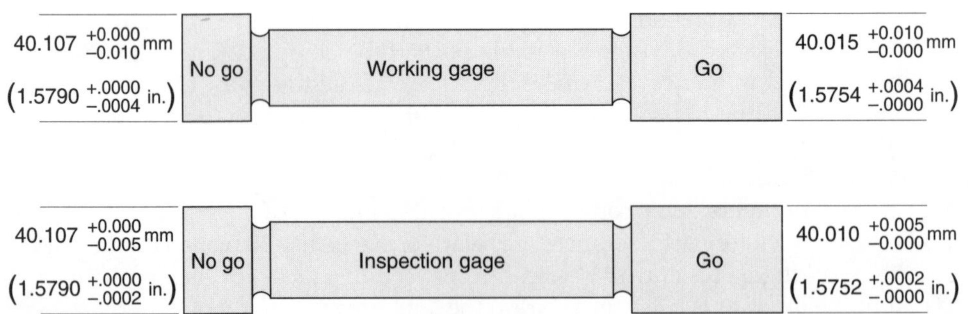

Figure III.15 Specifications on working and inspection limit plug gages.

Reprinted with permission of the Society of Manufacturing Engineers, *Manufacturing Processes and Materials,* 4th Edition, Copyright 2000.

in.) for the working gage, and 10 percent of 0.10 mm (.004 in.) gives 0.010 mm (.0004 in.) for the inspection gage, applied unilaterally.

Indicating Gages and Comparators

Indicating gages and comparators magnify the amount a dimension deviates above or below a standard to which the gage is set. Most indicate in terms of actual units of measurement, but some show only whether a tolerance is within a given range. The ability to measure to 25 nanometers (nm) (.00001 in.) depends upon magnification, resolution, accuracy of the setting gages, and staging of the work piece and instrument. Graduations on a scale should be 1.5–2.5 mm (.06–.10 in.) apart to be clear. This requires magnification of 60,000x to 100,000x for a 25 nm (.00001 in.) increment; less is needed, of course, for larger increments. Mechanical, air, electronic, and optical sensors and circuits are available for any magnification needed and will be described in the following sections. However, measurements have meaning and are repeatable only if based upon reliable standards, like gage blocks. In addition, when measuring quantities such as roundness, cylindrical parts must be appropriately supported. Either the probe or part must be rotated on a spindle that must run true with an error much less than the increment to be measured.

Mechanical Indicating Gages. *Mechanical indicating gages* are comparators. Mechanical indicating gages and comparators employ a variety of devices. One type is the dial indicator depicted in Figure III.16. Movement of stem *A* is transmitted from the rack to compound gear train *B* and *C* to pointer *D*, which moves around a dial face. Springs exert a constant force on the mechanism and return the pointer to its original position after the object being measured is removed.

Dial indicators are used for many kinds of measuring and gauging operations. One example is that of inspecting a work piece such as the one illustrated in Figure III.17. They also serve to check machines and tools, alignments, and cutter runout. Dial indicators are often incorporated in special gages in measuring instruments, as exemplified by the indicating micrometer of Figure III.9.

Electric and Electronic Gages. Certain gages are called *electric limit gages* because they have the added feature of a rack stem that actuates precision switches. The switches connect lights or buzzers to show limits and also may energize sorting and corrective devices.

An *electronic gage* gives a reading in proportion to the amount a stylus is displaced. It may also actuate switches electronically to control various functions. Figure III.18 shows an example of an electronic gage, and diagrams of the most common kinds of gage heads. The *variable inductance* or *inductance-bridge transducer* has an alternating current fed into two coils connected into a bridge circuit. The reactance of each coil is changed as the position of the magnetic core is changed. This changes the output of the bridge circuit. The *variable transformer* or *linear variable displacement transformer* (LVDT) *transducer* has two opposed coils into which currents are induced from a primary coil. The net output depends on the displacement of the magnetic core. The deflection of a strain gage transducer is sensed by the changes in length and resistance of strain gages on its surface. This is also a means for measuring forces. Displacement of a variable

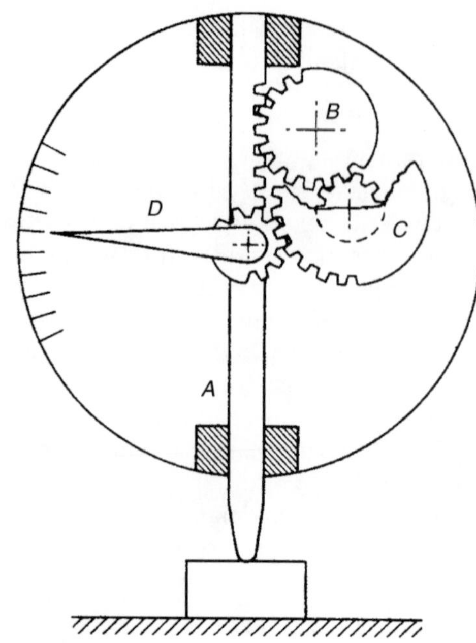

Figure III.16 Simple dial indicator mechanism.

Reprinted with permission of the Society of Manufacturing Engineers, *Manufacturing Processes and Materials,* 4th Edition, Copyright 2000.

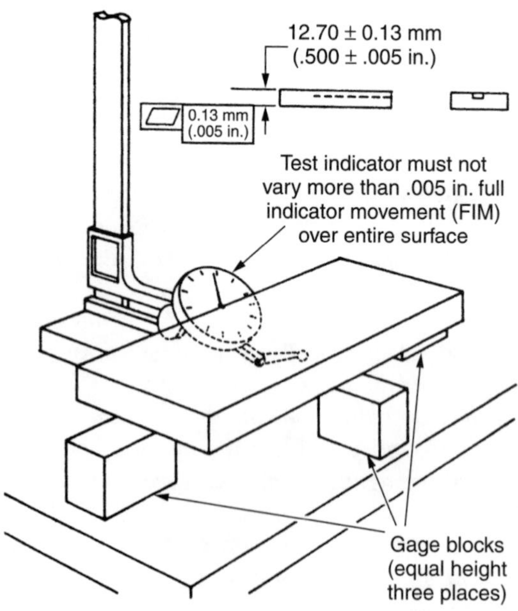

Figure III.17 An application of dial indicators for inspecting flatness by placing the work piece on gage blocks and checking full indicator movement (FID).

Reprinted with permission of the Society of Manufacturing Engineers, *Manufacturing Processes and Materials,* 4th Edition, Copyright 2000.

capacitance head changes the air gap between plates of a condenser connected in a bridge circuit. In every case, an alternating current is fed into the gage as depicted in Figure III.18e. The output of the gage head circuit is amplified electronically and displayed on a dial or digital readout. In some cases, the information from the gage may be recorded on tape or stored in a computer.

Depending on capacity, range, resolution, quality, accessories, and so on, electronic gages are priced from a little under $1000 to many thousands of dollars. An electronic height gage like the one shown in Figure III.18e with an amplifier and digital display lists for about $1700. A digital-reading height gage like the instrument shown in Figure III.18f can be used for transferring height settings in increments of 0.0025 mm (.00010 in.) with an accuracy of 0.001127 mm (.000050 in.). The instrument costs about $2000.

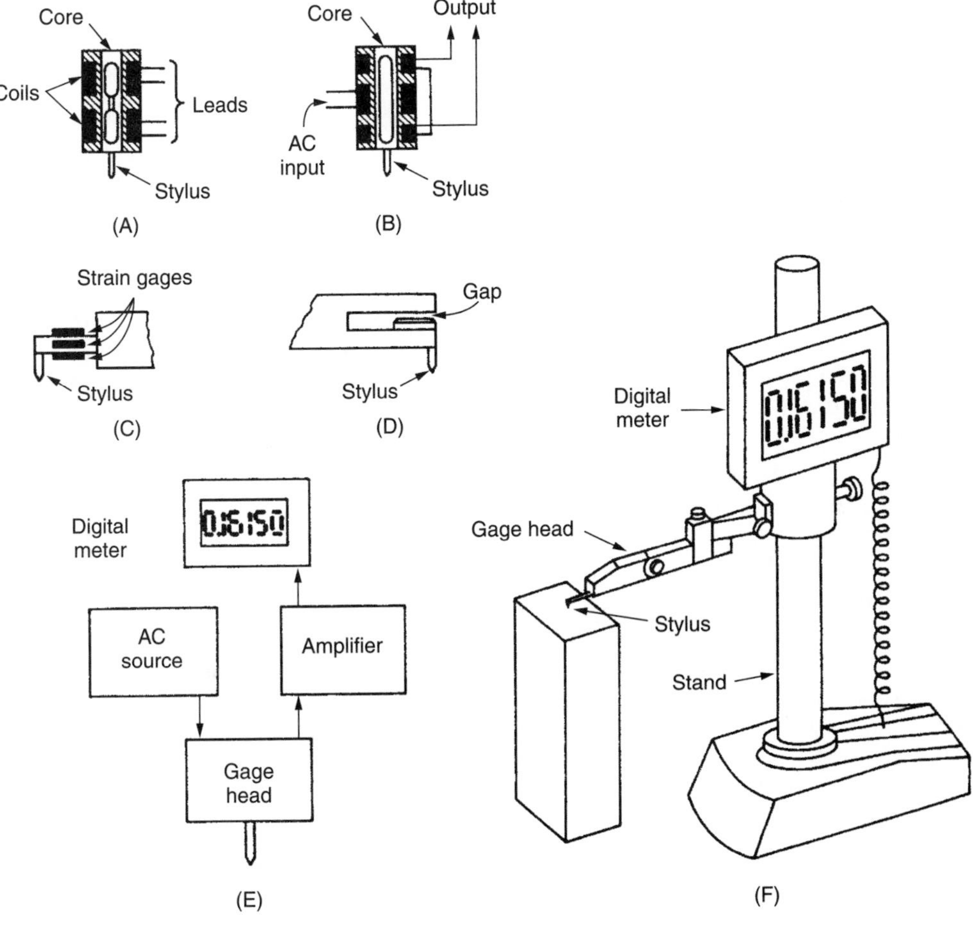

Figure III.18 Elements of electronic gages.

Reprinted with permission of the Society of Manufacturing Engineers, *Manufacturing Processes and Materials*, 4th Edition, Copyright 2000.

Electronic gages have several advantages: they are very sensitive (they commonly read to a few micrometers); output can be amplified as much has desired; a high-quality gage is quite stable; and they can be used as an absolute measuring device for thin pieces up to the range of the instrument. The amount of amplification can be switched easily, and three or four ranges are common for one instrument. Two or more heads may be connected to one amplifier to obtain sums or differences of dimensions, as for checking thickness, parallelism, and so on.

Air Gages. An *air gage* is a means of measuring, comparing, or checking dimensions by sensing the flow of air through the space between a gage head and work piece surface. The gage head is applied to each work piece in the same way, and the clearance between the two varies with the size of the piece. The amount the airflow is restricted depends upon the clearance. There are four basic types of air gage sensors shown in Figure III.19. All have a controlled constant-pressure air supply.

The *back-pressure gage* responds to the increase in pressure when the airflow is reduced. It can magnify from 1000:1 to over 5000:1, depending on range, but is somewhat slow because of the reaction of air to changing pressure. The *differential gage* is more sensitive. Air passes through this gage in one line to the gage head and in a parallel line to the atmosphere though a setting valve. The pressure between the two lines is measured. There is no time lag in the *flow gage*, where the rate of airflow raises an indicator in a tapered tube. The dimension is read from the position of the indicating float. This gage is simple, does not have a mechanism to wear, is free from hysteresis, and can amplify to over 500,000:1 without accessories. The *venturi gage* measures the drop in pressure of the air flowing through a venturi tube. It combines the elements of the back-pressure and flow gages and is fast, but sacrifices simplicity.

A few of the many kinds of gage heads and applications are also shown in Figure III.19. An air gage is basically a comparator and must be an asset to a master for dimension or to two masters for limits. The common single gage head is the plug. Practically all inside and outside linear and geometric dimensions can be checked by air gauging. Air *match gauging*, depicted in Figure III.19i, measures the clearance between two mating parts. This provides a means of controlling an operation to machine one part to a specified fit with the other. A *multidimension gage* has a set of cartridge or contact gage heads (Figure III.19h) to check several dimensions on a part at the same time. The basic gage sensor can be used for a large variety of jobs, but a different gage head and setting master are needed for almost every job and size.

A major advantage of an air gage is that the gage head does not have to tightly fit the part. A clearance of up to 0.08 mm (.003 in.) between the gage head and work piece is permissible, and even more in some cases. Thus no pressure is needed between the two to cause wear, and the gage head may have a large allowance for any wear that does occur. The flowing air helps keep surfaces clean. The lack of contact makes air gauging particularly suitable for checking against highly finished and soft surfaces. Because of its loose fit, an air gage is easy and quick to use. An inexperienced worker can measure the diameter of a hole to 25 nm (.000001 in.) in a few seconds with an air gage. The same measurement (to 25 µm .001 in.) with a vernier caliper by a skilled inspector may take up to 1 min. The faster types of air gages are adequate for high-rate automatic gauging in production.

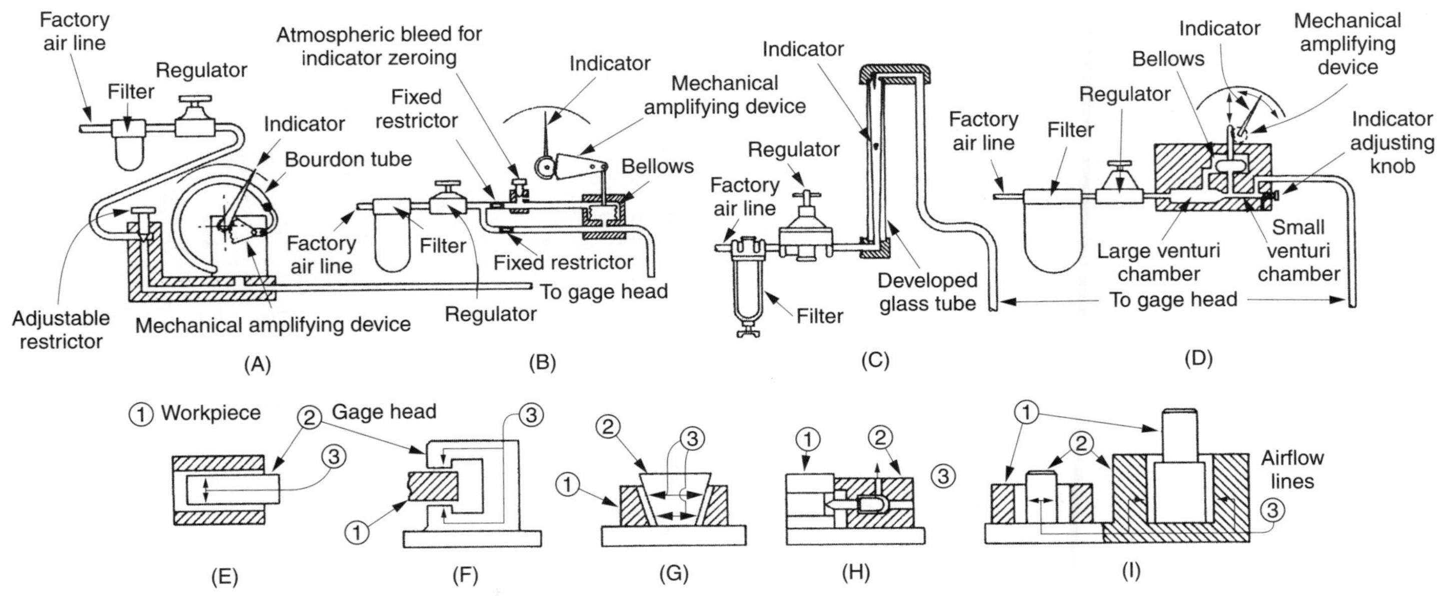

Figure III.19 Diagrams of air gage principles.

Reprinted with permission of the Society of Manufacturing Engineers, *Manufacturing Processes and Materials,* 4th Edition, Copyright 2000.

Optical Comparators. Many industrial products and component parts are so small and of such complex configuration that they require magnification for accurate discernment. For this purpose, a number of measuring and gauging instruments using various optical systems (such as the toolmakers' microscope, the binocular microscope, and the optical projecting comparator) find wide application for the inspection of small parts and tools.

The *optical projecting comparator* projects a magnified image of the object being measured on to a screen. A work piece is staged on a table to cast a shadow in a beam of light in *diascopic projection*, as shown in Figure III.20. The outline of the part is magnified and displayed on a screen. In *episcopic projection*, the light rays are directed against the side of the object and then reflected back through the projection lens.

Optical projection provides a means to check complex parts quickly to small tolerances. Commonly, a translucent drawing is placed over the screen with lines drawn to scale for the contour of the part, the limits of the outline, or critical features such as angles. For instance, the outline of a part can be compared with a drawing on the screen and deviations in the whole contour can be quickly seen. A fixture or stage may be supplied for a part to mount all pieces in the same way in rapid succession. The table can be adjusted in coordinate directions by micrometer screws or servomotors to 2 μm (.0001 in.). Table positions can be determined from the micrometer readings or from digital readout devices. Thus, a part can be displaced to measure precisely how far a line is from a specified position. In addition, the screen can be rotated to a vernier scale to measure angular deviations in minutes or small fractions of a degree. Magnifications for commercial comparators range from 5× to as much as 500×. For example, at 250× magnification, 0.0020 mm (.0008 in.) on a part becomes 0.500 mm (.0197 in.) on the screen, which is readily discernible. The horizontal optical comparator shown in Figure III.21 is table mounted and has a 356 mm (14 in.) diameter viewing screen. The designation "horizontal" means that the lens system is mounted horizontally, as illustrated

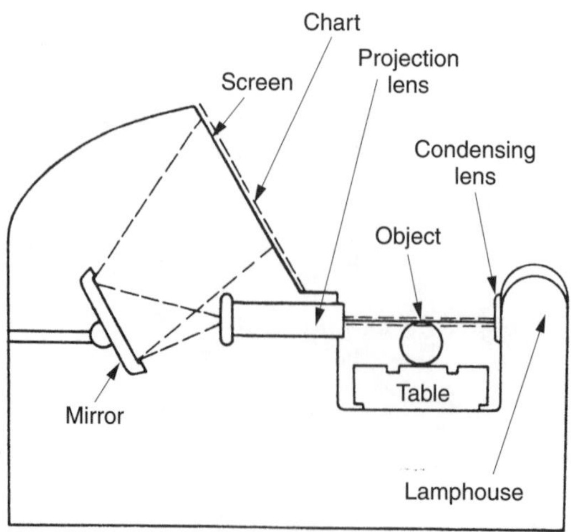

Figure III.20 Optical comparator system.

Reprinted with permission of the Society of Manufacturing Engineers, *Manufacturing Processes and Materials*, 4th Edition, Copyright 2000.

in Figure III.20. Comparators are also commercially available with a vertical lens configuration to facilitate the staging of thin parts.

One of the features of the comparator shown in Figure III.21 is a computerized digital readout (DRO) located on the top of the machine. The DRO has a two-axis digital display for establishing measurements in the *X*-*Y* plane. In addition, a 12-character, alphanumeric readout displays help messages, setup options, and the results of calculations. A fiber-optic edge-sensing device is also shown extending down the upper left portion of the screen. This device permits the digital readout to precisely indicate the edges of a part. A 16-key external keypad mounted on the lower bases provides the option of using the dedicated keys as they are identified or redefining any or all of those keys to execute any of 20 different programs containing up to 100 keystrokes each. The keypad includes a joystick capable of *X*-, *Y*-, and *Z*-axis control.

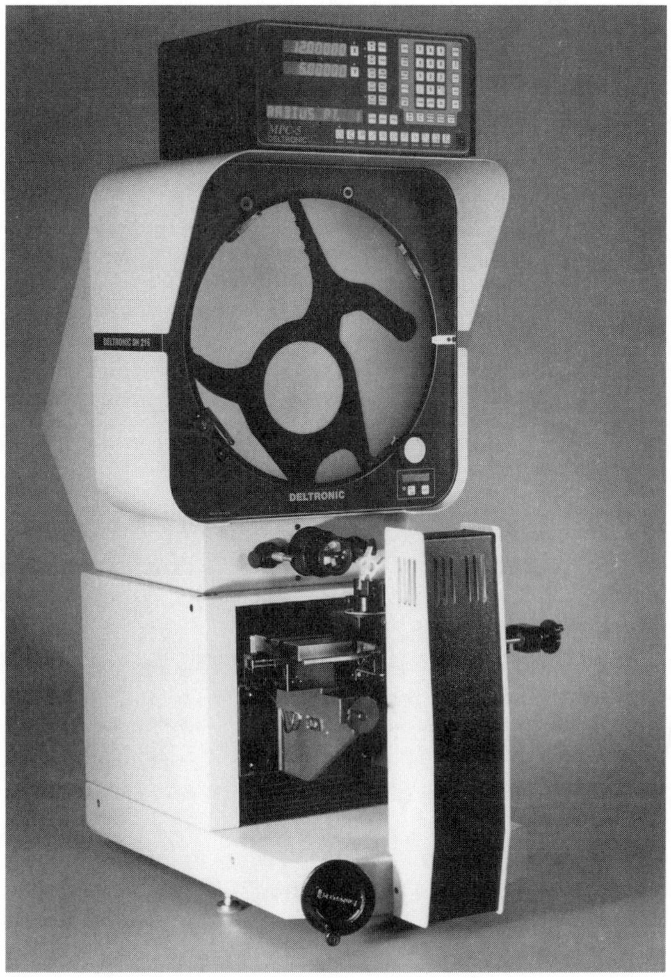

Figure III.21 Horizontal optical comparator with a 356 mm (14 in.) viewing screen, digital readout, and edge-sensing device. (Courtesy Deltronic Corporation)

Another feature of the comparator shown in Figure III.21 is an electric screen protractor that reads angles directly to either a minute or 0.01°. The angular setting of the protractor is displayed on an LED readout at the bottom-right of the screen. The machine has built-in provisions for either diascopic projection (contour illumination) or episcopic projection (surface illumination) via a high-intensity, tungsten-halogen light source. Lens changing is facilitated by the use of quick-change, bayonet-type lens holders. Seven different lens magnifications are available, ranging from 5× to 100×, all with an optical focusing range of 76 mm (3 in.). This comparator costs about $9700, which includes the edge-sensing device, the computerized digital readout, and one lens. Additional lenses cost about $550 each.

Other Measuring Standards

Along with working standards for length and angle measurements, there must be standards of geometric shape to serve as masters for the inspection of manufactured components and systems. Standards of this type are simply defined in common geometric terms and require no special definition. Taking the form of flats, straightedges, right angles, circles, balls, and the like, they are manufactured of hardened and stabilized steel to extremely close tolerances (as close as manufacturing technology permits) so that they approximate the geometric shape that they embody. A precision straightedge may be used to determine the straightness of travel of a slide on a machine tool. A master square may be used to determine the deviation from orthogonality of machine axes. A master circle may be used to inspect the truth of rotation of a machine-tool spindle. Such measurements are ultimately essential to the quality of manufactured parts, since a machine tool cannot produce parts to precise specifications if it is not precisely produced itself.[2]

Surface Metrology

Surface metrology may be broadly defined as the measurement of the difference between what the surface actually is and what it is intended to be. It is treated separately from length measurement, which is concerned with the relationship of two surfaces on a work piece. *Surface measurement*, however, is involved with the relationship of a surface on the work piece to a reference that is not actually on the work piece. The most common aspect of surface metrology is the measurement of surface roughness as an average deviation from a mean center line.[3]

The quality of surface finish is commonly specified along with linear and geometric dimensions. This is becoming more common as product demands increase because surface quality often determines how well a part performs. Heat-exchanger tubes transfer heat better when their surfaces are slightly rough rather than highly finished. Brake drums and clutch plates work best with some degree of surface roughness. On the other hand, bearing surfaces for high-speed engines wear-in excessively and fail sooner if not highly finished, but still need certain surface textures to hold lubricants. Thus there is a need to control all surface features, not just roughness alone.

Surface Characteristics

The American National Standards Institute (ANSI) has provided a set of standard terms and symbols to define such basic surface characteristics as profile, roughness, waviness, flaws, and lay. A *profile* is defined as the contour of any section through a surface. *Roughness* refers to relatively finely spaced surface irregularities such as might be produced by the action of a cutting tool or grinding wheel during a machining operation. *Waviness* consists of those surface irregularities that are of greater spacing than roughness. Waviness may be caused by vibrations, machine or work deflections, warping, and so on. *Flaws* are surface irregularities or imperfections that occur at infrequent intervals and at random locations. Such imperfections as scratches, ridges, holes, cracks, pits, checks, and so on, are included in this category. *Lay* is defined as the direction of the predominant surface pattern. These characteristics are illustrated in Figure III.22.

Surface Quality Specifications

Standard symbols to specify surface quality are included in Figure III.22c. Roughness is most commonly specified and is expressed in units of micrometers (μm), nanometers (nm), or microinches (μin.). According to ANSI/ASME B46.1-1985, the standard measure of surface roughness adopted by the United States and approximately 25 countries

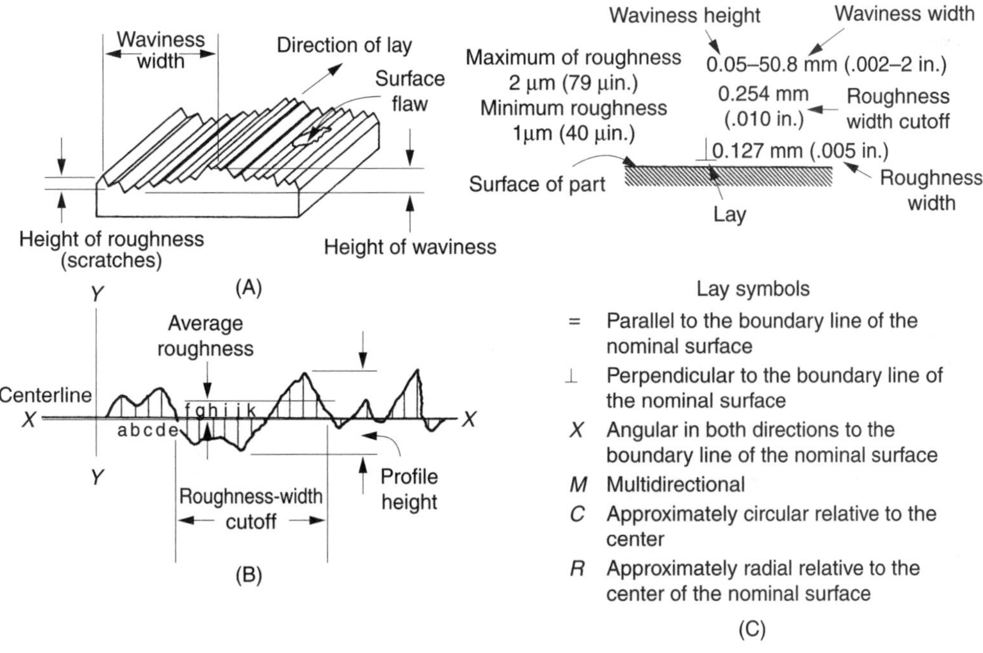

Figure III.22 (A) Typical surface highly magnified; (B) profile of surface roughness; (C) surface quality specifications.

Reprinted with permission of the Society of Manufacturing Engineers, *Manufacturing Processes and Materials*, 4th Edition, Copyright 2000.

around the world is the arithmetic average roughness, R_a (formerly AA or CLA). R_a represents the arithmetic average deviation of the ordinates of profile height increments of the surface from the centerline of that surface. An approximation of the average roughness may be obtained by:

$$R_{a+} = \frac{y_a + y_b + y_c + \ldots + y_n}{n}$$

where

R_{a+} = approximation of the average roughness

$y_a \ldots y_n$ = absolute values of the surface profile coordinates

n = number of sample measurements

The longest length along the centerline over which the measurements are made is the roughness-width cutoff or sampling length. In many cases, the maximum peak-to-valley height on a surface (R_y) is about four to five times greater than the average surface roughness as measured by R_a. This may present a problem for precision parts having small dimensional tolerances. For example, a flat surface on a part with an R_a of 0.4 μm (16 μin.) might very well have a peak-to-valley height (R_y) of 1.6 μm (64 μin.) or greater. If the tolerance on that dimension is 0.0025 mm (.0001 in.), then the 0.4 μm (16 μin.) surface finish represents nearly two-thirds of the permissible tolerance.

Prior to 1955, the root-mean-square (rms) was used to designate surface roughness. If measurements are made (plus or minus) from the centerline like the ones in Figure III.19b, the rms average is:

$$\left[\left(\Sigma y_i^2\right)/n\right]^{\frac{1}{2}}$$

where

y_i = sum of measurements taken from the centerline

n = number of measurements

Rms values are about 11 percent larger than R_a figures. Some surface roughness measuring instruments have a scale with numbers labeled "rms" and a scale calibrated in R_a values. On such instruments, the number called "rms" is root-mean-square values only when the profile is sinusoidal.

Waviness height alone may be specified, or it may be accompanied by a width specification. Thus, in Figure III.22c, the specification 0.05–50.8 mm (.002–2 in.) means that no waves over 0.05 mm (.002 in.) high are allowed in any 50.8 mm (2 in.) of length. If no width specification is given, it is usually implied that the waviness height specified must be held over the full length of the work. Other specifications in Figure III.22(C) are less common.

Measurement of Surface Finish

Waviness and roughness are measured separately. Waviness may be measured by sensitive dial indicators. A method of detecting gross waviness is to coat a surface with a high-gloss film, such as mineral oil, and then reflect it in a regular pattern, such as a wire grid. Waviness is revealed by irregularities or discontinuities in the reflected lines.

Many optical methods have been developed to evaluate surface roughness. Some are based on interferometry. One method of interference contrast makes different levels stand out from each other by lighting the surface with two out-of-phase rays. Another method projects a thin ribbon of light at 45° onto a surface. This appears in a microscope as a wavy line depicting the surface irregularities. For a method of replication, a plastic film is pressed against a surface to take its imprint. The film then may be plated with a thin silver deposit for microscopic examination or may be sectioned and magnified. These are laboratory methods and are only economical in manufacturing where other means are not feasible, such as on a surface inaccessible to a probe.

Except for extremely fine surface finishes that require laboratory measurement, most manufacturers measure surface texture at or near the workplace. A variety of instruments, called surface finish gages, are commercially available as either hand-held or table mounted. These require only moderate sill, and roughness measurements are displayed on a dial, digital readout, chart, or a digital output for statistical process control (SPC), depending on the type of instrument used. Most of these instruments employ a diamond-tipped stylus that is moved across the surface of the part to sense the point-to-point roughness of that surface. As illustrated in Figure III.23, there are two basic types of gages, the *skid* or the *skidless* type. The skid type shown in Figure III.23a has a hinged probe that rides the work surface in close proximity to a fairly large skid that also contacts the work surface. The skid type instruments usually have inductive transducers and are used predominantly for averaging measurements of surface roughness, but not waviness. The skid filters out waviness. Most portable or hand-held instruments are the skid type and they are reasonably accurate for roughness measurements in the range of 0.30–0.51 µm (12–20 µin.) R_a.

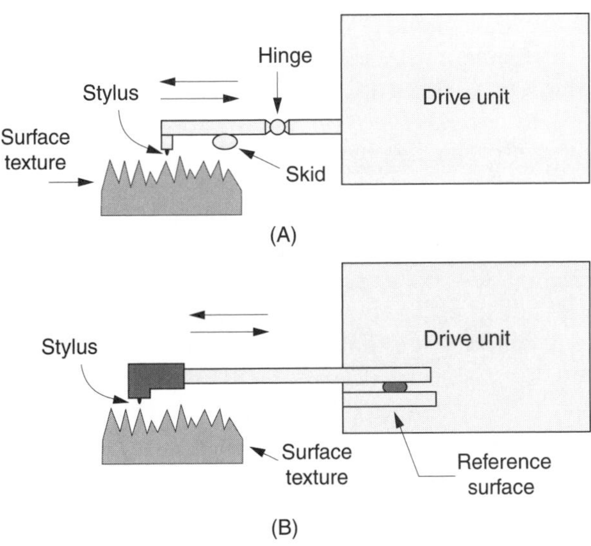

Figure III.23 (A) Skid type or average surface-finish measuring gage; (B) skidless or profiling gage.

Reprinted with permission of the Society of Manufacturing Engineers, Manufacturing Processes and Materials, 4th Edition, Copyright 2000.

The skidless type of instrument illustrated in Figure III.23b has a built-in reference surface that permits the probe to sense both long- and short-wavelength variations in surface conditions. Thus, these can be used to measure both waviness and roughness, as well as surface inclination (straightness). These instruments are often referred to as "profiling" gages and they usually generate a profile chart on paper or on a computer screen.

The international standard for the assessment of surface texture, ISO/R468, defines three parameters: R_a (CLA), R_z, and R_{max}, all measured relative to a straight mean line[4]:

1. R_a (center line average) value is the arithmetic mean of the departures of a profile from the mean line. It is normally determined as the mean result of several consecutive sample lengths L.
2. R_z (ten-point height) is the average distance between the five height peaks and five deepest valleys within the sampling length and measured perpendicular to it.
3. R_{max} is the maximum peak-to-valley height within the sampling length.

Other parameters of surface measurement are defined as follows[5]:

1. R_{tm} is the average value of R_{max}'s for five consecutive sampling lengths.
2. R_p is the maximum profile height from the mean line within the sampling length. R_{pm} is the mean value of R_p's determined over five sampling lengths.
3. PC (peak count) is the number of peak/valley pairs per inch projecting through a band of width *b* centered about the mean line.

Coordinate Measuring Machines

The *coordinate measuring machine* (CMM) is a flexible measuring device capable of providing highly accurate dimensional position information along three mutually perpendicular axes. This instrument is widely used in manufacturing industries for the post-process inspection of a large variety of products and their components. It is also very effectively used to check dimensions on a variety of process tooling, including mold cavities, die assemblies, assembly fixtures, and other work holding or tool positioning devices.

Over the last decade, coordinate measuring machines have become a primary means of dimensional quality control for manufactured parts of complex form, where the volume of production does not warrant the development of functional gauging. The advent of increasingly inexpensive computing power and more fully integrated manufacturing systems will continue to expand the use of these machines into an even larger role in the overall quality assurance of manufactured parts.

Coordinate measuring machines (CMMs) can most easily be defined as physical representations of a three-dimensional rectilinear coordinate system. Coordinate measuring machines now represent a significant fraction of the measuring equipment used for defining the geometry of different shaped work pieces. Most dimensional characteristics of many parts can be measured within minutes with these machines. Similar measurements would take hours using older measuring equipment and procedures. Besides flexibility and speed, coordinate measuring machines have several additional advantages:

1. Different features of a part can be measured in one setup. This eliminates errors introduced due to setup changes.
2. All CMM measurements are taken from one geometrically fixed measuring system, eliminating the accumulation of errors resulting from using functional gauging and transfer techniques.
3. The use of digital readouts eliminates the necessity for the interpretation of readings, such as with the dial or vernier-type measuring scales.
4. Most CMMs have automatic data recording, which minimizes the operator influence.
5. Part alignment and setup procedures are greatly simplified by using software supplied with computer-assisted CMMs. This minimizes the setup time for measurement.
6. Data can be automatically saved for further analysis.

Coordinate Measuring Machines Classification

Although coordinate measuring machines can be thought of as representations of a simple rectilinear coordinate system for measuring the dimensions of different shaped work pieces, they naturally are constructed in many different configurations, all of which offer different advantages. CMMs provide means for locating and recording the coordinate location of points in their measuring volumes. Traditional coordinate measuring machines are classified according to their configurations, as follows[6]:

1. Cantilever configuration, in which the probe is attached to a vertical machine ram (z-axis) moving on a mutually perpendicular overhang beam (y-axis) that moves along a mutually perpendicular rail (x-axis). Cantilever configuration is limited to small- and medium-sized machines. It provides for easy operator access and the possibility of measuring parts longer than the machine table.
2. Bridge-type configuration, in which a horizontal beam moves along the x-axis, carrying the carriage which provides the y-motion. In other configurations, the horizontal beam (bridge structure) is rigidly attached to the machine base and the machine table moves along the x-axis. This is called *fixed bridge configuration*. A bridge-type coordinate measuring machine provides more rigid construction, which in turn provides better accuracy. The presence of the bridge on the machine table makes it a little more difficult to load large parts.
3. Column-type configuration, in which a moving table and saddle arrangement provides the x and y motions and the machine ram (z-axis) moves vertically relative to the machine table.
4. Horizontal-arm configuration features a horizontal probe ram (z-axis) moving horizontally relative to a column (y-axis), which moves in a mutually perpendicular motion (x-axis) along the machine base. This configuration provides the possibility for measuring large parts. Other arrangements of horizontal-arm configuration feature a fixed horizontal-arm configuration in which the probe is attached and moving vertically (y-axis) relative to a column which slides along

the machine base in the x-direction. The machine table moves in a mutually perpendicular motion (z-axis) relative to the column.

5. Gantry-type configuration comprises a vertical ram (z-axis) moving vertically relative to a horizontal beam (x-axis), which in turn moves along two rails (y-axis) mounted on the floor. This configuration provides an easy access and allows the measurements of large components.

6. L-shaped bridge configuration comprises a ram (z-axis) moving vertically relative to a carriage (x-axis), which moves horizontally relative to an L-shaped bridge moving in the y-direction.

Figure III.24 shows CMM types according to this classification. The most advanced configuration, the ring-bridge, is not illustrated.

In addition to classifying coordinate measuring machines according to their physical configuration, they can also be classified according to their mode of operation: manually oriented, computer-assisted, or direct computer-controlled. In manual machines, the operator moves the probe along the machine's axes to establish and manually record the measurement values that are provided by digital readouts. In some machines, digital printout devices are used.

Computer-assisted coordinate measuring machines can be either manually positioned (free-floating mode) by moving the probe to measurement locations, or manually driven by providing power-operated motions under the control of the operator. In either case, a computer accomplishes the data processing. Some computer-assisted CMMs can perform some or all of the following functions: inch to metric conversion, automatic compensation for misalignment, storing of pre-measured parameters and measurement sequences, data recording, means for disengagement of the power drive to allow manual adjustments and manipulations of the machine motions, and geometric and analytical evaluations.

Direct computer-controlled CMMs use a computer to control all machine motions and measuring routines and to perform most of the routinely required data processing. These machines are operated in much the same way as CNC machine tools. Both control and measuring cycles are under program control. Off-line programming capability is also available.

The effective use of computers for CMM applications is a principal feature differentiating available CMM systems. The value of a measurement system depends a great deal on the sophistication and ease of use of the associated software and its functional capabilities. The functional capabilities of a CMM software package depend on the number and types of application programs available. The following is a list of many of the different types of system software available for coordinate measuring machines:

1. Printout instructions, measurement sequence, zero reference, and so on.

2. Automatic compensation for misalignment of the work piece with the machine axes.

3. Coordinate conversion between cartesian and polar coordinates.

4. Tolerance calculations providing out-of-tolerance conditions.

5. Defining geometric elements such as points, lines, circles, planes, cylinders, spheres, cones, and their intersections.

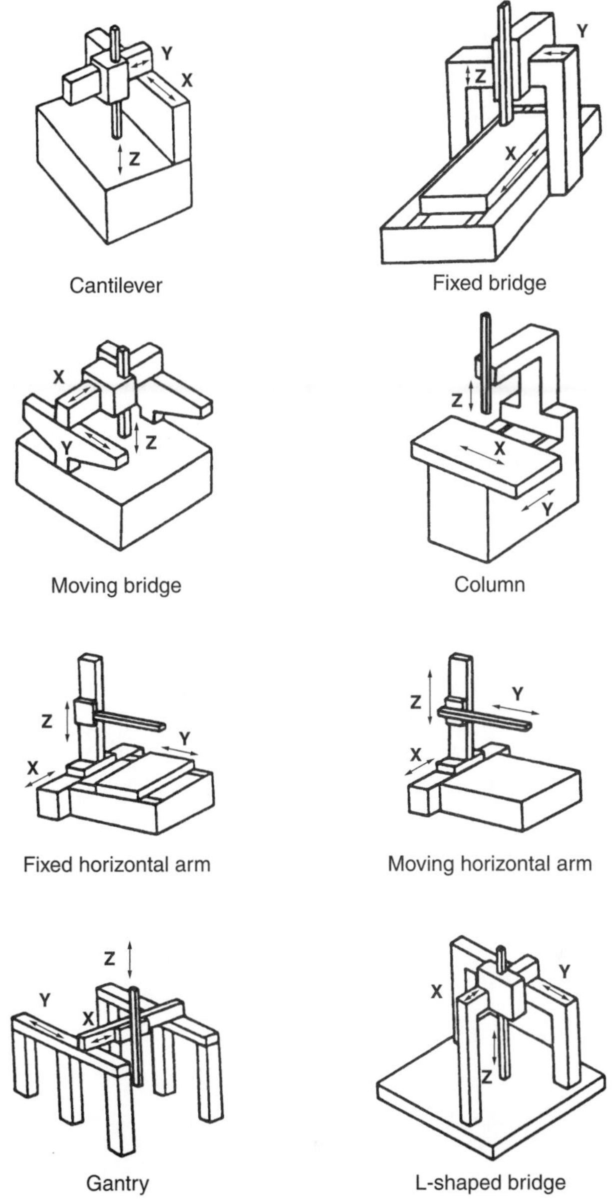

Figure III.24 Coordinate measuring machine classifications.

6. Automatic redefinition of coordinate systems or machine axes, and printout of origin and inspection planes.
7. Inspection of special shapes or contours, such as gears and cams.
8. Multiple-point hole checking using least square techniques for determining best fit center, mean diameter, roundness, and concentricity.

9. Evaluating geometric tolerance conditions by defining type of form and positional relationship, such as roundness, flatness, straightness, parallelism, or squareness.
10. Hold diameter and location checking considering maximum and minimum material conditions as defined in ANSI Y14.5.
11. Friendly operator interfaces for self-teaching or part programs.
12. Other software for statistical analysis includes graphic data display, histograms, integration of areas under a curve, contour plotting, automatic part or lot acceptance or rejection based on statistical evaluation, and so on.

Moving Bridge CMM

The two most common structural configurations for CMMs are the moving bridge and the cantilever type. The basic elements and configuration of a typical moving-bridge type coordinate measuring machine are shown in Figure III.25. The base or work table of most CMMs is constructed of granite or some other ceramic material to provide a stable work locating surface and an integral guide way for the superstructure. As indicated in Figure III.25, the two vertical columns slide along precision guide ways on the base to provide *y*-axis movement. A traveling block on the bridge gives *x*-axis movement to the quill, and the quill travels vertically for a *z*-axis coordinate.

The moving elements along the axes are supported by air bearing to minimize sliding friction and compensate for any surface imperfections on the guide ways. Movement along the axes can be accomplished manually on some machines by light hand pressure or rotation of a handwheel. Movement on more expensive machines is accomplished by axis drive motors, sometimes with joystick control. Direct computer

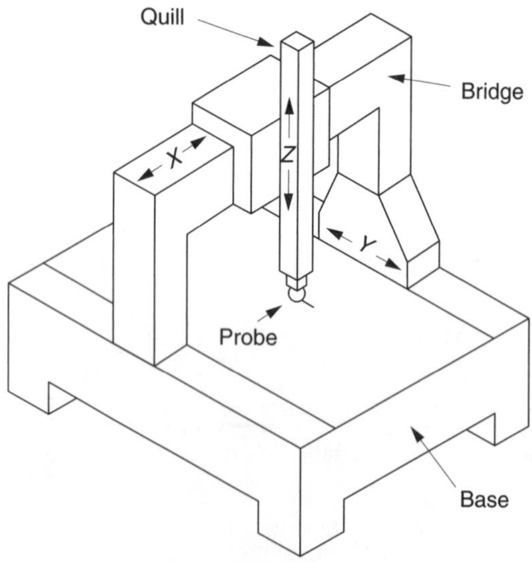

Figure III.25 Typical moving bridge coordinate measuring machine configuration.

Reprinted with permission of the Society of Manufacturing Engineers, *Manufacturing Processes and Materials,* 4th Edition, Copyright 2000.

controlled (DCC) CMMs are equipped with axis drive motors, which are programmed to automatically move the sensor element (probe) through a sequence of positions.

To establish a reference point for coordinate measurement, the CMM and probe being used must be *datumed*. In the datuming process, the probe, or set of probes, is brought into contact with a calibrated sphere located on the worktable. The center of the sphere is then established as the origin of the *x-y-z* axes coordinate system.

The coordinate measuring machine shown in Figure III.26 has a measuring envelope of about 0.5 × 0.5 × 0.4 m (18 × 20 × 16 in.), and is equipped with a disengagable drive that enables the operator to toggle between manual and direct computer control (DCC). It has a granite worktable, and the *X*-beam and *Y*-beam are made of an extruded aluminum to provide the rigidity and stability needed for accurate measuring. The measurement system has a readout resolution of 1 μm (.0004 in.) and the DCC system can be programmed to accomplish 445–600 measurement points/min. A CMM of this size costs about $58,000 with computer support, joystick control, and an electronic touch probe. It can also be equipped with a video camera for noncontact measurement.

Contacting Probes. CMM measurements are taken by moving the small stylus (probe) attached to the end of the quill until it makes contact with the surface to be measured.

Figure III.26 Coordinate measuring machine. (Courtesy Brown and Sharpe Manufacturing Company)

The position of the probe is then observed on the axes readouts. On early CMMs, a rigid (hard) probe was used as the contacting element. The hard probe can lead to a variety of measurement errors, depending on the contact pressure applied, deflection of the stylus shank, and so on. These errors are minimized by the use of a pressure-sensitive device called a *touch trigger probe*.

The touch trigger probe permits hundreds of measurements to be made with repeatabilites in the 0.25–1.0 μm (.00001–.00004 in.) range. Basically, this type of probe operates as an extremely sensitive electrical switch that detects surface contact in three dimensions. The manual indexable touch-trigger probe shown in Figure III.27 can be used to point and probe without redatuming for each position measured. A probe of this type for use on manually operated CMMs costs about $4000. Motorized probe heads are available at a cost between $16,000–$19,000 for use on DCC CMMs.

Noncontacting Sensors. Many industrial products and components that are not easily and suitably measured with surface contacting devices may require the use of non-contact sensors or probes on CMMs to obtain the necessary inspection information. This may include: two-dimensional parts, such as circuit boards and very thin stamped parts; extremely small or miniaturized microelectronic devices and medical instrument parts; and very delicate, thin-walled products made of plastic or other light-weight materials.

There are several noncontacting sensor systems available that have been adapted either individually or in combination with the coordinate measuring process. All of these involve optical measuring techniques and include microscopes, lasers, and video cameras. The automated, three-dimensional, video-based coordinate measuring system

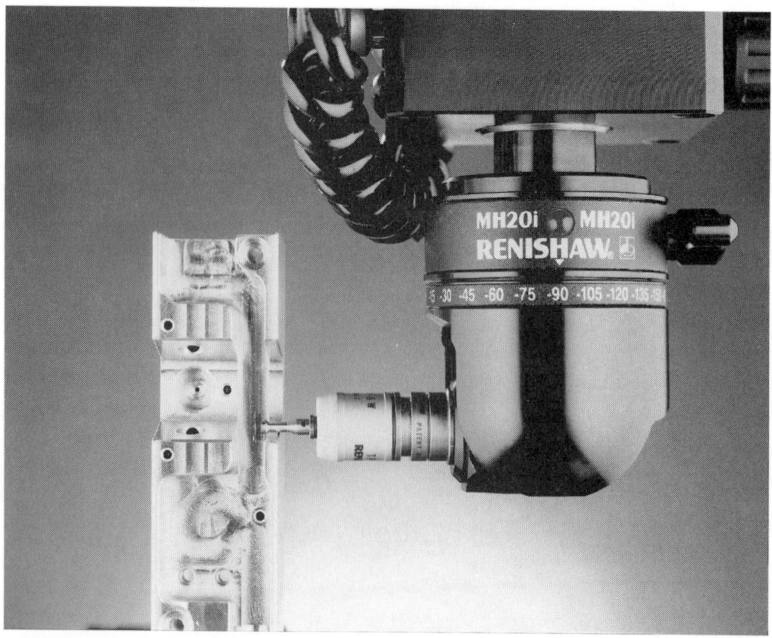

Figure III.27 Manual indexable probe. (Courtesy Renishaw, Inc.)

appears to offer many advantages because of its ability to accomplish multiple measurements within a single video frame. Thus, it is often possible to obtain data from several hundred coordinate points with a video measuring system in the same time it would take to obtain a single-point measurement with a conventional touch-probe system. A large number of points on a part can be imaged with CCD (charged couple device) video cameras, depending on the optical view and array or pixel size of the camera. For example, one commercially available system has a field of view range from 0.5–7.6 mm (.02–.30 in.) with a 756 × 581 pixel array, and can image the field of view at 30 video frames/second.

Video-based systems do not have the same throughput advantage for height (z-axis) measurements as they do for two-dimensional (x-y) measurements because of the time involved for focusing. On some machines, this disadvantage is overcome by integrating laser technology with the video system.

The *multisensor coordinate measuring machine* (MSCMM) shown in Figure III.28 incorporates three sensing technologies for highly accurate noncontact and/or contact inspection tasks: optical, laser, and touch probe. The machine uses two quills or measuring heads to accomplish high-speed data acquisition within a four-axis (x, y, $z1$, $z2$)

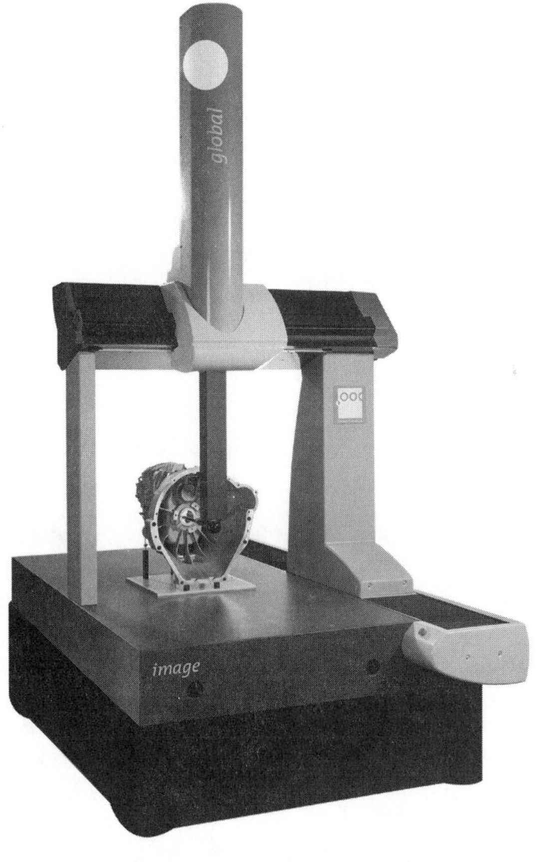

Figure III.28 A multisensor coordinate measuring machine with optical, laser, and touch probes for noncontact and contact measurements. (Courtesy Brown and Sharpe Manufacturing Company)

configuration, thus permitting noncontact or contact inspection of virtually any part in a single setup.

The sensing head on the left quill in Figure III.28 contains an optical/laser sensor with a high-resolution CCD video and a coaxial laser. The video camera has advanced image processing capabilities via its own microprocessor, enabling subpixel resolutions of 0.05 μm (2μin.). The coaxial laser shares the same optical path as the video image and assists in the focusing of the CCD camera. This eliminates focusing errors associated with optical systems and increases the accuracies of Z measurements. Single-point measurements can be obtained in less than 0.2 sec. and high-speed laser scanning/digitizing can be accomplished at up to 5000 points/second.

The right-hand quill of Figure III.28 contains the z2-axis touch-probe sensor used to inspect features that are either out of sight of the optical/laser sensor or are better suited to be measured via the contact method.

The MSCMM of Figure III.28 is being used to inspect a valve body with the *z*1-axis optical/laser probe and a transmission case with the *z*2-axis touch probe. The machine shown is a bench-top type with a maximum measuring range of 900 mm (≈ 35 in.), 800 mm (≈ 32 in.), and 600 mm (≈ 24 in.) for the *x*, *y*, and *z*1 and *z*2 axes, respectively. Positioning of the moving elements is accomplished by backlash-free, recirculating-ball lead screws and computer-controlled DC motors. Position information is provided by high-precision glass scales. A multisensor coordinate measuring machine of this type with Windows-based computer control costs about $275,000.

Automatic Gauging Systems

As industrial processes are automated, gauging must keep pace. Automated gauging is performed in two general ways. One is in-process or on-the-machine control by continuous gauging of the work. The second way is post-process or after-the-machine gauging control. Here, the parts coming off the machine are passed through an automatic gage. A control unit responds to the gage to sort pieces by size, and adjusts or stops the machine if parts are found out of limits.

Measuring With Light Rays

Interferometry

Light waves of any kind are of invariable length and are the standards for ultimate measures of distance. Basically, all interferometers divide a light beam and send it along two or more paths. Then the beams are recombined and always show interference in some proportion to the differences between the lengths of the paths. One of the simplest illustrations of the phenomenon is the optical flat and a monochromatic light source of known wavelength.

The optical flat is a plane lens, usually a clear fused quartz disk, from about 51–254 mm (2–10 in.) in diameter and 13–25 mm (.5–1 in.) thick. The faces of a flat are accurately polished to nearly true planes; some have surfaces within 25 nm (.000001 in.) of true flatness.

Helium is commonly used in industry as a source of monochromatic or single-wavelength light because of its convenience. Although helium radiates a number of wavelengths of light, that portion that is emitted with a wavelength of 587 nm

(.00002313 in.) is so much stronger than the rest that the other wavelengths are practically unnoticeable.

The principle of light-wave interference and the operation of the optical flat are illustrated in Figure III.29a, wherein an optical flat is shown resting at a slight angle on a work piece surface. Energy, in the form of light waves, is transmitted from a monochromatic light source to the optical flat. When a ray of light reaches the bottom surface of the flat, it is divided into two rays. One ray is reflected from the bottom of the flat toward the eye of the observer, while the other continues on downward and is reflected and loses one-half wavelength on striking the top of the work piece. If the rays are in phase when they re-form, their energies reinforce each other, and they appear bright. If they are out of phase, their energies cancel and they are dark. This phenomenon produces a series of light and dark fringes or bands along the work piece surface and the bottom of the flat, as illustrated in Figure III.29b. The distance between the work piece and the bottom surface of the optical flat at any point determines which effect takes place. If the distance is equivalent to some whole number of half wavelengths of the same monochromatic light, the reflected rays will be out of phase, thus producing dark bands. This condition exists at positions X and Z of Figure III.29a. If the distance is equivalent to some odd number of quarter wavelengths of the light, the reflected rays will be in phase with each other and produce light bands. The light bands would be centered between the dark bands. Thus a light band would appear at position Y in Figure III.29a.

Since each dark band indicates a change of one-half wavelength in distance separating the work surface and flat, measurements are made very simply by counting the number of these bands and multiplying that number by one-half the wavelength of the light source. This procedure may be illustrated by the use of Figure III.29b. There, the diameter of a steel ball is compared with a gage block of known height. Assume a monochromatic light source with a wavelength of 0.5875 μm (23.13 μin.). From the block, it is obvious that the difference in elevations of positions *A* and *B* on the flat is equal to $(4 \times 0.5875)/2$ or 1.175 μm ($[4 \times 23.13]/2$ or 46.26 μin.). By simple proportion, the difference in elevations between points *A* and *C* is equal to $(1.175 \times 63.5)/12.7 = 5.875$ μm ($[46.26 \times 2.5]/.5 = 231.3$ μin.). Thus the diameter of the ball is $19.05 + 0.005875 = 19.055875$ mm ($.750 + .0002313 = .7502313$ in.).

Optical flats are often used to test the flatness of surfaces. The presence of interference bands between the flat and the surface being tested is an indication that the surface is not parallel with the surface of the flat.

The way dimensions are measured by interferometry can be explained by moving the optical flat of Figure III.29a in a direction perpendicular to the face of the work piece or mirror. It is assumed that the mirror is rigidly attached to a base, and the optical flat is firmly held on a true slide. As the optical flat moves, the distance between the flat and mirror changes along the line of traverse, and the fringes appear to glide across the face of the flat or mirror. The amount of movement is measured by counting the number of fringes and fraction of a fringe that pass a mark. It is difficult to precisely superimpose a real optical flat on a mirror or the end of a piece to establish the end points of a dimension to be measured. This difficulty is overcome in sophisticated instruments by placing the flat elsewhere and by optical means reflecting its image in the position relative to the mirror in Figure III.29a. This creates interference bands that appear to lie on the face of and move with the work piece or mirror. The image of the optical flat can be merged into the planes of the work piece surfaces to establish beginning and end points of dimensions.

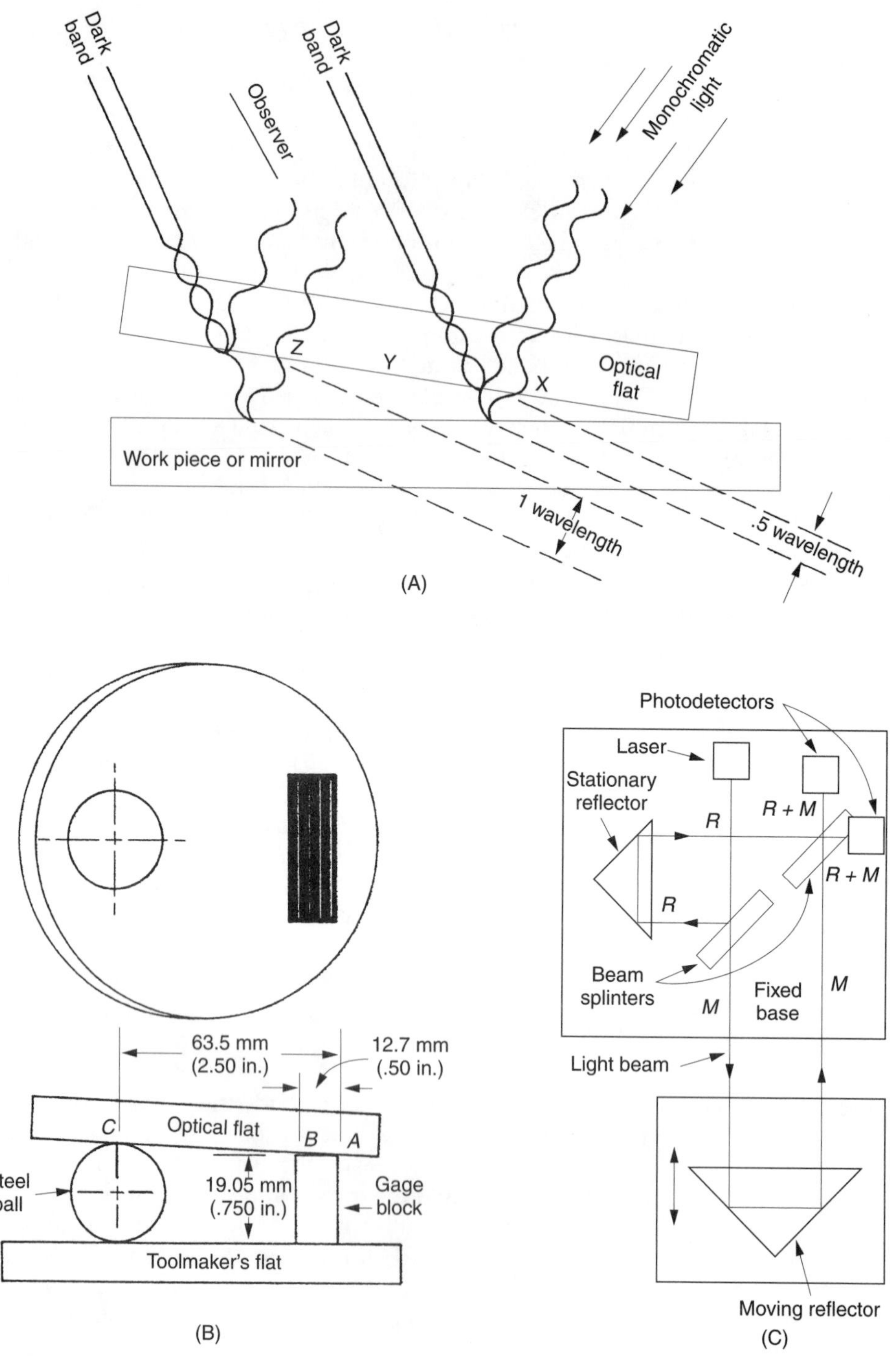

Figure III.29 (A) Light-wave interference with an optical flat; (B) application of an optical flat; (C) diagram of an interferometer.

Reprinted with permission of the Society of Manufacturing Engineers, *Manufacturing Processes and Materials*, 4th Edition, Copyright 2000.

A simple interferometer for measuring movements of a machine tool slide to nanometers (millionths of an inch) is depicted in Figure III.29c. A strong light beam from a laser is split by a half mirror. One component becomes the reference *R* and is reflected solely over the fixed machine base. The other part *M* travels to a reflector on the machine side and is directed back to merge with ray *R* at the second beam splitter. Their resultant is split and directed to two photodetectors. The rays pass in and out of phase as the slide moves. The undulations are converted to pulses by an electronic circuit; each pulse stands for a slide movement equal to one-half the wavelength of the laser light. The signal at one photodetector leads the other according to the direction of movement.

When measurements are made to nanometers (millionths of an inch) by an interferometer, they are meaningful only if all causes of error are closely controlled. Among these are temperature, humidity, air pressure, oil films, impurities, and gravity. Consequently, a real interferometer is necessarily a highly refined and complex instrument; only its basic elements have been described here.

Optical Tooling

Telescopes and accessories to establish precisely straight, parallel, perpendicular, or angled lines are called *optical tooling*. Two of many applications are shown in Figure III.30a and b. One is to check the straightness and truth of ways of a machine tool bed at various places along the length. The other is to establish reference lanes for measurements on a major aircraft or missile component. Such methods are especially necessary for large structures. Accuracy of one part in 200,000 is regularly realized; this means that a point at a distance of 2.5 m (100 in) can be located within 13 µm (.0005 in.). Common optical tooling procedures are autocollimation, autoreflection, planizing, leveling, and plumbing.

Autocollimation is done with a telescope having an internal light that projects a beam through the crosshairs to a target mirror as indicated in Figure III.30a. If the mirror face is truly perpendicular to the line of sight, the crosshair image will be reflected back on itself. The amount the reflected image deviates from the actual reticle image is an indication of the tilt in the target. A target may have a cross-line pattern for alignment with the line of sight. An autocollimated image is not clear for distances over 15.2 m (50 ft), and then a somewhat less accurate method must be used. This is *autoreflection*, with an optical flat containing a cross-line pattern mounted on the end of the illuminated telescope and focused to twice the distance of the target mirror. Then if the mirror is perpendicular to the line of sight, the pattern of the flat is reflected in coincidence with the crosshairs in the telescope.

Planizing is comprised of fixing planes at 90° with other planes or with a line of sight. This may be done from accurately placed rails on which transits are mounted in a tooling dock as indicated in Figure III.30b. A transit is a telescope mounted to swing in a plane perpendicular to a horizontal axis. Square lines also may be established with an optical square or planizing prism mounted on or in front of a telescope as depicted in Figure III.30c. Angles may be precisely set by autocollimating on the precisely located faces of an optical polygon as in Figure III.30d.

Leveling establishes a horizontal line of sight or plane. This may be done with a telescope fitted with a precision spirit level to fix a horizontal line of sight. A transit or sight level set in this manner may be swiveled around a vertical axis to generate a horizontal plane. *Plumbing*, shown in Figure III.30e, consists of autocollimating a telescope from the surface of a pool of mercury to establish a vertical axis.

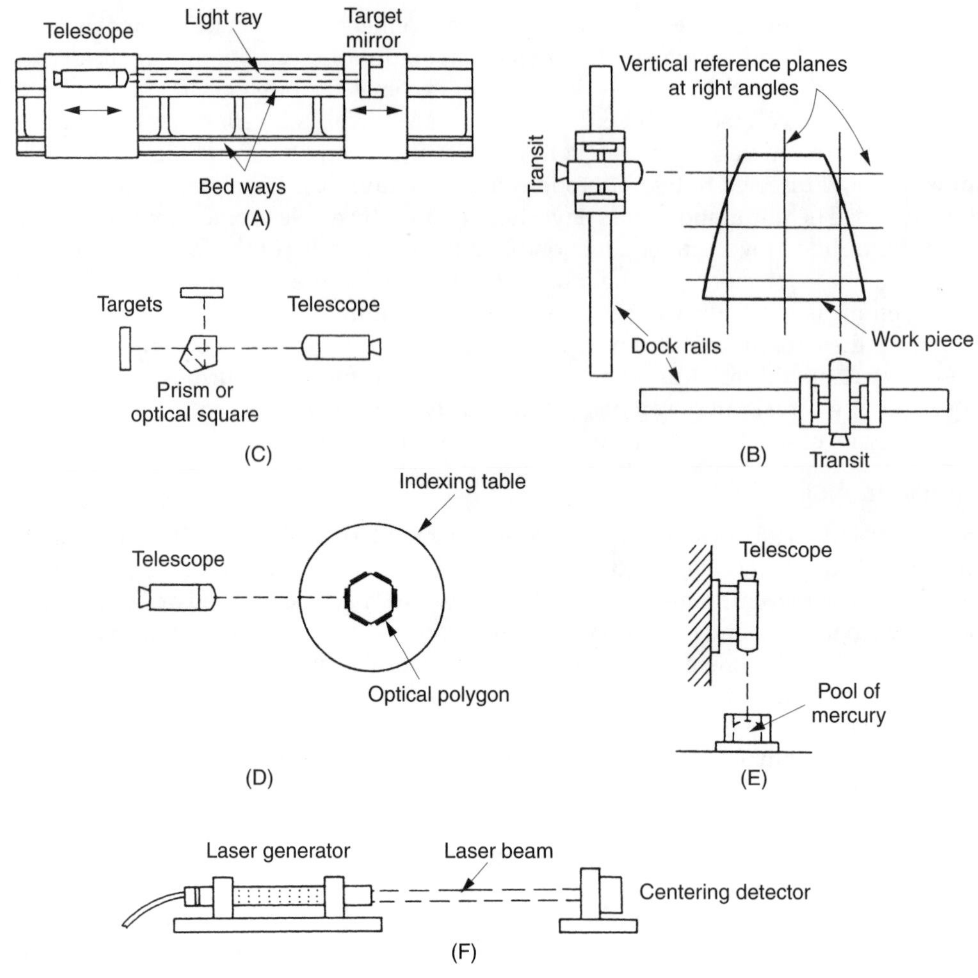

Figure III.30 Optical tooling.

Reprinted with permission of the Society of Manufacturing Engineers, *Manufacturing Processes and Materials,* 4th Edition, Copyright 2000.

An advanced step in optical tooling is the use of the intense light beam of a laser. A centering detector, shown in Figure III.30f, has four photocells equally spaced (top and bottom and on each side) around a point. Their output is measured and becomes equalized within the device and is centered with the beam. This provides a means to obtain alignment with a straight line. Squareness may be established by passing a laser beam through an optical square.

Hardness Testing

Hardness of metals is usually determined using either the Brinnell or Rockwell methods. In each case, a load is applied to a penetrator. For the Brinnell test, the diameter of the indentation is measured. For the Rockwell test, the depth of penetration is measured.

Force Testing

A force is defined as a push or pull, typically as a result of contact between objects. Forces are conveniently measured in pounds or kilograms using various testing devices.

Weight Testing

The weight of an object is a measure of the force that gravity exerts on it, whereas mass measures its inertia. Therefore, for example, an object would have the same mass whether on Earth or on the moon, but would have different weights. Weight and mass are proportional in a given gravitational field. Scales must be given the same type of attention regarding maintenance and calibration as other gages.

B. CALIBRATION PROCEDURES

Calibration refers to measurements where the individual values are reported, rather than to measurements indicating only that an instrument is functioning within prescribed limits. It also refers to the disciplines necessary to control measuring systems to assure their functioning within prescribed accuracy objectives.[7] The aim of all calibration activities is ascertaining that a measuring system will function to assure attainment of its accuracy objectives.

The general calibration provisions for a measuring system include[8]:

1. Acceptance calibration of a new system
2. Periodic calibration of the system in use or when placed in use after storage
3. Availability of standards traceable to the national standard for the unit of measure under consideration

Normally, a calibration chain or pyramid of echelons is involved in the discipline of metrology control and surveillance. The levels include[9]:

1. *Level 1*: the product tolerance or measured quantity
2. *Level 2*: the calibration of the product measuring system
3. *Level 3*: the calibration of the measuring system used to calibrate the product measurement system
4. *Level 4*: local standards, such as gage blocks or standard cells (volts), used for calibration of Level 3
5. *Level 5*: referencing local standards of Level 4 to the national standard

Each of these levels attempts to achieve an accuracy/tolerance ratio that will satisfy requirements of the preceding level. This achievement is, of course, subject to the limitations of the state of the art, as well as cost–accuracy tradeoffs that may come into play.[10]

Periodic calibration of measuring and test equipment is accepted by most as necessary for measurement accuracy. A little more controversial is the question of determining the basis of the period of recalibration. There are a number of techniques in use to establish calibration intervals initially and to adjust the intervals thereafter. These methods include the same interval for all equipment in the user's inventory, the same interval for families of instruments (for example, oscilloscopes, digital volumeters [DVMs], gage blocks, and so on), and the same interval for a given manufacturer and model number. Adjustments of these initial intervals are then made for the entire inventory, individual families, or manufacturer and model numbers, respectively, based on analyses or history. A study conducted for NIST in connection with a review of government laboratory practices identifies these and other methods.[11]

Calibration Programs

A typical calibration program may involve all or most of the following tasks[12]:

1. Evaluation of equipment to determine its capability
2. Identification of calibration requirements
3. Selection of standards to perform calibration
4. Selection of methods/procedures to carry out the measurements necessary for the calibration
5. Establishment of the initial interval and the rules for adjusting the interval thereafter
6. Establishment of a recall system to assure instruments due for calibration are returned
7. Implementation of a labeling system to visually identify the instrument's due date
8. Use of a quality assurance program to evaluate the calibration system (process, control, audit, corrective action, and so on)

Selection of the standards, methods, and procedures to carry out the calibration includes the decision relating to where the calibration will be performed. Some instruments may require use of a laboratory's highest level of standards and thus must be performed in the laboratory. Other instruments, however, may be calibrated in the using area by the transport of suitable standards to that area.

The recall system must be designed to assure that the calibration organization and the using organization are both aware in advance that an instrument will be due for calibration. Depending on the number of instruments being controlled and their different geographic locations, the system may be as simple as a card file or as sophisticated as a fully automated data processing system. The more sophisticated the system, the more that can be expected from it beyond the basic purpose of providing recall notification (for example, history of previous calibrations, interval assignments, labor standards or actual costs, parts replaced, and so on).

Labeling instruments to visually display their calibration due dates is a companion feature to the recall system. Labels indicate (by dates, color codes, or similar symbols) the date the instrument is due for its next calibration. This visual identification may be used by the quality assurance organization to assure that the instrument is not used beyond its due date.

Intervals are established in a variety of ways, as discussed previously. Principal objectives of an interval adjustment program include minimizing the potential for out-of-tolerance instruments in using areas, minimizing the costs of calibration, and assuring the required accuracy of instrumentation. The effectiveness of the interval adjustment programs can be estimated by measuring the average interval and its trend by measuring the quality level.

Quality-level goals that vary from about 75 percent to above 95 percent have been established by different organizations. The relationship between intervals and quality levels is complicated by such factors as age of equipment in the inventory (new items are added to inventories), the makeup of the inventory (mechanical instrumentation, electronic test equipment, fixtures, and so on), and the accuracy assignments of the instruments in the inventory. The quality level, however, is one indicator of the effectiveness of the interval adjustment program. When combined with other indicators (such as the average interval, the minimum and maximum observed intervals, and a corrective-action system that is triggered by low intervals), the quality level is a sound method for evaluating the total calibration control system.

Gage Traceability

Traceability is a process intended to quantify a laboratory's measurement uncertainty in relation to the national standards. It is based on analyses of error contributions present in each of the measurement transfers: the calibration of the laboratory's reference standards by NIST, the measurements made in the calibration transfers within the laboratory, and the measurements made on a product. Evidence of traceability is normally required; it may be as simple as retention of certificates and reports on calibration, or as complex as reproduction of the analyses demonstrating the uncertainties claimed for the measurements.[13]

A laboratory that maintains its own reference standards (that is, it relies on no laboratory other than NIST for calibration of its standards) must continuously monitor its own performance. Measurements on check standards, intercomparisons of standards, and participation in measurement assurance programs sponsored by NIST are meant to quantify laboratory error sources, as well as to provide indications of the causes.[14]

Classification of Standards

The National Institute of Standards and Technology (NIST) is this nation's custodian of the standards of measurement. It was established by an act of Congress in 1901, although the need for such a body had been noted by the founders of the Constitution. NIST's two main campuses are in Gaithersburg, Maryland, and Boulder, Colorado, where research into the phenomenon of measurement, the properties of materials, and calibration of the reference standards submitted by laboratories from throughout the United States is carried out. The following is a generalization of the echelons of standards in the national measurement system[15]:

- *National standards.* Include prototype and natural phenomena of SI (Systems International, the worldwide system of weight and measures standards) base units and reference and working standards for derived and other units.
- *Metrology standards.* Reference standards of industrial or governmental laboratories.
- *Calibration standards.* Working standards of industrial or governmental laboratories.

Frequently, there are various levels within these echelons.[16]

In order to maintain accuracy, standards in a vast industrial complex must be traceable to a single source, usually the country's national standards. Since the national laboratories of well-developed countries maintain close connections with the International Bureau of Weights and Measures, there is assurance that items manufactured to identical dimensions in different countries will be compatible.[17]

Application of precise measurement has increased so much during the past few years that it is no longer practical for a single national laboratory to perform directly all the calibrations and standardization required by a large country with high technical development. This has led to the establishment of a considerable number of standardizing laboratories in industry and in various branches of the state and national governments. In order that results of calibrations be uniform, the standardizing laboratories must maintain close rapport with the national laboratory. This is facilitated by use of uniform terminology when discussing standards.[18]

Gage Repeatability and Reproducibility

In any production process, natural or inherent variability is the cumulative effect of many small causes. When other causes are present, these are referred to as *special* or *assignable causes*. This variability usually arises from sources such as improperly adjusted machines or equipment, operator errors, or defective raw materials. Such variability is generally large when compared to the natural process variability and it usually represents an unacceptable level of process performance. A process that is operating in the presence of assignable causes is said to be "out-of-control." Often, production processes operate in the in-control state. Occasionally, however, assignable causes occur, seemingly at random, resulting in a shift to a state of out-of-control. A control chart is widely used to quickly detect the occurrence of assignable causes, and corrective action may be undertaken before many nonconforming units are manufactured.

Control charts mainly detect the presence of assignable causes. The concept of gage repeatability and reproducibility (GR&R)[19] can be employed to identify real root causes of the problem in a process. After process adjustment, factors that affect the measurement system variation can then be studied using the gage repeatability and reproducibility (GR&R) technique. Measurement system variation can be characterized by location (stability, bias, linearity) and width or spread (repeatability and reproducibility). A general discussion for estimating total measurement variation is outlined below.

GR&R study is appropriate to apply in most manufacturing-related measurement systems. It may be used as:

- A criterion for judging new measuring equipment
- A comparison among measuring devices
- A means for improving performance of measuring instruments
- A comparison for measuring equipment before and after repair
- A required component for calculating process variation and the acceptability level for a production process
- A measure of the need for training in how to use measuring instruments

Repeatability is the variation in measurement obtained with one measuring instrument when used several times by the same operator measuring an identical characteristic on the same part. The standard deviation for repeatability or instrument variation (σ_e) is estimated by:

$$\frac{\overline{R}}{d_2^*}$$

where $\overline{R}$ is the average range of the repeated measurements.

Reproducibility, on the other hand, is the variation in the average of measurements made by different operators using the same measuring instrument when measuring the identical characteristic on the same part. Operator variation or reproducibility is estimated by determining the overall average for each appraiser and then finding the range (R_0) by subtracting the smallest operator average from the largest. The standard deviation for reproducibility (σ_0) is estimated by R_0/d_2^*.

The measurement system variance ($\sigma^2_{R\&R}$) can then be estimated by:

$$\sigma^2_{R\&R} = \sigma_e^2 + \sigma_0^2$$

The measurement system variation (R&R) or gage R&R is represented by $\sigma_{R\&R}$.

Part-to-Part Variation

Part-to-part variation also makes a contribution to the total variation in a measurement and can be determined from the measurement system data or an independent process capability study. If the measurement system study is used, the part standard deviation σ_P (PV) is estimated by R_p/d_2^*. R_p can be estimated as the average range of part measurements.

Total Variation

Total variation (TV or σ_{TV}) for the study is calculated by summing the square of both the repeatability and reproducibility (R&R) variation and the part-to-part variation PV, and taking the square root, as follows:

$$TV = \sqrt{(R\&R)^2 + (PV)^2}$$

The contribution of the equipment variation contribution EV is calculated as 100(EV/TV). The contribution of other factors to the total variation TV can be similarly calculated, as follows:

$$\%AV = 100\frac{AV}{TV}$$

$$\%AV = 100\frac{R\&R}{TV}$$

$$\%AV = 100\frac{PV}{TV}$$

Example: This example illustrates the use of GR&R study as a means for improving performance of measuring instruments. At a quality assurance department of a PCB plant, experiments were conducted in order to compare two types of instruments.

Instrument	Purpose	Specification
Coating measuring instrument (CMI)	To measure Ni/Au plating thickness of boards	Thickness must be at least 0.76 micron ($\geq$ 0.76 μm)
Vernier caliper	To measure board's dimensions	5.77 $\pm$ 0.01 inches

Samples of 10 parts were taken. Three operators, A, B, and C, made the measurements using the above instruments. Measurements of the 10 parts were made in a random order. Operators A, B, and C did the same measurement for all 10 parts without seeing each other's reading. Measured values are recorded on a sheet separated by each operator. The procedure was repeated using a different random order of parts and operators. The above formulae were used to obtain the following results:

Results of Variations for Both Instruments

Variation	CMI	Vernier Caliper
% EV	76.60	21.33
% AV	22.13	90.76
% R&R	79.73	93.23

From this study, the measurement variation by those who used CMI for measurement provided more equipment variation *EV* than vernier caliper, but provided less operator variation *AV* than vernier caliper. Investigations have revealed that:

- CMI is more sensitive to use. It is affected by temperature, vibration, humidity, and so on.
- This instrument is used for measurements with very high precision (10^{-6} m).
- The calibration method may not be suitable.

Therefore, corrective action should focus on equipment improvement rather than operator improvement.

For the vernier caliper, the following observations were made:

- Operators do not understood enough to use and read the equipment.
- The different skills and experiences of each operator had an effect on reading scales.
- The measuring method of each operator was different.

Therefore, corrective action should focus on operator improvement by providing training rather than instrument improvement. Variation results of both instruments after improvement are shown below.

Coating Measuring Instrument

Variation	Improvement 1	Improvement 2
% EV	48.80	27.01
% AV	12.29	14.86
% R&R	50.32	30.82

Vernier Caliper		
Variation	**Improvement 1**	**Improvement 2**
% EV	24.10	13.02
% AV	1.60	0.00
% R&R	24.15	13.02

Endnotes

1. R. B. Zipin, "Dimensional Measurements and Standards in Manufacturing," *Bendix Technical Journal* 1, no. 4 (1971): 15–19.
2. Ibid.
3. J. A. Bosch, *66 Centuries of Measurement* (Dayton, OH: Sheffield Measurement Division, 1984).
4. R. C. Spragg, "Advanced System for the Measurement of Errors of Form," *SME Paper* No. IQ 76-807, 1976.
5. Machinability Data Center, *Machining Data Handbook* (Cincinnati, OH: TechSolve, 1980).
6. ASME, *ANSI/ASME B89.1.12M-1985 Methods for Performance Evaluation of Coordinate Measuring Machines* (New York: ASME, 1985).
7. W. J. Darmody, "Elements of a Generalized Measuring System," in *Handbook of Industrial Metrology* (Englewood Cliffs, NJ: Prentice Hall, 1967).
8. Ibid.
9. Ibid.
10. Ibid.
11. T. L. Voft, "Optimizing Calibration Recall Intervals and Algorithms," *NIST Publication* NBS-GCR-80-283, 1980.
12. G. O. Rice, "Metrology," in *Quality Management Handbook*, eds. L. Walsh, R. Wurster, and R. J. Kimber (Milwaukee: ASQC Quality Press; and New York: Marcel Dekker, 1986).
13. Ibid.
14. Ibid.
15. Ibid.
16. D. A. Mack, "Instrument Calibration" (workshop conference on the Management of Laboratory Instruments, Cairo, Egypt, November 7–11, 1976). Conference proceedings collected in *Management Systems for Laboratory Instrument Services* (Research Triangle Park, NC: Instrument Society of America).
17. A. McNish, "The Nature of Measurement," in *Handbook of Industrial Metrology* (Englewood Cliffs, NJ: Prentice Hall, 1967).
18. Ibid.
19. Ford, GM, and Chrysler Corporations, *Measurement System Analysis Reference Manual* (Detroit, MI: AIAG, 1995).

References

American Society of Mechanical Engineers. *ANSI/ASME B46.1-1095 Surface Texture—Surface Roughness, Waviness, and Lay.* New York: ASME, 1986.

———. *ANSI/ASME B89.1.12M-1985 Methods for Performance Evaluation of Coordinate Measuring Machines.* New York: ASME, 1985.

———. *ANSI Y14.5M-1982 Dimensioning and Tolerancing.* New York: ASME, 1983.

American Society for Testing and Materials. *ASTM Standards on Precision and Accuracy for Various Applications.* Philadelphia: ASTM, 1977.

Bosch, J. A. *66 Centuries of Measurement.* Dayton, OH: Sheffield Measurement Division, 1984.
———, ed. *Coordinate Measuring Machines and Systems.* New York: Marcel Dekker, 1995.
Busch, T. *Fundamentals of Dimensional Metrology.* Albany, NY: Delmar, 1966.
Busch, T., R. Harlow, and R. Thompson. *Fundamentals of Dimensional Metrology,* 3rd ed. Albany, NY: Delmar, 1998.
Darmody, W. J. "Elements of a Generalized Measuring System." In *Handbook of Industrial Metrology.* Englewood Cliffs, NJ: Prentice Hall (ASTME), 1967.
Elshennawy, A. K., I. Ham, and P. H. Cohen. "Evaluating the Performance of Coordinate Measuring Machines." ASQ *Quality Progress* (January 1988): 59–65.
Farrago, F. T. *Handbook of Dimensional Measurement.* New York: Industrial Press, 1968.
Gaylor, J. F. W., and C. R. Shotbolt. *Metrology for Engineers.* London: Cassell & Company, 1964.
International Organization for Standardization. *International Standard (ISO) 1000.* New York: ANSI, 1973.
Mack, D. A. "Instrumentation Calibration." Workshop conference on the Management of Laboratory Instruments, Cairo, Egypt, November 7–11, 1976. Conference proceedings collected in *Management Systems for Laboratory Instrument Services.* Research Triangle Park, NC: Instrument Society of America.
McNish, A. "The Nature of Measurement." In *Handbook of Industrial Metrology.* Englewood Cliffs, NJ: Prentice Hall, 1967.
MIL-STD-45662 Calibration System Requirements. Washington, DC: Department of Defense, 1980.
National Institute for Standards and Technology. *Special Publication 304A.* U.S. Department of Commerce, 1981.
Rashed, A. F., and A. M. Hamouda. *Technology for Real Quality.* Alexandria, Egypt: Egyptian University House, 1974.
Reason, R. E. *The Measurement of Surface Texture.* London: CleaverHume Press, 1960.
Rice, G. O. "Measurement Systems and the Standards Laboratory." Workshop conference on the Management of Laboratory Instruments, Cairo, Egypt, November 7–11, 1976. Conference proceedings collected in *Management Systems for Laboratory Instrument Services.* Research Triangle Park, NC: Instrument Society of America, 1980.
———. "Metrology." In *Quality Management Handbook.* Eds. L. Walsh, R. Wurster, and R. J. Kimber. Milwaukee: ASQC Quality Press and New York: Marcel Dekker, 1986.
Simpson, J. A. "Foundations of Metrology." *Journal of Research of the National Bureau of Standards* 86, no. 3 (May/June 1981): 36–42.
Wunchell, W. *Inspection and Measurement in Manufacturing.* Dearborn, MI: Society of Manufacturing Engineers, 1996.

IV

Inspection and Test

A. MEASUREMENT TERMS AND DEFINITIONS

Measurement

A *measurement* is a series of manipulations of physical objects or systems according to a defined protocol, which results in a number. The number is purported to uniquely represent the magnitude (or intensity) of a certain satisfaction, which depends on the properties of the test object. This number is acquired to form the basis of a decision affecting some human goal or satisfying some human object need, the satisfaction of which depends on the properties of the test subject. These needs or goals can be usefully viewed as requiring three general classes of measurements[1]:

1. *Technical*. This class includes those measurements made to assure dimensional compatibility, conformation to design specifications necessary for proper function, or, in general, all measurements made to ensure fitness for intended use of some object.
2. *Legal*. This class includes those measurements made to ensure compliance with a law or regulation. This class is the concern of weights and measures bodies, regulators, and those who must comply with those regulations. The measurements are identical in kind with those of technical metrology but are usually embedded in a much more formal structure. Legal metrology is more prevalent in Europe than in the United States, although this is changing.
3. *Scientific*. This class includes those measurements made to validate theories of the nature of the universe or to suggest new theories. These measurements, which can be called *scientific metrology* (properly the domain of experimental physics), present special problems.

Concepts in Measurements

Measurement Error

Error in measurement is the difference between the indicated value and the true value of a measured quantity. The true value of a quantity to be measured is seldom known.

Errors are classified as random and systematic. *Random errors* are accidental in nature. They fluctuate in a way that cannot be predicted from the detailed employment of the measuring system or from knowledge of its functioning. Sources of error such as hysteresis, ambient influences, or variations in the work piece are typical but not completely all-inclusive in the random category. *Systematic errors* are those not usually detected by repetition of the measurement operations. An error resulting from either faulty calibration of a local standard or a defect in contact configuration of an internal measuring system is typical but not completely inclusive in the systematic class of errors.[2]

It is important to know all the sources of error in a measuring system, rather than merely to be aware of the details of their classification. Analysis of the causes of errors is helpful in attaining the necessary knowledge of achieved accuracy.[3]

There are many different sources of error that influence the precision of a measuring process in a variety of ways according to the individual situation in which such errors arise. The permutation of error sources and their effects, therefore, is quite considerable. In general, these errors can be classified under three main headings[4]:

1. Process environment
2. Measuring equipment
3. Operator fallibility

These factors constitute an interrelated three-element system for the measuring process as shown in Figure IV.1.

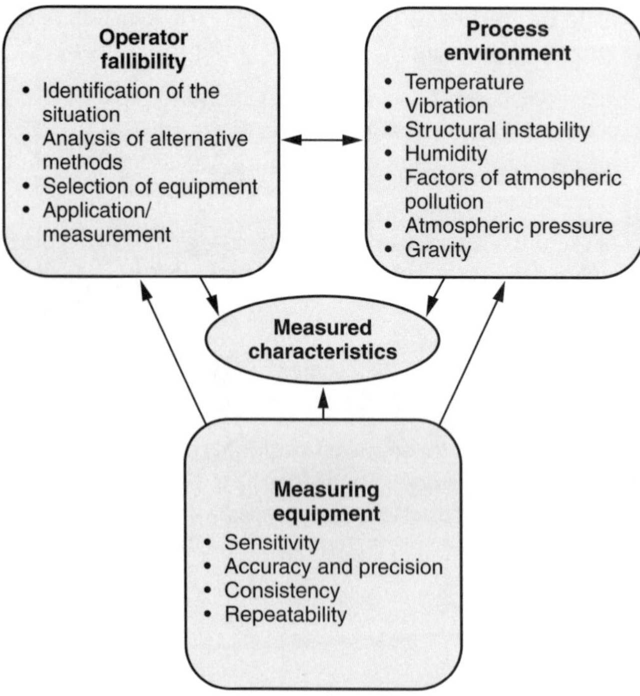

Figure IV.1 Factors affecting the measuring process.

The areas in which operator fallibility arises can be grouped as follows[5]:

1. Identification of the measuring situation
2. Analysis of alternative methods
3. Selection of equipment
4. Application (or measurement)

The identification of measuring situations becomes increasingly complex in modern metrology. As parts become smaller and more precise, greater attention has to be paid to geometric qualities such as roundness, concentricity, straightness, parallelism, and squareness. Deficiencies in these qualities may consume all of the permitted design tolerance, so that a simple dimensional check becomes grossly insufficient.

Operators have to be knowledgable about what they have to measure and how satisfactorily the requirements of the situation will be met by the measuring instrument. Correct identification of the measuring situation will eliminate those methods found unsuitable for the situation. A proper selection of measuring equipment can therefore be selected from a smaller range of measuring process alternatives. Method analysis can then be applied to such alternatives to determine which best satisfies the situation. This usually involves examining each method for different characteristics and evaluating the relative accuracies between the different methods.

Accuracy

Accuracy is the degree of agreement of individual or average measurements with an accepted reference value or level.[6]

Precision

Precision is the degree of mutual agreement among individual measurements made under prescribed like conditions,[7] or simply, how well identically performed measurements agree with each other. This concept applies to a process or a set of measurements, not to a single measurement, because in any set of measurements the individual results will scatter about the mean.[8]

Repeatability and Reproducibility

Repeatability refers to how close the measurements of an instrument are to each other if such measurements were repeated on a part under the same measuring conditions. *Reproducibility* is a measure of the degree of agreement between two single test results made on the same object in two different, randomly selected measuring locations or laboratories. While repeatability is normally used to designate precision for measurements made within a restricted set of conditions (for example, individual operators), reproducibility is normally used to designate precision for measurements involving variation between certain sets (for example, laboratories) as well as within them.

Inspection

Inspection is the evaluation of product quality by comparing the results of measuring one or several product characteristics with applicable standards. From this definition it is evident that the inspection function involves a number of tasks[9]:

1. Measurement, which could be on a qualitative or quantitative scale. The objective is to make a judgment about product's conformance to specifications.
2. Comparison of the measurement results to certain standards that reflect the intended use of the product by the customer and the various production costs. If the product is found to be nonconforming, a decision as to whether nonconforming products are fit for use may be reached.
3. Decision making regarding the disposition of the unit inspected, and, under sampling inspection, regarding the lot from which the sample was drawn.
4. Corrective action(s) in order to improve the quality of the product and/or process based upon the aggregate results of inspection over a number of units.

Uses of Inspection

The results of inspection can be used for different purposes as outlined below:

1. To determine if the production process is changing.[10]
2. To distinguish between good lots and bad lots, as in incoming material inspection and final product inspection, using acceptance sampling plans.
3. To distinguish between good products and bad products. In this case, a 100 percent inspection or a scheme of defect classification may be used.
4. To determine the status of process control and if the process is changing. This is usually done in conjunction with control charts.
5. To evaluate process capability, which is defined as the ratio between the difference between specification limits (tolerance) and the natural tolerance limits of the process, estimated as six standard deviation units (6σ). In this case, inspection is used to determine if the process exhibits excessive variation and if it is approaching or exceeding the specification limits.
6. To determine process adjustment. Based on inspection results of process output, as depicted by a histogram for example, process mean may require adjustment and/or process variation may need to be reduced. A process might require adjustment even though all the units produced to date conform to the quality standards agreed upon with the customer.
7. To rate the accuracy of inspectors or of inspection equipment by comparing the inspection results with corresponding standards. An inspection operation can result in two types of error: classification of a conforming unit as nonconforming, and classification of a nonconforming unit as conforming. The probabilities of both types of error could be easily estimated using probability theory and other statistical methods.[11]
8. To serve as a mechanism for evaluating vendors in terms of their products' quality. Vendors that consistently deliver high-quality products can receive preferred status involving reduced inspection and priority in bidding for new contracts, while vendors that do not stand up to quality requirements could be warned or discontinued altogether. This type of procedure is known as *vendor qualification* or *vendor certification.*

Quality Characteristics

Measurement is the process of evaluating a property or characteristic of an object and describing it with a numerical or nominal value. If the value is numerical, reflecting the extent of the characteristic, then the measurement is said to be on a quantitative scale and the actual property is referred to as a variable. Examples of variables inspection are measurements related to weight, length, temperature, and so on.

If the value assigned to each unit is other than numerical, then the measurement is on a qualitative or classification scale and is referred to as an *attribute.* In most inspection situations involving nominal or attribute data, there are two possible nominal values: conforming (good) and nonconforming (defective). Each product unit is assigned one of these two labels according to inspection operation results. It is then possible to derive a numerical measure of many units' quality or processes output from a qualitative scale. This is achieved by calculating the fraction nonconforming (fraction defective) as the ratio between the number of units labeled as nonconforming and the total number of units inspected.

A common method of inspection by attributes involves the use of limit gages, also known as go/no go gages. Limit gages are made to sizes essentially identical with the design specification limits of the dimension to be inspected. If a specific gage can properly mate with a part, then the part can be assembled with another part whose physical boundaries do not exceed those of the gage. Consequently, the part is acceptable for assembly. Limit gages designed to identify this condition are called go gages.

The "go" end of a go/no go gage contains the reverse physical replica of the dimension inspected at the maximum material condition (minimum size for interior features, maximum size for exterior features). The maximum material condition produces the minimum clearance required for assembly.

The "no go" end is designed to detect conditions of excessive clearance. It contains the reverse physical replica of the dimension inspected at its minimum material condition. A part will not mate with a no go gage unless the actual condition of the part feature is below the specified minimum. Thus, if the no go gage mates with the part, then the part dimension is incorrect and the part should be rejected.

In practice, go/no go gages are used together and often appear at opposite ends of an inspection instrument. An acceptable part should mate with the go end but should not mate with the no go end. Parts that mate with neither or both ends do not meet design specifications and should be rejected.

Most methods of inspection by attributes, other than gauging, are largely subjective and depend on the ability of human inspectors to make the right decision. In many cases, inspection by attributes involves visual characteristics, such as color, shape, smoothness, and other visual defects.

B. GEOMETRIC DIMENSIONING AND TOLERANCING

It is expected that drawings have dimensions that provide detailed information about sizes, shapes, and the location of different components and parts. It is also expected that part and component dimensions show acceptable variation. To produce any part or component with exact dimensions is nearly impossible, except by remote chance. Variations in materials, machines, manufacturing parameters, and humans make it necessary that dimensions have acceptable variations. Such variation is referred to as *tolerance.* Higher quality requires tighter tolerances that, in turn, require more expensive and strict production and inspection procedures to obtain. There are two types of tolerances: unilateral tolerance and bilateral tolerance. Unilateral tolerance specifies allowable variation in a dimension from a basic or nominal size in one direction in relation to that basic size.

For example, $2.000^{+0.000/-0.005}$ inches describes an allowable variation only in the lower limit: unilateral tolerance. Specifications on a part with this tolerance will be 2.000 inches and 1.995 inches as desired upper and lower limits, respectively. On the other hand, $2.000^{+0.005/-0.005}$ inches describes a bilateral tolerance. It does specify a dimension with allowable variations in both directions of the basic size. Specifications on a part with such bilateral tolerance will be 2.005 inches and 1.995 inches as desired upper and lower limits, respectively.

Geometric tolerancing defines tolerances for geometric features or characteristics on a part. Figure IV.2 shows some of the geometric dimensioning and tolerancing symbols as defined in ANSI Y14.5M. Figure IV.3 illustrates the interpretation of a geometric tolerance on a drawing.

The limit dimensions of the simple cylindrical piece at the top of Figure IV.4 define the maximum and minimum limits of a profile for the work. The form or shape of the part may vary as long as no portions of the part exceed the maximum profile

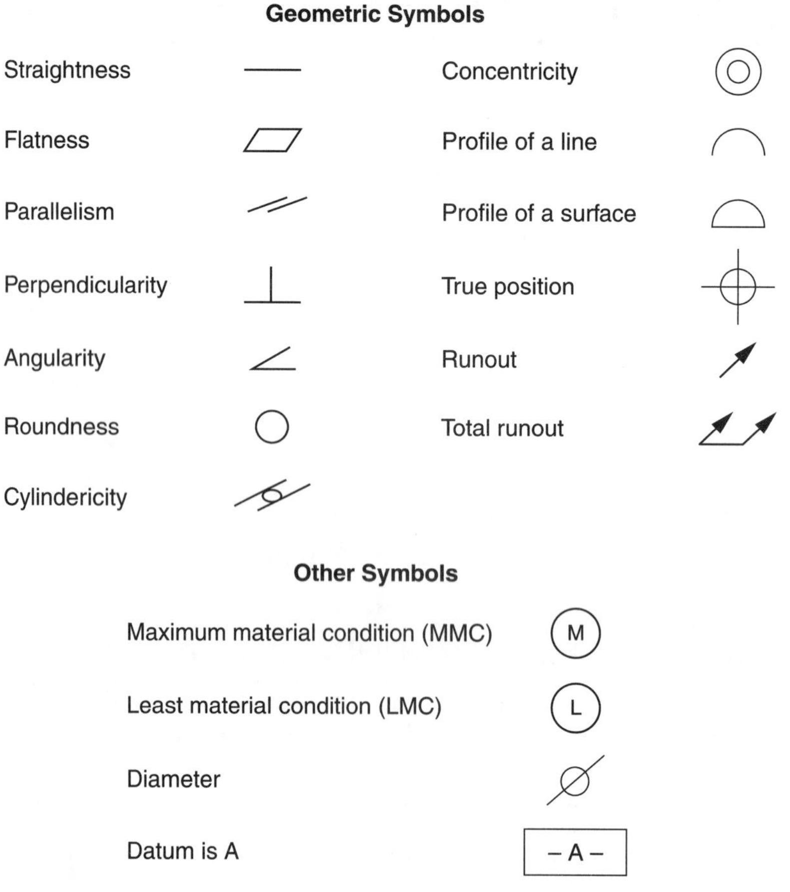

Figure IV.2 Some geometric dimensioning and tolerancing symbols.

limit or are inside the minimum profile limit. If a part measures its maximum material limit of size everywhere, it should be of perfect form. This is referred to as the *maximum material condition* (MMC) and is at the low limit for a hole or slot but at the high limit for parts, such as shafts, bolts, or pins.

If it is desired to provide greater control on the form than is imposed by the limit dimensions, then certain tolerances of form must be applied. In most cases, these tolerances appear in the form of notations on the drawing as illustrated at the bottom of Figure IV.4.

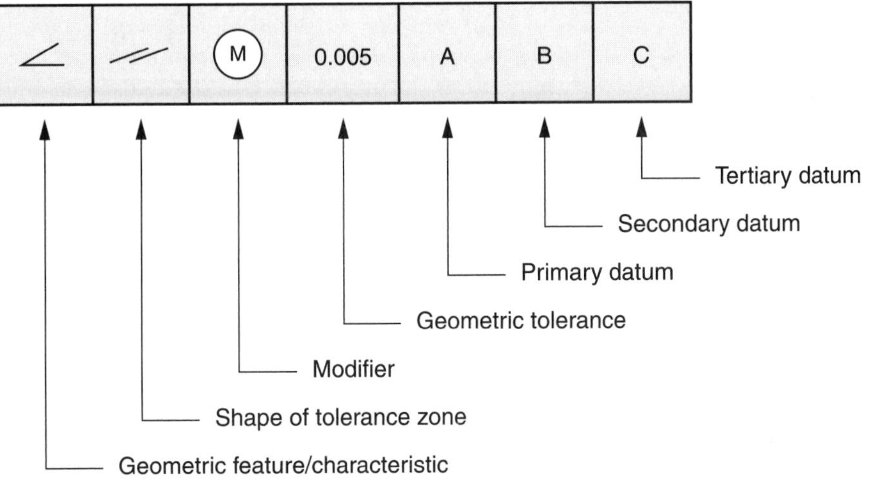

Figure IV.3 Interpretation of a geometric tolerance.

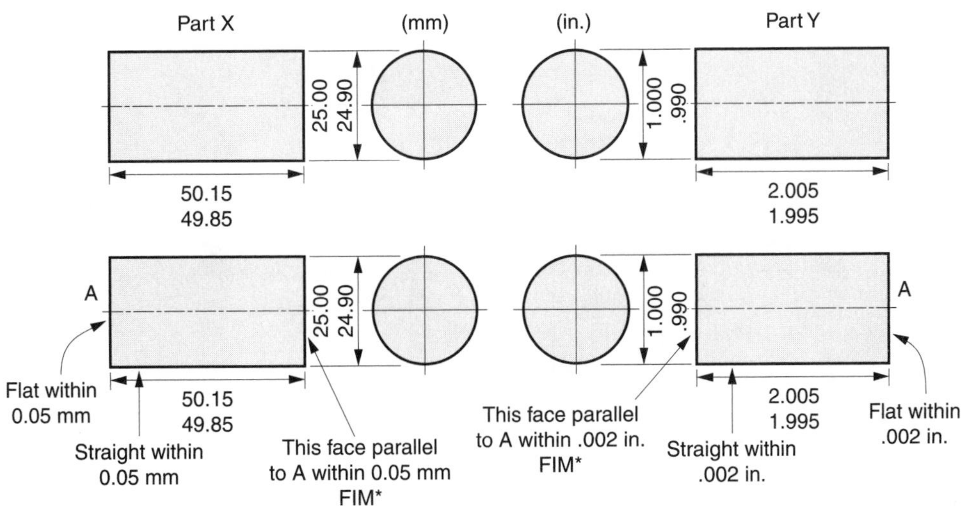

Figure IV.4 Part drawing with and without tolerances of form.

Reprinted with permission of the Society of Manufacturing Engineers, *Manufacturing Processes and Materials*, 4th Edition, Copyright 2000.

Positional Tolerances

Positional tolerancing is a system of specifying the true position, size, or form of a part feature and the amount it may vary from the ideal. The advantage of the system is that it allows the one responsible for making the part to divide tolerances between position and size as he or she finds fit. The principles are illustrated for two simple mating parts in Figure IV.5. The basic dimensions without tolerances are shown at the bottom and right side of each part. Beneath the size dimension for holes or posts is a box with the notations for positional tolerancing. Actually, a number of specifications are possible, but only onset is shown here as an example. The circle and cross in the first cell of the box is the convention that says the features are positionally toleranced.

Part I in Figure IV.5 introduces the idea of the MMC utilized in most positional tolerancing. This is designated by the letter *M* in a circle and means that the smallest hole (12.70 mm or .500 in.) determines the inner boundary for any hole. The "∅0.20 mm (.008 in.)" notation in the box specifies that the axis of any minimum-size hole must not be outside a theoretical cylinder of 0.20 mm (.008 in.) diameter around the true position. A 12.50 mm (.492 in.) diameter plug in true position will fit in any 12.70 mm (.500 in.) diameter hole with its axis on the 0.20 mm (.008 in.) diameter cylinder. Any hole that passes over such a plug is acceptable, provided that its diameter is within the high and low limits specified.

The letter *A* in the specification box designates that the theoretical cylinder bounding the hole axes must be perpendicular to the datum surface carrying the *A* flag. Features usually are referred with three coordinate datum surfaces, but for simplicity, in this case, the holes are related only to each other and surface *A*, and not to the sides of the part.

Part II of Figure IV.5 introduces the idea of zero maximum material condition specified by "∅0.000" before the MMC symbol. This means the axis of the largest-diameter post (12.50 mm [.492 in.]) must be exactly in the true position, but smaller sizes of posts may vary in position as long as they do not lie outside the boundary set by the largest.

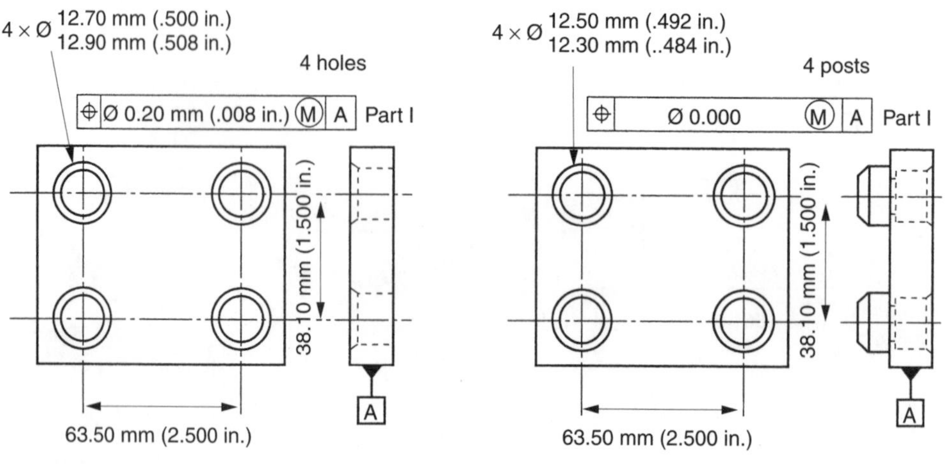

Figure IV.5 Two parts dimensioned with positional tolerances.

Reprinted with permission of the Society of Manufacturing Engineers, *Manufacturing Processes and Materials*, 4th Edition, Copyright 2000.

Thus, if the posts are held to a tolerance smaller than the 0.20 mm (.008 in.) specified, say to a tolerance of 0.05 mm (.002 in.), the difference (0.15 mm [.006 in.]) is then available for variations in post positions. The advantage of zero MMC is that only one limit of the feature, in this case the lower limit of the post diameter, needs to be checked along with position.

C. BLUEPRINT READING

The quality technician must be able to read and understand blueprints in order to make valid decisions about the acceptability of products. This text cannot provide comprehensive coverage of this topic, but the following list includes some of the more common concerns:

- Tolerances/specifications may be given with the dimension (20.000 ± .005, for example) or covered in a note in the title block (such as "Unless otherwise specified, dimensions with 3 decimal places have tolerance of ± .004," or "0.000: ± 0.004"). Sometimes a note covers tolerances for all dimensions ("all dimensions ± 1/64", for example). Occasionally, a company's standard procedures cover unspecified tolerances and may not be referenced on the print.
- Units used should be specified in the title block or elsewhere on the print; for example, "All dimensions in mm."
- "Typical" callouts refer to dimensions that have the same value but are not repeated on the drawing. For example, if five circles are located at 38° intervals along an arc, it is standard practice to dimension one angle with a note: "38° TYP."
- Multiple features with the same dimensions, such as several holes with the same diameter, may be specified with a note (for example, "∅ .250 5 holes" or "∅ .250 5×").
- Detail references indicate that more information is included on a separate drawing. The detail drawing may or may not be on the same sheet. Detail callouts are often identified with a dashed line around an area with a label such as "Detail A."
- Section references indicate that more information is included on a separate cross sectional drawing. The section drawing may or may not be on the same sheet. Sections are often specified with a heavy line through a part with arrows indicating the direction at which the section drawing is oriented. Letters near the arrows specify the section referenced. The section drawing will use these same letters elsewhere (for example, Section A-A).
- Geometric dimensioning and tolerancing symbols provide additional control over part features such as flatness, concentricity, parallelism, and so on.

D. CLASSIFICATION OF CHARACTERISTICS AND DEFECTS

In certain types of products, more than one defect could be present and a relatively small number of minor defects could be acceptable to the customer. Product quality in similar cases may be judged by the total number of defects or the number of defects per unit. Control charts for attributes are a tool that may be used for this purpose. In such cases, the objective of inspection is to determine the number of defects or nonconformities present, rather than to classify units as conforming or nonconforming.

Defect and nonconformity are two terms that may be used alternately in many situations. For other purposes, definitions for both terms are slightly different. A *nonconformity* is defined as a failure of a quality characteristic to meet its intended level or state, occurring with severity sufficient to cause the product not to meet a specification. A *defect* is a nonconformity severe enough to cause the product not to satisfy normal usage requirements. Thus, the difference between the term nonconformity and the term defect is based mainly on the perspective. The former is defined based on specifications, while the latter is defined based on fitness for use. Thus, the numerical result generated by inspection consists of the count of defects or nonconformities for each product unit. Often it is possible to classify the different types of defects according to their severity, then assign a weight to each class based on the importance of the affected quality characteristic regarding the product specifications. The selection of the weights should reflect the relative importance of the various defect categories and their likelihood of causing product failure or customer dissatisfaction. A typical seriousness classification includes four levels of defect seriousness:

1. Critical defect may lead directly to severe injury or catastrophic economic loss.
2. Serious defect may lead to injury or significant economic loss.
3. Major defect may cause major problems during normal use. A major defect will likely result in reducing the useability of the product.
4. Minor defect may cause minor problems during normal use.

E. INSPECTION PLANNING

Inspection planning includes the determination of the location of inspection and/or quality control methods and procedures at the various points in the production process. It also involves the determination of the types of inspections to be carried out and the acceptable quality levels, identification of critical characteristics to be inspected, and classification of defects.

Inspection planning includes the preparation of a list of characteristics to be inspected. The following guidelines may prove helpful:

- Inspect characteristics that affect the performance of the product. To the extent possible, product testing should be done under conditions that simulate actual use.
- Select characteristics that can be measured objectively, to the extent possible.
- Provide a seriousness classification in order to improve consistency for characteristics that are evaluated subjectively.
- Inspect characteristics that can be related to a specific production process in order to simultaneously obtain information about the process.

A detailed inspection plan should be prepared and approved by the customer and the production, engineering, and manufacturing departments prior to the start of full-scale production. The inspection plan should include the following items:

- The location of each inspection station in the sequence of production operations.
- The type of inspection or test to be carried out, including a description of the environment, equipment, and procedures.
- Accuracy requirements for the measurements.
- The conformance criteria, normally based on product specifications.
- The sample size and procedure for drawing the sample in case of sampling inspection.
- The lot size and the criteria for lot acceptance, if applicable.
- The disposition of nonconforming units, for example, repair, scrap, or salvage; and of rejected lots, for example, screen or return to vendor.
- The criteria for initiating a review of the process, vendor, or inspector.

Inspector Qualifications

Basic requirements for inspection personnel include:

1. The ability to perform the relevant measurements
2. Understanding of product specifications to the point of being capable of determining product quality
3. Basic mathematical skills for recording and analyzing data
4. Basic understanding of statistical concepts needed for sampling inspection and process characterization
5. Knowledge of measurements and measurement technology
6. Understanding of company's inspection policies, inspection procedure, products, materials, and processes

Inspector Training

Training refers to the formal procedures used to improve job-related capability. Training programs for inspection personnel should be designed to address three main generic aspects:

1. *Attitude*—This includes developing a genuine concern for the product and for the customer, as well as fostering a positive self-image of the inspection function. To a significant extent, attitude is affected by the leadership of management and supervisory staff.
2. *Knowledge*—This includes not only knowledge directly related to the inspection function, but also of the various production processes, materials, equipment, procedures, and so on.
3. *Skills*—This category refers to mastering the performance of the technical activities that are part of the inspector's job.

Training programs should be periodically aimed at new inspection personnel as well as those with on-the-job experience. On-the-job training by a supervisor or a training coordinator could be the most prevalent and least costly approach to training. Other training methods include:

- Classroom instruction by in-house experts or outside consultants. It is best suited for theoretical subjects, such as basic mathematics, statistics, experimental design, and computer use.
- Self-study, using audiovisual programs and self-instruction training manuals. This method allows the inspectors to study at their own pace and during convenient times.
- Outside programs, offered by professional organizations and their local chapters, and by universities and community colleges through their extension divisions.

F. INSPECTION POINTS

The location of inspection stations can be determined based on the following considerations:

- Inspect incoming materials to prevent the entry of defective components into the production system. This could be eliminated if the suppliers provide sufficient evidence of the use of process control techniques to maintain product quality.
- Inspect prior to costly operations in order to avoid further investment in an already nonconforming product.
- Inspect prior to processing operations that may mask defects, for example, surface finish should be inspected prior to painting.
- Inspect prior to processing operations that may cause an increase in repair costs. For example, inspect and test circuit boards prior to assembly into their enclosures.
- Inspect following operations known to have a relatively high defect rate.
- Inspect final or finished goods before moving the product to another department or plant prior to shipping to the customer.
- Inspect the first few units of each new batch in order to verify that the setup is correct.

G. INSPECTION TECHNIQUES AND PROCESSES

Testing

Two terms are normally associated with inspection—gauging and testing. *Gauging* determines product conformance with specification, with the aid of measuring instruments such as calipers, micrometers, templates, and other mechanical, optical, and electronic devices. *Testing* refers to the determination of the capability of an item to meet specified requirements by subjecting it to a set of physical, chemical, environmental, or other operating conditions and actions similar to or more severe than those expected under normal use.

Testing might be destructive or nondestructive. In testing, the product is subjected to measuring procedures that render its usefulness to the customer. Gauging, however, is the more common form of inspection and is less costly; this operation has no effect on the product's service capability. Of course, certain product characteristics, mainly those related to failure modes, may only be observed and measured by exposing the product to conditions beyond its designed limits, such as determining the maximum current that an electronic component can carry and the maximum tensile force that a mechanical part can withstand. Most of these procedures are normally destructive testing procedures and may be performed in cases where mandatory requirements are to be met. Nondestructive testing (NDT) of products is usually applied by subjecting the product to some tests, such as eddy current, ultrasonic resonance, or x-ray testing.

Nondestructive Testing (NDT) Techniques

Screening or 100 percent inspection cannot be used when the product is subjected to a destructive testing procedure or the time of performing inspection is too long. Another constraint is that the cost of inspection is too high to justify the economics of inspection. NDT techniques are more common for automated inspection or 100 percent inspection. A list of the most common NDT techniques includes:

- Eddy current testing involves the application of an AC current passing through a coil that is placed near the surface of the part to be inspected. Thus, its application is limited to conductive materials and the test results are made by comparison.
- Ultrasonic testing is normally used to check for surface defects that cause deflection of an ultrasonic wave directed on the part surface, thus giving an indication of the presence of a surface defect. For ultrasonic testing, reference standards are required.
- X-ray techniques cause the internal characteristics of the part to be displayed and thus provide information about the presence of defects, cracks, or other impurities.
- Liquid penetration is more common for detecting defects on the part surface. It is used for different part configurations and, unlike magnetic particle testing, it can be used for nonmagnetic materials. However, liquid penetration cannot be used to locate subsurface discontinuities.
- Magnetic particle testing is used when the part material can be magnetized. Discovery of part defects, like cracks or discontinuities, can then be detected by the presence of paring magnetic fields. Magnetic particle testing is limited to parts made of iron, steel, or allied materials.
- Other common NDT techniques include the application of some phenomenon, such as thermal, chemical, holographic interferometry (employing interference patterns for checking surface displacements), or optical phenomena. These are used for special testing procedures and are often too expensive to be widely applied.

H. SAMPLING

Sampling versus 100 Percent Inspection

Inspection can be done with screening (also called sorting or 100 percent inspection), in which all units are inspected, or with sampling. *Acceptance sampling* is the process of inspecting a portion of the product in a lot for the purpose of making a decision regarding classification of the entire lot as either conforming or nonconforming to quality specifications. Sampling provides the economic advantage of lower inspection costs due to fewer units being inspected. In addition, the time required to inspect a sample is substantially less than that required for the entire lot and there is less damage to the product due to reduced handling. Most inspectors find that selection and inspection of a random sample is less tedious and monotonous than inspection of the complete lot. Another advantage of sampling inspection is related to the supplier/customer relationship. By inspecting a small fraction of the lot, and forcing the supplier to screen 100 percent in case of lot rejection (which is the case for rectifying inspection), the customer emphasizes that the supplier will be more concerned about quality. On the other hand, variability is inherent in sampling, resulting in sampling errors: rejection of lots of conforming quality and acceptance of lots of nonconforming quality.

Acceptance sampling is most appropriate when inspection costs are high and when 100 percent inspection is monotonous and can cause inspector fatigue and boredom, resulting in degraded performance and increased error rates. Obviously, sampling is the only choice available for destructive inspection. Rectifying sampling is a form of acceptance sampling. Sample units detected as nonconforming are discarded from the lot, replaced by conforming units, or repaired. Rejected lots are subject to 100 percent screening, which can involve discarding, replacing, or repairing units detected as nonconforming.

In certain situations, it is preferable to inspect 100 percent of the product. This would be the case for critical or complex products, where the cost of making the wrong decision would be too high. Screening is appropriate when the fraction nonconforming is extremely high. In this case, most of the lots would be rejected under acceptance sampling and those accepted would be so as a result of statistical variations rather than better quality. Screening is also appropriate when the fraction nonconforming is not known and an estimate based on a large sample is needed.

It should be noted that the philosophy now being espoused in supplier relations is that the supplier is responsible for ensuring that the product shipped meets the user's requirements. Many larger customers are requiring evidence of product quality through the submission of process control charts that show the product was produced by a process that was in control and capable of meeting the specifications.

Sampling Plans

Sampling may be performed according to the type of quality characteristics to be inspected. There are three major categories of sampling plans: sampling plans for attributes, sampling plans for variables, and special sampling plans. It should be noted that acceptance sampling is not advised for processes in continuous production and in a state of statistical control. For these processes, Deming provides decision rules for selecting either 100 percent inspection or no inspection.[12]

Lot-by-Lot versus Average Quality Protection

Sampling plans based on average quality protection from continuing processes have their characteristics based on the binomial and/or Poisson distributions. Plans used for lot-by-lot protection, not considered to have been manufactured by a continuing process, have their characteristics based on the hypergeometric distribution, which takes the lot size into consideration for calculation purposes.

Sampling plans based on the Poisson and binomial distributions are more common than those based on the hypergeometric distribution. This is due to the complexity of calculating plans based on the hypergeometric distribution. New software on personal computers, however, may eliminate this objection.

The Operating Characteristic (OC) Curve

No matter which type of attribute sampling plan is being considered, the most important evaluation tool is the operating characteristic (OC) curve. The OC curve allows a sampling plan to be almost completely evaluated at a glance, giving a pictorial view of the probabilities of accepting lots submitted at varying levels of percent defective. The OC curve illustrates the risks involved in acceptance sampling. Figure IV.6 shows an OC curve for a sample size n of 50 drawn from an infinite lot size, with an acceptance number c of 3.

As can be seen by the OC curve, if the lot were 100 percent to specifications, the probability of acceptance P_a would also be 100 percent. But if the lot were 13.4 percent defective, there would be a 10 percent probability of acceptance.

There are two types of OC curves to consider: (1) Type-A OC curves, and (2) Type-B OC curves. Type-A OC curves are used to calculate the probability of acceptance on a lot-by-lot basis when the lot is not a product of a continuous process. These OC curves are calculated using the hypergeometric distribution.

Type-B OC curves are used to evaluate sampling plans for a continuous process. These curves are based on the binomial and/or Poisson distributions when the requirements for

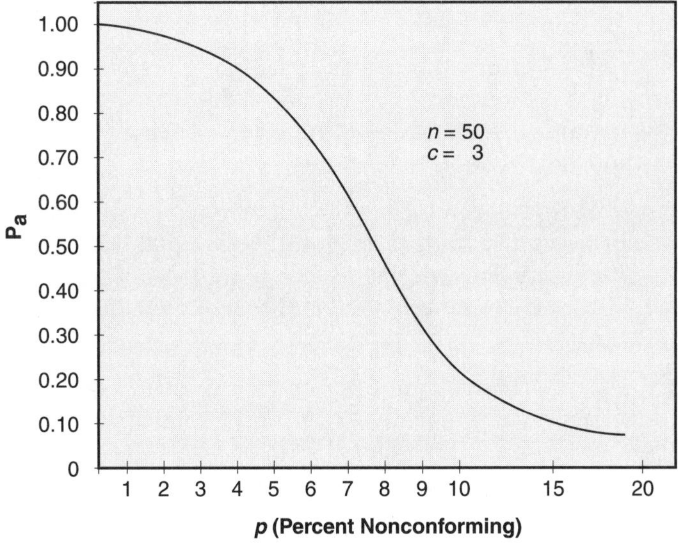

Figure IV.6 An operating characteristic (OC) curve.

usage are met. In general, the ANSI/ASQC Z1.4-1993 standard OC curves are based on the binomial distribution for sample sizes through 80 and the Poisson approximation to the binomial is used for sample sizes greater than 80.

Acceptance Sampling by Attributes

Acceptance sampling by attributes is generally used for two purposes: (1) protection against accepting lots from a continuing process whose average quality deteriorates beyond an acceptable quality level, and (2) protection against isolated lots that may have levels of nonconformances greater than can be considered acceptable. The most commonly used forms of acceptance sampling are sampling plans by attributes. The most widely used standard of all attribute plans, although not necessarily the best, is ANSI/ASQC Z1.4-1993. The following sections provide more details on the characteristics of acceptance sampling and discussion of military standards in acceptance sampling.

Acceptable Quality Level

Acceptable quality level (AQL) is defined as the maximum percent or fraction of nonconforming units in a lot or batch that, for the purposes of acceptance sampling, can be considered satisfactory as a process average. This means that a lot that has a fraction defective equal to the AQL has a high probability (generally in the area of 0.95, although it may vary) of being accepted. As a result, plans that are based on AQL, such as ANSI/ASQC Z1.4-1993, favor the producer in getting lots accepted that are in the general neighborhood of the AQL for fraction defective in a lot.

Lot Tolerance Percent Defective

The lot tolerance percent defective (LTPD), expressed in percent defective, is the poorest quality in an individual lot that should be accepted. The LTPD has a low probability of acceptance. In many sampling plans, the LTPD is the percent defective having a 10 percent probability of acceptance.

Producer's and Consumer's Risks

There are risks involved in using acceptance sampling plans. The risks involved in acceptance sampling are: (1) producer's risk, and (2) consumer's risk. These risks correspond with Type 1 and Type 2 errors in hypothesis testing. The definitions of producer's and consumer's risks are:

- *Producer's risk* (α)—The producer's risk for any given sampling plan is the probability of rejecting a lot that is within the acceptable quality level.[13] This means that the producer faces the possibility (at level of significance a) of having a lot rejected even though the lot has met the requirements stipulated by the AQL level.
- *Consumer's risk* (β)—The consumer's risk for any given sampling plan is the probability of acceptance (usually 10 percent) for a designated numerical value of relatively poor submitted quality.[14] The consumer's risk, therefore, is the probability of accepting a lot that has a quality level equal to the LTPD.

Average Outgoing Quality

The average outgoing quality (AOQ) is the expected average quality of outgoing products, including all accepted lots, plus all rejected lots which have been sorted 100 percent and have had all of the nonconforming units replaced by conforming units.

There is a given AOQ for specific fractions nonconforming of submitted lots sampled under a given sampling plan. When the fraction nonconforming is very low, a large majority of the lots will be accepted as submitted. The few lots that are rejected will be sorted 100 percent and have all nonconforming units replaced with conforming units. Thus, the AOQ will always be less than the submitted quality. As the quality of submitted lots becomes poor in relation to the AQL, the percent of lots rejected becomes larger in proportion to accepted lots. As these rejected lots are sorted and combined with accepted lots, an AOQ lower than the average fraction of nonconformances of submitted lots emerges. Therefore, when the level of quality of incoming lots is good, the AOQ is good; when the incoming quality is bad and most lots are rejected and sorted, the result is also good.

To calculate the AOQ for a specific fraction nonconforming and a sampling plan, the first step is to calculate the probability of accepting the lot at that level of fraction nonconforming. Then, multiply the probability of acceptance by the fraction nonconforming for the AOQ. Thus:

$$AOQ = P_a p[1 - \text{sample size/lot size}]$$

If the desired result is a percentage, multiply by 100.

The average outgoing quality limit (AOQL) is the maximum AOQ for all possible levels of incoming quality.

Average Outgoing Quality Limit

The average outgoing quality limit (AOQL) is a variable dependent upon the quality level of incoming lots. When the AOQ is plotted for all possible levels of incoming quality, a curve as shown in Figure IV.7 results. The AOQL is the highest value on the AOQ curve.

Assuming an infinite lot size, the AOQ may be calculated as AOQ = $P_a p$. Probability of acceptance (P_a) may be obtained from tables as explained earlier and then multiplied by p (associated value of fraction nonconforming) to produce a value for AOQ as shown in the next example, using the previous equation.

Example: Given an OC with curve points (P_a and p) as shown, construct the AOQ curve. Note that P_a and p are calculated as explained in the previous example.

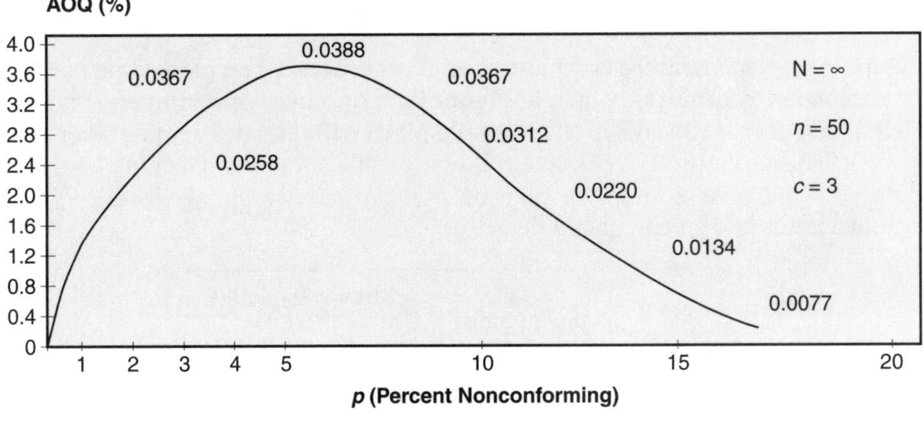

Figure IV.7 Average outgoing quality curve for: N = ∞, $n = 50$, $c = 3$.

Probability of Acceptance	Fraction Defective	AOQ
0.998	0.01	0.00998
0.982	0.02	0.01964
0.937	0.03	0.02811
0.861	0.04	0.03444
0.760	0.05	0.03800
0.647	0.06	0.03882
0.533	0.07	0.03731
0.425	0.08	0.03400
0.330	0.09	0.02970
0.250	0.10	0.02500

As can be seen, the AOQ rises until the incoming quality level of 0.06 nonconforming is reached. The maximum AOQ point is 0.03882, which is called the AOQL. This is the AOQL for an infinite lot size, sample size = 50, accept on three or less nonconformances.

Lot Size, Sample Size, and Acceptance Number

For any single sampling plan, the plan is completely described by the lot size, sample size, and acceptance number. In this section, the effect of changing the sample size, acceptance number, and lot size on the behavior of the sampling plan will be explored along with the risks of constant percentage plans.

The effect on the OC curve caused by changing the sample size while holding all other parameters constant is shown in Figure IV.8. The probability of acceptance changes considerably as sample size changes. The P_a for the given sample sizes for a 10 percent nonconforming lot and an acceptance number of zero are shown below.

Sample Size	Probability of Acceptance (P_a%)
10	35
4	68
2	82
1	90

The effect of changing the acceptance number on a sampling plan while holding all other parameters constant is shown in Figure IV.9. Another point of interest is that for $c = 0$, the OC curve is concave in shape, while plans with larger accept numbers have a "reverse s" shape. Figure IV.9 and the following table show the effect of changing the acceptance number of a sampling plan on the indifference quality level (IQL: 50-50 chance of accepting a given percent defective).

Sample Size	Acceptance Number	Percent Defective at Indifference Quality Level (%)
10	2	27
10	1	17
10	0	7

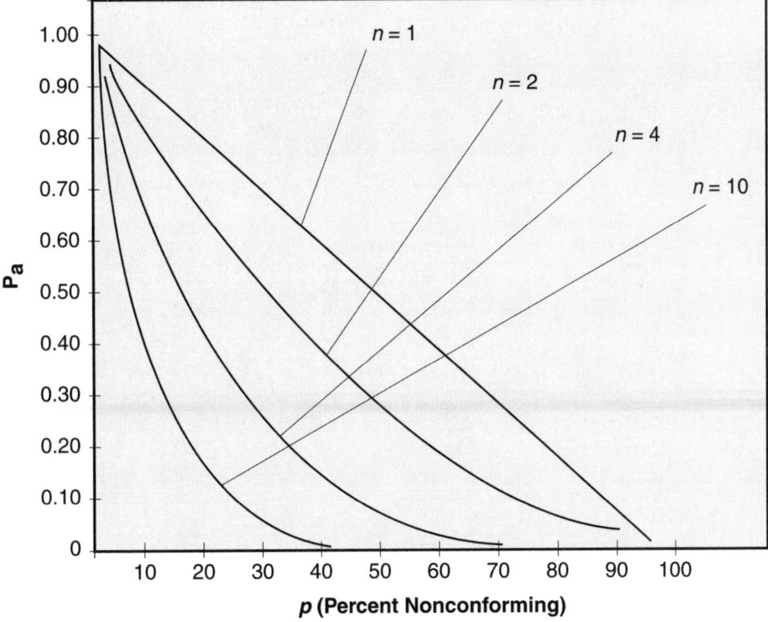

Figure IV.8 Effect on an OC curve of changing sample size n when accept number c is held constant.

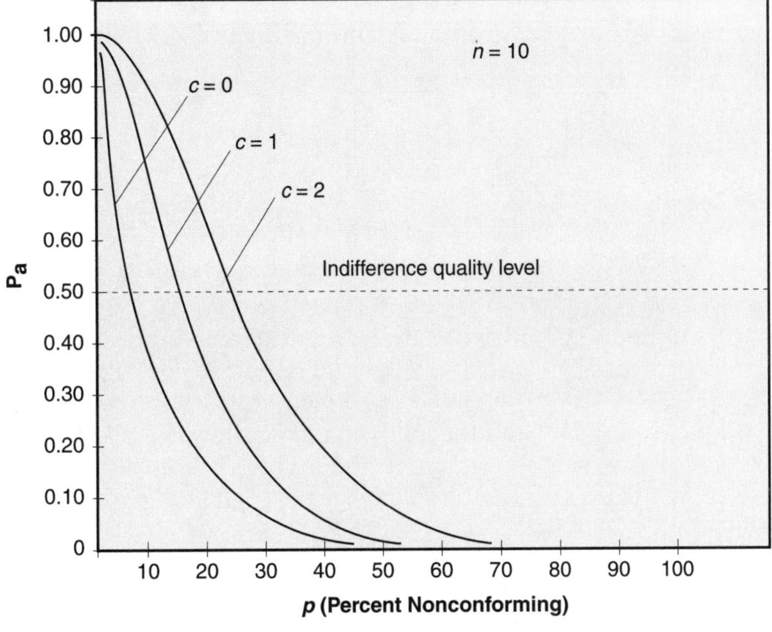

Figure IV.9 Effect of changing accept number c when sample size n is held constant.

The parameter having the least effect on the OC curve is the lot size N. For this reason, using the binomial and Poisson approximations, even when lot sizes are known (and are large compared to sample size), results in little error in accuracy. Figure IV.10 shows the changes in the OC curve for a sample size of 10, accept number of 0, and lot sizes of 100, 200, and 1000. As can be seen, the differences due to lot size are minimal. Some key probabilities of acceptance points for the three lot sizes follow.

Fraction Defective	Probability of Acceptance (P_a)	Lot Size
0.10	0.330	100
0.30	0.023	100
0.50	0.001	100
0.10	0.340	200
0.30	0.026	200
0.50	0.001	200
0.10	0.347	1000
0.30	0.028	1000
0.50	0.001	1000

Computing the sample size as a percentage of the lot size has a large effect on risks and protection, as shown in Figure IV.11. In this case, plans having a sample size totaling 10 percent of the lot size are shown. As can be seen, the degree of protection changes dramatically with changes in lot size, which results in low protection for small lot sizes and gives excessively large sample requirements for large lot sizes.

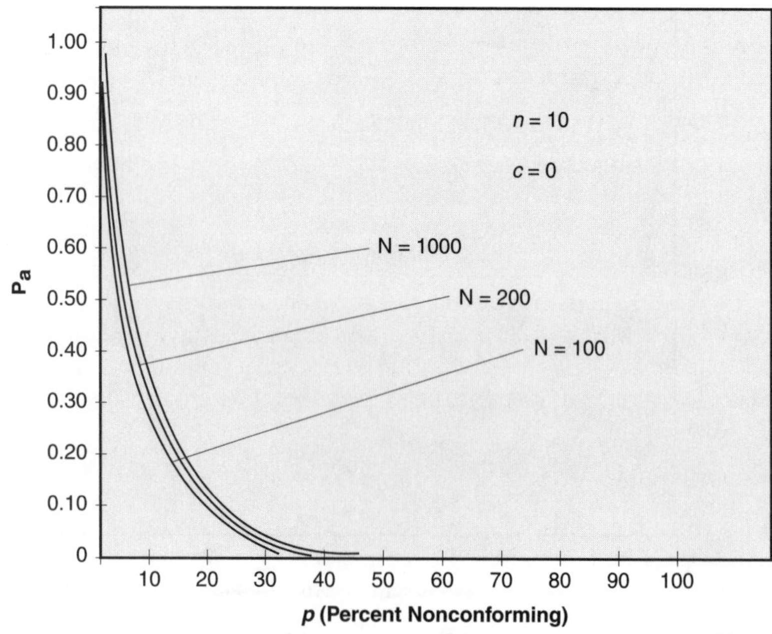

Figure IV.10 Effect of changing lot size N when accept number c and sample size n are held constant.

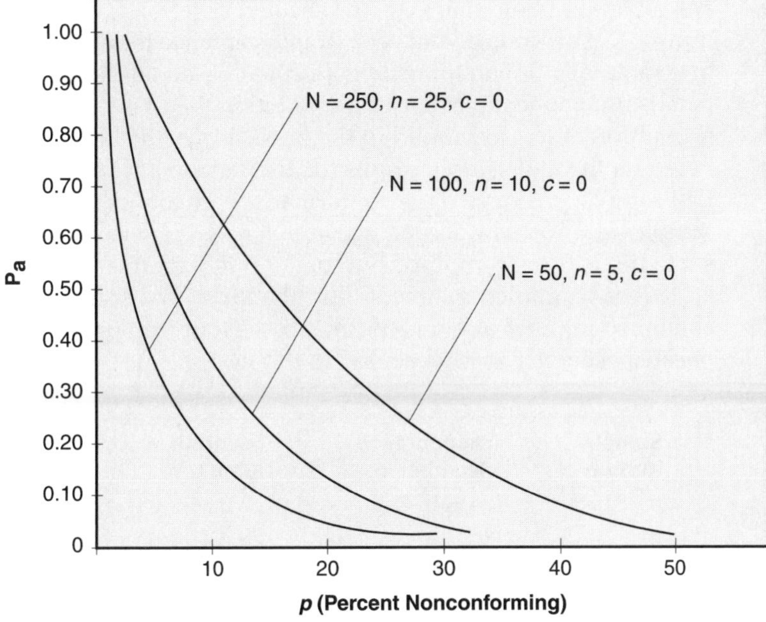

Figure IV.11 Operating characteristic curves for sampling plans having the sample size equal to 10 percent of the lot size.

Types of Attribute Sampling Plans

There are several types of attribute sampling plans in use, with the most common being single, double, multiple, and sequential sampling plans. The type of sampling plan used is determined by ease of use and administration, general quality level of incoming lots, average sample number, and so on.

Single Sampling Plans

When single sampling plans are used, the decision to either accept or reject the lot is based on the results of the inspection of a single sample of n items from a submitted lot. In the example shown earlier, the OC curve and AOQ curve were calculated for a single sampling plan where $n = 50$ and $c = 3$. Single sampling plans have the advantage of ease of administration, but due to the unchanging sample size, they do not take advantage of potential cost savings of reduced inspection when incoming quality is either excellent or poor.

Double Sampling Plans

When using double sampling plans, a smaller first sample is taken from the submitted lot, and one of three decisions is made: (1) accept the lot, (2) reject the lot, or (3) draw another sample. If a second sample is drawn, the lot will either be accepted or rejected after the second sample. Double sampling plans have the advantage of a lower total sample size when the incoming quality is either excellent or poor because the lot is either accepted or rejected on the first sample.

Example: A double sampling plan is to be executed as follows: take a first sample (n_1) of 75 units and set c_1 (the acceptance number for the first sample) = 0. The lot will be accepted based on the first sample results if no nonconformances are found in the first sample. If three nonconformances are found in the first sample, the lot will be rejected based on the first sample results. If, after analyzing the results of the first sample, one or two nonconformances are found, take a second sample (n_2 = 75). The acceptance number for the second sample (c_2) is set to three. If the combined number of nonconformances in the first and second samples is three or less, the lot will be accepted and if the combined number of nonconformances is four or more, the lot will be rejected. The plan is represented as follows:

Sample Number	Acceptance Number *c*	Rejection Number *r*
$n_1 = 75$	$c_1 = 0$	$r_1 = 3$
$n_2 = 75$	$c_2 = 3$	$r_2 = 4$

Multiple Sampling Plans

Multiple sampling plans work in the same way as double sampling with an extension of the number of samples to be taken up to seven, according to ANSI/ASQC Z1.4-1993. In the same manner that double sampling is performed, acceptance or rejection of submitted lots may be reached before the seventh sample, depending on the acceptance/rejection criteria established for the plan.

ANSI/ASQC Z1.4-1993

ANSI/ASQC Z1.4-1993 is probably the most commonly used standard for attribute sampling plans. The wide recognition and acceptance of the plan could be due to government contracts stipulating the standard, rather than its statistical importance. Producers submitting products at a nonconformance level within AQL have a high probability of having the lot accepted by the customer.

When using ANSI/ASQC Z1.4-1993, the characteristics under consideration should be classified. The general classifications are critical, major, and minor defects:

- *Critical defect.* A critical defect is a defect that judgment and experience indicate is likely to result in hazardous or unsafe conditions for the individuals using, maintaining, or depending on the product; or a defect that judgment and experience indicate is likely to prevent performance of the unit. In practice, critical characteristics are commonly inspected to an AQL level of 0.40 to 0.65 percent if not 100 percent inspected. One hundred percent inspection is recommended for critical characteristics if possible. Acceptance numbers are always zero for critical defects.

- *Major defect.* A major defect is a defect, other than critical, that is likely to result in failure or to reduce materially the usability of the unit of product for its intended purpose. In practice, AQL levels for major defects are generally about 1 percent.

- *Minor defect.* A minor defect is a defect that is not likely to reduce materially the usability of the unit of product for its intended purpose. In practice, AQL levels for minor defects generally range from 1.5 percent to 2.5 percent.

Levels of Inspection

There are seven levels of inspection used in ANSI/ASQC Z1.4-1993: reduced inspection, normal inspection, tightened inspection, and four levels of special inspection. The special inspection levels should only be used when small sample sizes are necessary and large risks can be tolerated. When using ANSI/ASQC Z1.4-1993, a set of switching rules must be followed as to the use of reduced, normal, and tightened inspection.

The following guidelines are taken from ANSI/ASQC Z1.4-1993:

- *Initiation of inspection.* Normal inspection Level II will be used at the start of inspection unless otherwise directed by the responsible authority.
- *Continuation of inspection.* Normal, tightened, or reduced inspection shall continue unchanged for each class of defect or defectives on successive lots or batches except where the following switching procedures require change. The switching procedures shall be applied to each class of defects or defectives independently.

Switching Procedures

Switching rules are graphically shown in Figure IV.12.

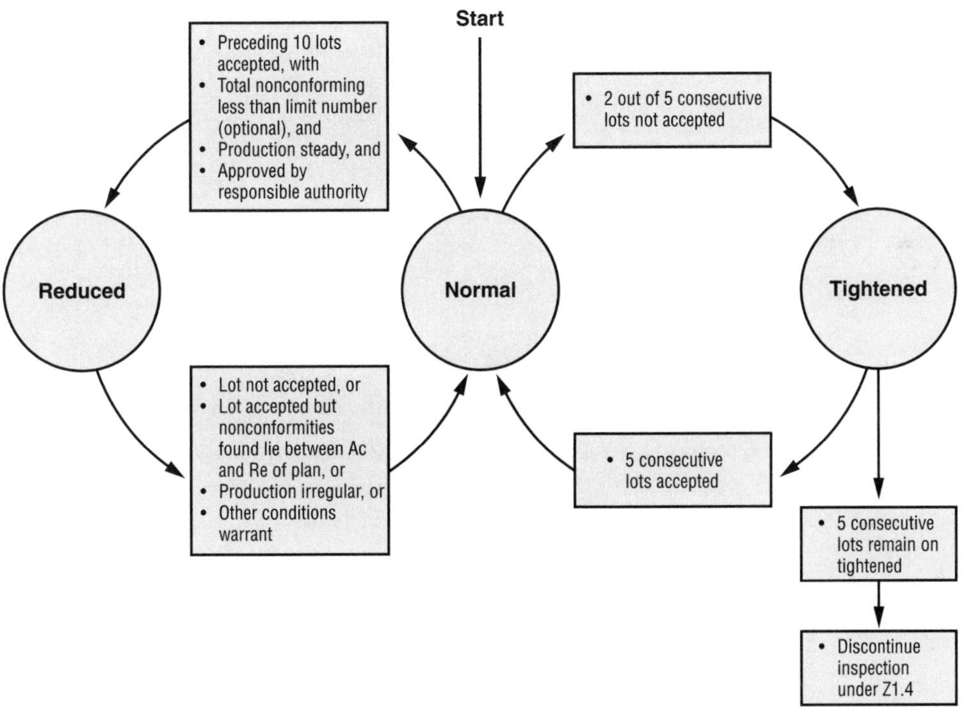

Figure IV.12 Switching rules for normal, tightened, and reduced inspection.

- *Normal to tightened.* When normal inspection is in effect, tightened inspection shall be instituted when two out of five consecutive lots or batches have been rejected on original inspection (that is, ignoring resubmitted lots or batches for this procedure).
- *Tightened to normal.* When tightened inspection is in effect, normal inspection shall be instituted when five consecutive lots or batches have been considered acceptable on original inspection.
- *Normal to reduced.* When normal inspection is in effect, reduced inspection shall be instituted providing that all of the following conditions are satisfied:
  a. The preceding 10 lots or batches (or more), as indicated by the note on ANSI/ASQC Z1.4-1993 Table I, shown as Figure IV.15 at the end of this chapter, have been on normal inspection and none has been rejected on original inspection.
  b. The total number of defectives (or defects) in the sample from the preceding 10 lots or batches (or such other number as was used for condition (a) above) is equal to or less than the applicable number given in Table VIII of ANSI/ASQC Z1.4-1993 (shown as Figure IV.14 at the end of this chapter). If double or multiple sampling is in use, all samples inspected should be included, not "first" samples only.
  c. Production is at a steady rate.
  d. Reduced inspection is considered desirable by the responsible authority.
- *Reduced to normal.* When reduced inspection is in effect, normal inspection shall be instituted if any of the following occur on original inspection:
  a. A lot or batch is rejected.
  b. A lot or batch is considered acceptable under reduced inspection but the sampling procedures terminated without either acceptance or rejection criteria having been met. In these circumstances, the lot or batch will be considered acceptable, but normal inspection will be reinstated starting with the new lot or batch.
  c. Production becomes irregular or delayed.
  d. Other conditions warrant that normal inspection shall be instituted.
- *Discontinuation of inspection.* In the event that 10 consecutive lots or batches remain on tightened inspection (or such other number as may be designated by the responsible authority), inspection under the provisions of this document should be discontinued pending action to improve the quality of submitted material.

Types of Sampling

ANSI/ASQC Z1.4-1993 allows for three types of sampling:

1. Single sampling
2. Double sampling
3. Multiple sampling

The choice of the type of plan depends on many variables. Single sampling is the easiest to administer and perform, but usually results in the largest average total inspection. Double sampling in ANSI/ASQC Z1.4-1993 results in a lower average total inspection than single sampling, but requires more decisions to be made, such as:

- Accept the lot after first sample.
- Reject the lot after first sample.
- Take a second sample.
- Accept the lot after second sample.
- Reject the lot after second sample.

Multiple sampling plans further reduce the average total inspection but also increase the number of decisions to be made. As many as seven samples may be required before a decision to accept or reject the lot can be made. This type of plan requires the most administration.

A general procedure for selecting plans from ANSI/ASQC Z1.4-1993 is as follows:

1. Decide on an AQL.
2. Decide on the inspection level.
3. Determine the lot size.
4. Find the appropriate sample size code letter. See Table I from ANSI/ASQC Z1.4-1993, also shown as Figure IV.15 at the end of this chapter.
5. Determine the type of sampling plan to be used: single, double, or multiple.
6. Using the selected AQL and sample size code letter, enter the appropriate table to find the desired plan to be used.
7. Determine the normal, tightened, and reduced plans as required from the corresponding tables.

Example: A lot of 1750 parts has been received and are to be checked to an AQL level of 1.5 percent. Determine the appropriate single, double, and multiple sampling plans for general inspection Level II.

Steps to define the plans are as follows:

1. Table I on page 10 of ANSI/ASQC Z1.4-1993, also shown as Figure IV.15 at the end of this chapter, stipulates code letter K.
2. Normal inspection is applied. For code letter K, using Table II-A of ANSI/ASQC Z1.4-1993 on page 11 of the standard, also shown as Figure IV.16 at the end of this chapter, a sample of 125 is specified.
3. For double sampling, two samples of 80 may be required. Refer to Table III-A on page 14 of the standard, shown as Figure IV.17 at the end of this chapter.
4. For multiple sampling, at least two samples of 32 are required and it may take up to seven samples of 32 before an acceptance or rejection decision is made. Refer to Table IV-A on page 17 of the standard, shown as Figure IV.18 at the end of this chapter.

A breakdown of all three plans follows:

Sampling Plan	Sample(s) Size	AC	RE
Single sampling	125	5	6
Double sampling			
First	80	5	
Second	80	7	
Multiple sampling			
First	32	*	4
Second	32	1	5
Third	32	2	6
Fourth	32	3	7
Fifth	32	5	8
Sixth	32	7	9
Seventh	32	9	10

AC = Acceptance Number
RE = Rejection Number
* Acceptance not permitted at this sample size.

Dodge-Romig Tables

Dodge-Romig tables were designed as sampling plans to minimize average total inspection (ATI). These plans require an accurate estimate of the process average nonconforming in selection of the sampling plan to be used. The Dodge-Romig tables use the AOQL and LTPD values for plan selection, rather than AQL as in ANSI/ASQC Z1.4-1993. When the process average nonconforming is controlled to requirements, Dodge-Romig tables result in lower average total inspection, but rejection of lots and sorting tend to minimize the gains if process quality deteriorates.

Note that if the process average nonconforming shows statistical control, acceptance sampling should not be used. The most economical course of action in this situation is either no inspection or 100 percent inspection.[15]

Variables Sampling Plans

Variables sampling plans use the actual measurements of sample products for decision making rather than classifying products as conforming or nonconforming, as in attribute sampling plans. Variables sampling plans are more complex in administration than attribute plans, thus they require more skill. They provide some benefits, however, over attribute plans. Two of these benefits are:

1. Equal protection to an attribute sampling plan but with a much smaller sample size. There are several types of variables sampling plans in use, including: (1) known; (2) unknown but can be estimated using sample standard deviation *S*; and (3) unknown and the range R is used as an estimator. If an attribute sampling plan sample size is determined, the variables plans previously listed can be compared as a percentage to the attribute plan.

Plan	Sample Size (Percent)
Attribute	100
σ unknown, range method	60
σ unknown and estimated from sample	40
σ known	15

2. Variables sampling plans allow the determination of how close to nominal or a specification limit the process is performing. Attribute plans either accept or reject a lot; variables plans give information on how well or poorly the process is performing.

Variables sampling plans, such as ANSI/ASQC Z1.9-1993, have some disadvantages and limitations:

1. The assumption of normality of the population from which the samples are being drawn.
2. Unlike attribute sampling plans, separate characteristics on the same parts will have different averages and dispersions, resulting in a separate sampling plan for each characteristic.
3. Variables plans are more complex in administration.
4. Variables gauging is generally more expensive than attribute gauging.

ANSI/ASQC Z1.9-1993

The most common standard for variables sampling plans is ANSI/ASQC Z1.9-1993, which has plans for: (1) variability known, (2) variability unknown—standard deviation method, and (3) variability unknown—range method. Using the aforementioned methods, this sampling plan can be used to test for a single specification limit, a double (or bilateral) specification limit, estimation of the process average, and estimation of the dispersion of the parent population.

As in ANSI/ASQC Z1.4-1993, several AQL levels are used and specific switching procedures for normal—reduced—tightened inspection are followed. ANSI/ASQC Z1.9-1993 allows for the same AQL value for each specification limit of double specification limit plans or the use of different AQL values for each specification limit. The AQL values are designated M_L for the lower specification limit and M_U for the upper specification limit.

There are two forms used for every specification limit ANSI/ASQC Z1.9-1993 plan: Form 1 and Form 2. Form 1 provides only acceptance or rejection criteria, whereas Form 2 estimates the percent below the lower specification and the percent above the upper specification limit. These percentages are compared to the AQL for acceptance/rejection criteria. Figure IV.13 summarizes the structure and organization of ANSI/ASQC Z1.9-1993.

There are 14 AQL levels used in ANSI/ASQC Z1.9-1993 that are consistent with the AQL levels used in ANSI/ASQC Z1.4-1993. Section A of ANSI/ASQC Z1.9-1993 contains both an AQL conversion table and a table for selecting the desired inspection

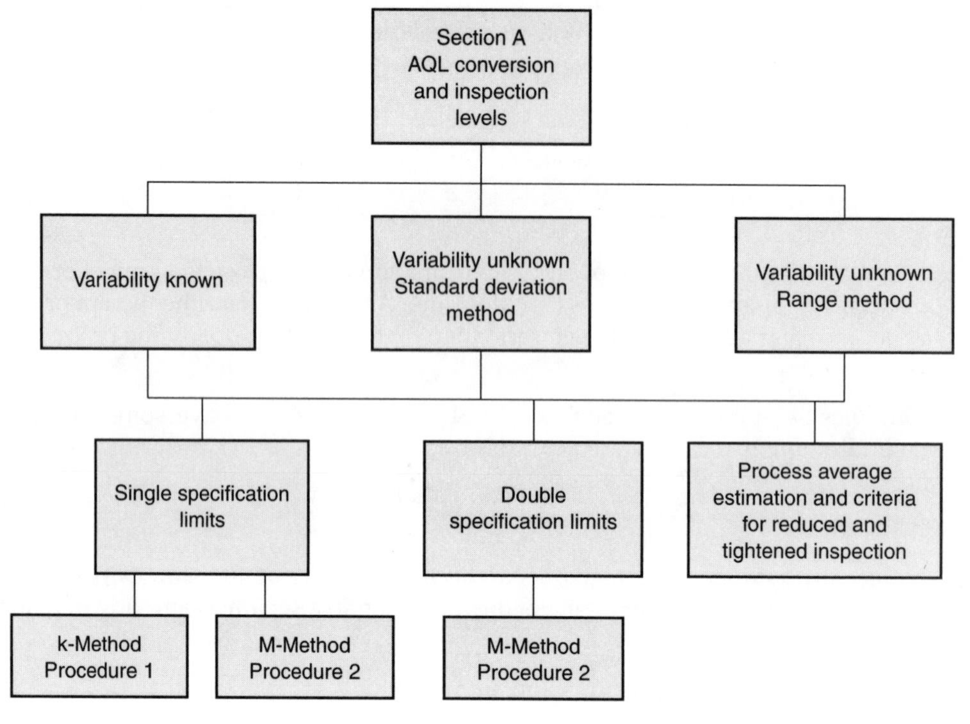

Figure IV.13 Structure and organization of ANSI/ASQC Z1.9-1993.

level. Level IV is generally considered normal inspection, with Level V being tightened inspection and Levels I, II, and III being reduced inspection. Table A-3 on page 7 of ANSI/ASQC Z1.9-1993 contains the OC curves for the sampling plans in Sections B, C, and D.

Section B contains sampling plans used when the variability is unknown and the standard deviation method is used. Part I is used for a single specification limit; Part II is used for a double specification limit; and Part III is used for estimation of process average and criteria for reduced and tightened inspection.

Section C contains sampling plans used when the variability is unknown and the range method is used. Parts I, II, and III are the same as Parts I, II, and III in Section B.

Section D contains sampling plans used when variability is known. Parts I, II, and III are the same as Parts I, II, and III in Section B.

Variability Unknown—Range Method. An example from Section C will be used here to illustrate the use of the variability unknown—range method for a single specification limit. The quality indices for a single specification limit are:

$$\frac{U-\overline{X}}{\overline{R}} \text{ or } \frac{\overline{X}-L}{\overline{R}}$$

where:

U = upper specification limit

L = lower specification limit

$\overline{X}$ = sample average

$\overline{R}$ = average range of the sample

The acceptance criterion is a comparison of the quality $(U - \overline{X})/\overline{R}$ or $(\overline{X} - L)/\overline{R}$ to the acceptability constant k. If the calculated quantity is equal to or greater than k, the lot is accepted; if the calculated quantity is negative or less than k, the lot is rejected.

The following example illustrates the use of the variability unknown—range method, Form I variables sampling plan and is similar to examples from Section C of ANSI/ASQC Z1.9-1993.

Example: The lower specification limit for electrical resistance of a certain electrical component is 620 ohms. A lot of 100 items is submitted for inspection. Inspection Level IV, normal inspection, with AQL = 0.4 percent, is to be used. From ANSI/ASQC Z1.9-1993 Table A-2 and Table C-1, shown on pages 158 and 159 as Figure IV.19 and Figure IV.20 respectively, it is seen that a sample of size 10 is required. Suppose that values of the sample resistances (in the order reading from left to right) are:

645, 651, 621, 625, 658 (R = 658 – 621 = 37)

670, 673, 641, 638, 650 (R = 673 – 638 = 35)

Determine compliance with the acceptability criterion.

Line	Information Needed	Value	Explanation
1.	Sample size: n	10	
2.	Sum of measurement: ΣX	6472	
3.	Sample mean $\overline{X}: \Sigma X/n$	647.2	6472/10
4.	Average range $\overline{R}: \Sigma R$/no. of subgroups	36	(37 + 35)/2
5.	Specification limit (lower): L	620	
6.	The quantity: $(\overline{X} - L)/R$	756	(647.2 – 620)/36
7.	Acceptability constant: k	.811	See Table C-1 (Figure IV.20 on page 159)
8.	Acceptability criterion: Compare $(X - L)/R$ with k	.756 ≤ .811	

The lot does not meet the acceptability criterion, since $(X - L)/R$ is less than k.

Note: If a single upper specification limit U is given, then compute the quantity $(U - X)/R$ in line 6, and compare it with k. The lot meets the acceptability criterion if $(U - X)/R$ is equal to or greater than k.

Variability Unknown—Standard Deviation Method. In this section, a sampling plan is shown for the situation where the variability is not known and the standard deviation is estimated from the sample data. The sampling plan will be that for a double specification limit, and it is found in Section B of the standard with one AQL value for both upper and lower specification limits combined.

The acceptability criterion is based on comparing an estimated percent nonconforming to a maximum allowable percent nonconforming for the given AQL level. The estimated percent nonconforming is found in ANSI/ASQC Z1.9-1993 Table B-5, shown as Figure IV.21 on page 160.

The quality indices for this sampling plan are:

$$\frac{U-\overline{X}}{s} \text{ or } \frac{\overline{X}-L}{s}$$

where

U = upper specification limit

L = lower specification limit

$\overline{X}$ = sample mean

s = estimate of lot standard deviation

The quality level of the lot is in terms of the lot percent defective. Three values are calculated: P_U, P_L, and p. P_U is an estimate of conformance with the upper specification limit; P_L is an estimate of conformance with the lower specification limit; and p is the sum of P_U and P_L.

The value of p is then compared with the maximum allowable percent defective. If p is less than or equal to M (ANSI/ASQC Z1.9-1993 Table B-5, shown as Figure IV.20 on page 159) or if either Q_U or Q_L is negative, the lot is rejected. The following example illustrates the above procedure.

Example: The minimum temperature of operation for a certain device is specified as 180°F. The maximum temperature is 209°F. A lot of 40 items is submitted for inspection. Inspection Level IV, normal inspection with AQL = 1 percent, is to be used. ANSI/ASQC Z1.9-1993 Table A-2, shown as Figure IV.19 on page 158, gives code letter D, which results in a sample size of five from ANSI/ASQC Z1.9-1993 Table B-3, shown as Figure IV.22 on page 161. The results of the five measurements in degrees Fahrenheit are as follows: 197, 188, 184, 205, 201. Determine if the lot meets acceptance criteria.

Line	Information Needed	Value Obtained	Explanation
1.	Sample size: n	5	
2.	Sum of measurements: ΣX	975	
3.	Sum of squared measurements: ΣX^2	190,435	
4.	Correction factor: $(\Sigma X^2)/n$	190,125	$975^2/5$
5.	Corrected sum of squares (SS): $\Sigma X^2 - \text{CF}$	310	190,435 – 190,125
6.	Variance V: SS/$n - 1$	77.5	310/4
7.	Standard deviation s: $\sqrt{V}$	8.81	77.5
8.	Sample mean $\overline{X}$: $\Sigma X/n$	195	975/5
9.	Upper specification limit: U	209	
10.	Lower Specification limit: L	180	
11.	Quality index: $Q_U = (U - \overline{X})/s$	1.59	(209 – 195)/8.81
12.	Quality index: $Q_L = (\overline{X} - L)/s$	1.7	(195 – 180)/8.81
13.	Estimate of lot percent defective above U: P_U	2.19%	See Table B-5 (Figure IV.22 at the end of this chapter)
14.	Estimate of lot percent defective below L: P_L	0.66%	See Table B-5 (Figure IV.22 at the end of this chapter)
15.	Total estimate of percent defective in lot: $p = P_U + P_L$	2.85%	2.19 +.66
16.	Maximum allowable percent defective: M	3.32%	See Table B-3 (Figure IV.23 at the end of this chapter)
17.	Acceptibility criterion: Compare $p = P_U + P_L$ with M.	2.85% < 3.32%	

The lot meets the acceptability criterion, since $p = P_U + P_L$ is less than M.

ANSI/ASQC Z1.9-1993 provides a variety of other examples for variables sampling plans.

Number of sample units from last 10 lots or batches	Acceptance Quality Level																									
	0.010	0.015	0.025	0.040	0.065	0.10	0.15	0.25	0.40	0.65	1.0	1.5	2.5	4.0	6.5	10	15	25	40	65	100	150	250	400	650	1000
20–29	*	*	*	*	*	*	*	*	*	*	*	*	*	*	*	0	0	2	4	8	14	22	40	68	115	181
30–49	*	*	*	*	*	*	*	*	*	*	*	*	*	*	0	0	1	3	7	13	22	36	63	105	178	277
50–79	*	*	*	*	*	*	*	*	*	*	*	*	*	0	0	2	3	7	14	25	40	63	110	181	301	
80–129	*	*	*	*	*	*	*	*	*	*	*	*	0	0	2	4	7	14	24	42	68	105	181	297		
130–199	*	*	*	*	*	*	*	*	*	*	*	0	0	2	4	7	13	25	42	72	115	177	301	490		
200–319	*	*	*	*	*	*	*	*	*	*	0	0	2	4	8	14	22	40	68	115	181	277	471			
320–499	*	*	*	*	*	*	*	*	*	0	0	1	4	8	14	24	39	68	113	189						
500–799	*	*	*	*	*	*	*	*	0	0	2	3	7	14	25	40	63	110	181							
800–1249	*	*	*	*	*	*	*	0	0	2	4	7	14	24	42	68	105	181								
1250–1999	*	*	*	*	*	*	0	0	2	4	7	13	24	40	69	110	169									
2000–3149	*	*	*	*	*	0	0	2	4	8	14	22	40	68	115	181										
3150–4999	*	*	*	*	0	0	1	4	8	14	24	38	67	111	186											
5000–7999	*	*	*	0	0	2	3	7	14	25	40	63	110	181												
8000–12499	*	*	0	0	2	4	7	14	24	42	68	105	181													
12500–19999	*	0	0	2	4	7	13	24	40	69	110	169														
20000–31499	0	0	2	4	8	14	22	40	68	115	181															
31500 & Over	0	1	4	8	14	24	38	67	111	186																

* = Denotes that the number of sample units from the last ten lots or batches is not sufficient for reduced inspection for this AQL. In this instance more than ten lots or batches may be used for calculation, provided that the lots or batches used are the most recent ones in sequence, that they have all been on normal inspection, and that none has been rejected while on original inspection.

Figure IV.14 ANSI/ASQC Z1.4-1993 Table VIII: Limit numbers for reduced inspection. Used by permission.

Lot or batch size			Special inspection levels				General inspection levels		
			S-1	S-2	S-3	S-4	I	II	III
2	to	8	A	A	A	A	A	A	B
9	to	15	A	A	A	A	A	B	C
16	to	25	A	A	B	B	B	C	D
26	to	50	A	B	B	C	C	D	E
51	to	90	B	B	C	C	C	E	F
91	to	150	B	B	C	D	D	F	G
151	to	280	B	C	D	E	E	G	H
281	to	500	B	C	D	E	F	H	J
501	to	1200	C	C	E	F	G	J	K
1201	to	3200	C	D	E	G	H	K	L
3201	to	10000	C	D	F	G	J	L	M
10001	to	35000	C	D	F	H	K	M	N
35001	to	150000	D	E	G	J	L	N	P
150001	to	500000	D	E	G	J	M	P	Q
500001	and	over	D	E	H	K	N	Q	R

Figure IV.15 ANSI/ASQC Z1.4-1993 Table I: Sample size code letters inspection. Used by permission.

Sample Size Code Letter	Sample Size	Acceptance Quality Limit, *AQL*, in Percent Nonconforming Items and Nonconformities per 100 Items (Normal Inspection)																									
		0.010	0.015	0.025	0.040	0.065	0.10	0.15	0.25	0.40	0.65	1.0	1.5	2.5	4.0	6.5	10	15	25	40	65	100	150	250	400	650	1000
		Ac Re	*Ac Re*	*Ac Re*	*Ac Re*	*Ac Re*	*Ac Re*	*Ac Re*	*Ac Re*	*Ac Re*	*Ac Re*	*Ac Re*	*Ac Re*	*Ac Re*	*Ac Re*	*Ac Re*	*Ac Re*	*Ac Re*	*Ac Re*	*Ac Re*	*Ac Re*	*Ac Re*	*Ac Re*	*Ac Re*	*Ac Re*	*Ac Re*	*Ac Re*
A	2	↓	↓	↓	↓	↓	↓	↓	↓	↓	↓	↓	↓	↓	↓	0 1	↓	↓	1 2	2 3	3 4	5 6	7 8	10 11	14 15	21 22	30 31
B	3	↓	↓	↓	↓	↓	↓	↓	↓	↓	↓	↓	↓	↓	0 1	↑	↓	1 2	2 3	3 4	5 6	7 8	10 11	14 15	21 22	30 31	44 45
C	5	↓	↓	↓	↓	↓	↓	↓	↓	↓	↓	↓	↓	0 1	↑	↓	1 2	2 3	3 4	5 6	7 8	10 11	14 15	21 22	30 31	44 45	↑
D	8	↓	↓	↓	↓	↓	↓	↓	↓	↓	↓	↓	0 1	↑	↓	1 2	2 3	3 4	5 6	7 8	10 11	14 15	21 22	30 31	44 45	↑	↑
E	13	↓	↓	↓	↓	↓	↓	↓	↓	↓	↓	0 1	↑	↓	1 2	2 3	3 4	5 6	7 8	10 11	14 15	21 22	30 31	44 45	↑	↑	↑
F	20	↓	↓	↓	↓	↓	↓	↓	↓	↓	0 1	↑	↓	1 2	2 3	3 4	5 6	7 8	10 11	14 15	21 22	↑	↑	↑	↑	↑	↑
G	32	↓	↓	↓	↓	↓	↓	↓	↓	0 1	↑	↓	1 2	2 3	3 4	5 6	7 8	10 11	14 15	21 22	↑	↑	↑	↑	↑	↑	↑
H	50	↓	↓	↓	↓	↓	↓	↓	0 1	↑	↓	1 2	2 3	3 4	5 6	7 8	10 11	14 15	21 22	↑	↑	↑	↑	↑	↑	↑	↑
J	80	↓	↓	↓	↓	↓	↓	0 1	↑	↓	1 2	2 3	3 4	5 6	7 8	10 11	14 15	21 22	↑	↑	↑	↑	↑	↑	↑	↑	↑
K	125	↓	↓	↓	↓	↓	0 1	↑	↓	1 2	2 3	3 4	5 6	7 8	10 11	14 15	21 22	↑	↑	↑	↑	↑	↑	↑	↑	↑	↑
L	200	↓	↓	↓	↓	0 1	↑	↓	1 2	2 3	3 4	5 6	7 8	10 11	14 15	21 22	↑	↑	↑	↑	↑	↑	↑	↑	↑	↑	↑
M	315	↓	↓	↓	0 1	↑	↓	1 2	2 3	3 4	5 6	7 8	10 11	14 15	21 22	↑	↑	↑	↑	↑	↑	↑	↑	↑	↑	↑	↑
N	500	↓	↓	0 1	↑	↓	1 2	2 3	3 4	5 6	7 8	10 11	14 15	21 22	↑	↑	↑	↑	↑	↑	↑	↑	↑	↑	↑	↑	↑
P	800	↓	0 1	↑	↓	1 2	2 3	3 4	5 6	7 8	10 11	14 15	21 22	↑	↑	↑	↑	↑	↑	↑	↑	↑	↑	↑	↑	↑	↑
Q	1250	0 1	↑	↓	1 2	2 3	3 4	5 6	7 8	10 11	14 15	21 22	↑	↑	↑	↑	↑	↑	↑	↑	↑	↑	↑	↑	↑	↑	↑
R	2000	↑	↑	1 2	2 3	3 4	5 6	7 8	10 11	14 15	21 22	↑	↑	↑	↑	↑	↑	↑	↑	↑	↑	↑	↑	↑	↑	↑	↑

↓ = Use the first sampling plan below the arrow. If sample size equals, or exceeds, lot size, carry out 100 percent inspection.

↑ = Use the first sampling plan above the arrow.

Ac = Acceptance number

Re = Rejection number

Figure IV.16 ANSI/ASQC Z1.4-1993 Table II-A: Single sampling plans for normal inspection. Used by permission.

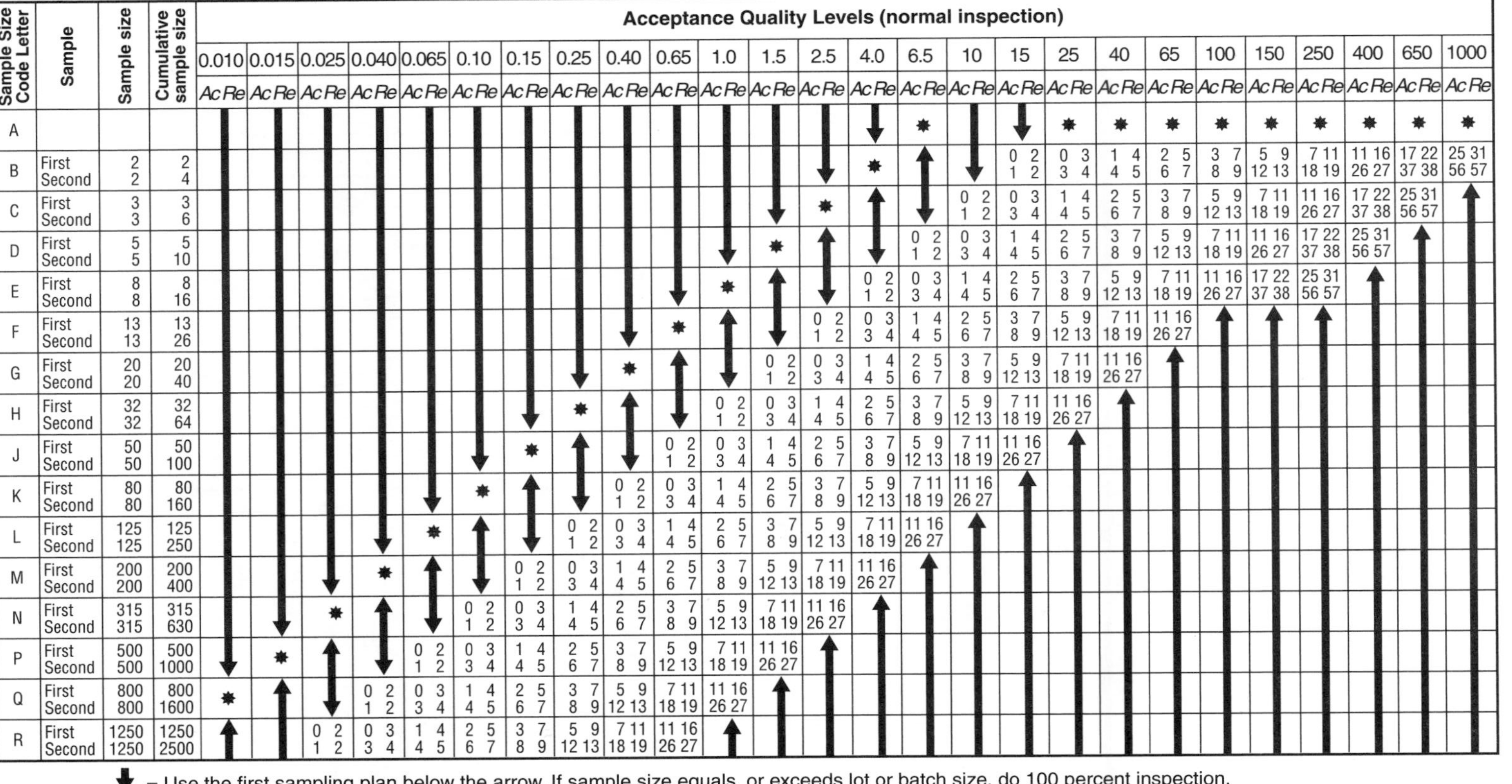

Sample Size Code Letter	Sample	Sample size	Cumulative sample size	Acceptance Quality Levels (normal inspection)																									
				0.010	0.015	0.025	0.040	0.065	0.10	0.15	0.25	0.40	0.65	1.0	1.5	2.5	4.0	6.5	10	15	25	40	65	100	150	250	400	650	1000
				Ac Re	Ac Re	Ac Re	Ac Re	Ac Re	Ac Re	Ac Re	Ac Re	Ac Re	Ac Re	Ac Re	Ac Re	Ac Re	Ac Re	Ac Re	Ac Re	Ac Re	Ac Re	Ac Re	Ac Re	Ac Re	Ac Re	Ac Re	Ac Re	Ac Re	Ac Re
A				↓	↓	↓	↓	↓	↓	↓	↓	↓	↓	↓	↓	↓	↓	*	↓	↓	*	*	*	*	*	*	*	*	*
B	First Second	2 2	2 4	↓	↓	↓	↓	↓	↓	↓	↓	↓	↓	↓	↓	↓	*	↕	↓	0 2 1 2	0 3 3 4	1 4 4 5	2 5 6 7	3 7 8 9	5 9 12 13	7 11 18 19	11 16 26 27	17 22 37 38	25 31 56 57
C	First Second	3 3	3 6	↓	↓	↓	↓	↓	↓	↓	↓	↓	↓	↓	↓	*	↕	↕	0 2 1 2	0 3 3 4	1 4 4 5	2 5 6 7	3 7 8 9	5 9 12 13	7 11 18 19	11 16 26 27	17 22 37 38	25 31 56 57	↑
D	First Second	5 5	5 10	↓	↓	↓	↓	↓	↓	↓	↓	↓	↓	↓	*	↕	↕	0 2 1 2	0 3 3 4	1 4 4 5	2 5 6 7	3 7 8 9	5 9 12 13	7 11 18 19	11 16 26 27	17 22 37 38	25 31 56 57	↑	↑
E	First Second	8 8	8 16	↓	↓	↓	↓	↓	↓	↓	↓	↓	↓	*	↕	↕	0 2 1 2	0 3 3 4	1 4 4 5	2 5 6 7	3 7 8 9	5 9 12 13	7 11 18 19	11 16 26 27	17 22 37 38	25 31 56 57	↑	↑	↑
F	First Second	13 13	13 26	↓	↓	↓	↓	↓	↓	↓	↓	↓	*	↕	↕	0 2 1 2	0 3 3 4	1 4 4 5	2 5 6 7	3 7 8 9	5 9 12 13	7 11 18 19	11 16 26 27	↑	↑	↑	↑	↑	↑
G	First Second	20 20	20 40	↓	↓	↓	↓	↓	↓	↓	↓	*	↕	↕	0 2 1 2	0 3 3 4	1 4 4 5	2 5 6 7	3 7 8 9	5 9 12 13	7 11 18 19	11 16 26 27	↑	↑	↑	↑	↑	↑	↑
H	First Second	32 32	32 64	↓	↓	↓	↓	↓	↓	↓	*	↕	↕	0 2 1 2	0 3 3 4	1 4 4 5	2 5 6 7	3 7 8 9	5 9 12 13	7 11 18 19	11 16 26 27	↑	↑	↑	↑	↑	↑	↑	↑
J	First Second	50 50	50 100	↓	↓	↓	↓	↓	↓	*	↕	↕	0 2 1 2	0 3 3 4	1 4 4 5	2 5 6 7	3 7 8 9	5 9 12 13	7 11 18 19	11 16 26 27	↑	↑	↑	↑	↑	↑	↑	↑	↑
K	First Second	80 80	80 160	↓	↓	↓	↓	↓	*	↕	↕	0 2 1 2	0 3 3 4	1 4 4 5	2 5 6 7	3 7 8 9	5 9 12 13	7 11 18 19	11 16 26 27	↑	↑	↑	↑	↑	↑	↑	↑	↑	↑
L	First Second	125 125	125 250	↓	↓	↓	↓	*	↕	↕	0 2 1 2	0 3 3 4	1 4 4 5	2 5 6 7	3 7 8 9	5 9 12 13	7 11 18 19	11 16 26 27	↑	↑	↑	↑	↑	↑	↑	↑	↑	↑	↑
M	First Second	200 200	200 400	↓	↓	↓	*	↕	↕	0 2 1 2	0 3 3 4	1 4 4 5	2 5 6 7	3 7 8 9	5 9 12 13	7 11 18 19	11 16 26 27	↑	↑	↑	↑	↑	↑	↑	↑	↑	↑	↑	↑
N	First Second	315 315	315 630	↓	↓	*	↕	↕	0 2 1 2	0 3 3 4	1 4 4 5	2 5 6 7	3 7 8 9	5 9 12 13	7 11 18 19	11 16 26 27	↑	↑	↑	↑	↑	↑	↑	↑	↑	↑	↑	↑	↑
P	First Second	500 500	500 1000	↓	*	↕	↕	0 2 1 2	0 3 3 4	1 4 4 5	2 5 6 7	3 7 8 9	5 9 12 13	7 11 18 19	11 16 26 27	↑	↑	↑	↑	↑	↑	↑	↑	↑	↑	↑	↑	↑	↑
Q	First Second	800 800	800 1600	*	↑	↕	0 2 1 2	0 3 3 4	1 4 4 5	2 5 6 7	3 7 8 9	5 9 12 13	7 11 18 19	11 16 26 27	↑	↑	↑	↑	↑	↑	↑	↑	↑	↑	↑	↑	↑	↑	↑
R	First Second	1250 1250	1250 2500	↑	↑	0 2 1 2	0 3 3 4	1 4 4 5	2 5 6 7	3 7 8 9	5 9 12 13	7 11 18 19	11 16 26 27	↑	↑	↑	↑	↑	↑	↑	↑	↑	↑	↑	↑	↑	↑	↑	↑

↓ = Use the first sampling plan below the arrow. If sample size equals, or exceeds lot or batch size, do 100 percent inspection.

↑ = Use the first sampling plan above the arrow.

Ac = Acceptance number.

Re = Rejection number.

* = Use corresponding single sampling plan (or alternatively, use double sampling plan below, where available).

Figure IV.17 ANSI/ASQC Z1.4-1993 Table III-A: Double sampling plans for normal inspection. Used by permission.

Acceptance Quality Levels (normal inspection)

Sample Size Code Letter	Sample	Sample size	Cumulative sample size	0.010	0.015	0.025	0.040	0.065	0.10	0.15	0.25	0.40	0.65	1.0
				Ac Re	*Ac Re*	*Ac Re*	*Ac Re*	*Ac Re*	*Ac Re*	*Ac Re*	*Ac Re*	*Ac Re*	*Ac Re*	*Ac Re*
A				↓	↓	↓	↓	↓	↓	↓	↓	↓	↓	↓
B														
C														
D	First	2	2											
	Second	2	4											
	Third	2	6											
	Fourth	2	8											
	Fifth	2	10											
	Sixth	2	12											
	Seventh	2	14											*
E	First	3	3											
	Second	3	6											
	Third	3	9											
	Fourth	3	12											
	Fifth	3	15											
	Sixth	3	18											
	Seventh	3	21											
F	First	5	5										*	↕
	Second	5	10											
	Third	5	15											
	Fourth	5	20											
	Fifth	5	25											
	Sixth	5	30											
	Seventh	5	35											
G	First	8	8									*	↕	
	Second	8	16											
	Third	8	24											
	Fourth	8	32											
	Fifth	8	40											
	Sixth	8	48											
	Seventh	8	56											
H	First	13	13								*	↕		# 2
	Second	13	26											# 2
	Third	13	39											0 2
	Fourth	13	52											0 3
	Fifth	13	65											1 3
	Sixth	13	78											1 3
	Seventh	13	91											2 3
J	First	20	20							*	↑		# 2	# 2
	Second	20	40										# 2	0 3
	Third	20	60										0 2	0 3
	Fourth	20	80										0 3	1 4
	Fifth	20	100										1 3	2 4
	Sixth	20	120										1 3	3 5
	Seventh	20	140										2 3	4 5

Sample Size Code Letter	Sample	1.5	2.5	4.0	6.5	10	15	25	40	65	100	150	250	400	650	1000
		Ac Re	*Ac Re*	*Ac Re*	*Ac Re*	*Ac Re*	*Ac Re*	*Ac Re*	*Ac Re*	*Ac Re*	*Ac Re*	*Ac Re*	*Ac Re*	*Ac Re*	*Ac Re*	*Ac Re*
A		↓	↓	↓	*	↓	↓	*	*	*	*	*	*	*	*	*
B				*	↕		++	++	++	++	++	++	++	++	++	++
C			*	↕		++	++	++	++	++	++	++	++	++	++	↑
D	First	*	↕		# 2	# 2	# 3	# 4	0 4	0 5	1 7	2 9	4 12	6 16	↑	
	Second				# 2	0 3	0 3	1 5	1 6	3 8	4 10	7 14	11 19	17 27		
	Third				0 2	0 3	1 4	2 6	3 8	6 10	8 13	13 19	19 27	29 39		
	Fourth				0 3	1 4	2 5	3 7	5 10	8 13	12 17	19 25	27 34	40 49		
	Fifth				1 3	2 4	3 6	5 8	7 11	11 15	17 20	25 29	36 40	53 58		
	Sixth				1 3	3 5	4 6	7 9	10 12	14 17	21 23	31 33	45 47	65 68		
	Seventh				2 3	4 5	6 7	9 10	13 14	18 19	25 26	37 38	53 54	77 78		
E	First	↕		# 2	# 2	# 3	# 4	0 4	0 5	1 7	2 9	4 12	6 16	↑		
	Second			# 2	0 3	0 3	1 5	1 6	3 8	4 10	7 14	11 19	17 27			
	Third			0 2	0 3	1 4	2 6	3 8	6 10	8 13	13 19	19 27	29 39			
	Fourth			0 3	1 4	2 5	3 7	5 10	8 13	12 17	19 25	27 34	40 49			
	Fifth			1 3	2 4	3 6	5 8	7 11	11 15	17 20	25 29	36 40	53 58			
	Sixth			1 3	3 5	4 6	7 9	10 12	14 17	21 23	31 33	45 47	65 68			
	Seventh			2 3	4 5	6 7	9 10	13 14	18 19	25 26	37 38	53 54	77 78			
F	First		# 2	# 2	# 3	# 4	0 4	0 5	1 7	2 9	↑	↑	↑			
	Second		# 2	0 3	0 3	1 5	1 6	3 8	4 10	7 14						
	Third		0 2	0 3	1 4	2 6	3 8	6 10	8 13	13 19						
	Fourth		0 3	1 4	2 5	3 7	5 10	8 13	12 17	19 25						
	Fifth		1 3	2 4	3 6	5 8	7 11	11 15	17 20	25 29						
	Sixth		1 3	3 5	4 6	7 9	10 12	14 17	21 23	31 33						
	Seventh		2 3	4 5	6 7	9 10	13 14	18 19	25 26	37 38						
G	First	# 2	# 2	# 3	# 4	0 4	0 5	1 7	2 9	↑						
	Second	# 2	0 3	0 3	1 5	1 6	3 8	4 10	7 14							
	Third	0 2	0 3	1 4	2 6	3 8	6 10	8 13	13 19							
	Fourth	0 3	1 4	2 5	3 7	5 10	8 13	12 17	19 25							
	Fifth	1 3	2 4	3 6	5 8	7 11	11 15	17 20	25 29							
	Sixth	1 3	3 5	4 6	7 9	10 12	14 17	21 23	31 33							
	Seventh	2 3	4 5	6 7	9 10	13 14	18 19	25 26	37 38							
H	First	# 2	# 3	# 4	0 4	0 5	1 7	2 9	↑							
	Second	0 3	0 3	1 5	1 6	3 8	4 10	7 14								
	Third	0 3	1 4	2 6	3 8	6 10	8 13	13 19								
	Fourth	1 4	2 5	3 7	5 10	8 13	12 17	19 25								
	Fifth	2 4	3 6	5 8	7 11	11 15	17 20	25 29								
	Sixth	3 5	4 6	7 9	10 12	14 17	21 23	31 33								
	Seventh	4 5	6 7	9 10	13 14	18 19	25 26	37 38								
J	First	# 3	# 4	0 4	0 5	1 7	2 9	↑								
	Second	0 3	1 5	1 6	3 8	4 10	7 14									
	Third	1 4	2 6	3 8	6 10	8 13	13 19									
	Fourth	2 5	3 7	5 10	8 13	12 17	19 25									
	Fifth	3 6	5 8	7 11	11 15	17 20	25 29									
	Sixth	4 6	7 9	10 12	14 17	21 23	31 33									
	Seventh	6 7	9 10	13 14	18 19	25 26	37 38									

↓ = Use the first sampling plan below the arrow (refer to continuation of table on following page, when necessary). If sample size equals or exceeds lot or batch size, do 100 percent inspection.

↑ = Use first sampling plan above arrow.

* = Use corresponding single sampling plan (or alternatively, use double sampling plan below, where available).

++ = Use corresponding double sampling plan (or alternatively, use multiple sampling plan below, where available).

Ac = Acceptance number.

Re = Rejectiion number.

\# = Acceptance not permitted at this sample size.

Figure IV.18 ANSI/ASQC Z1.4-1993 TABLE IV-A: Multiple sampling plans for normal inspection. Used by permission.

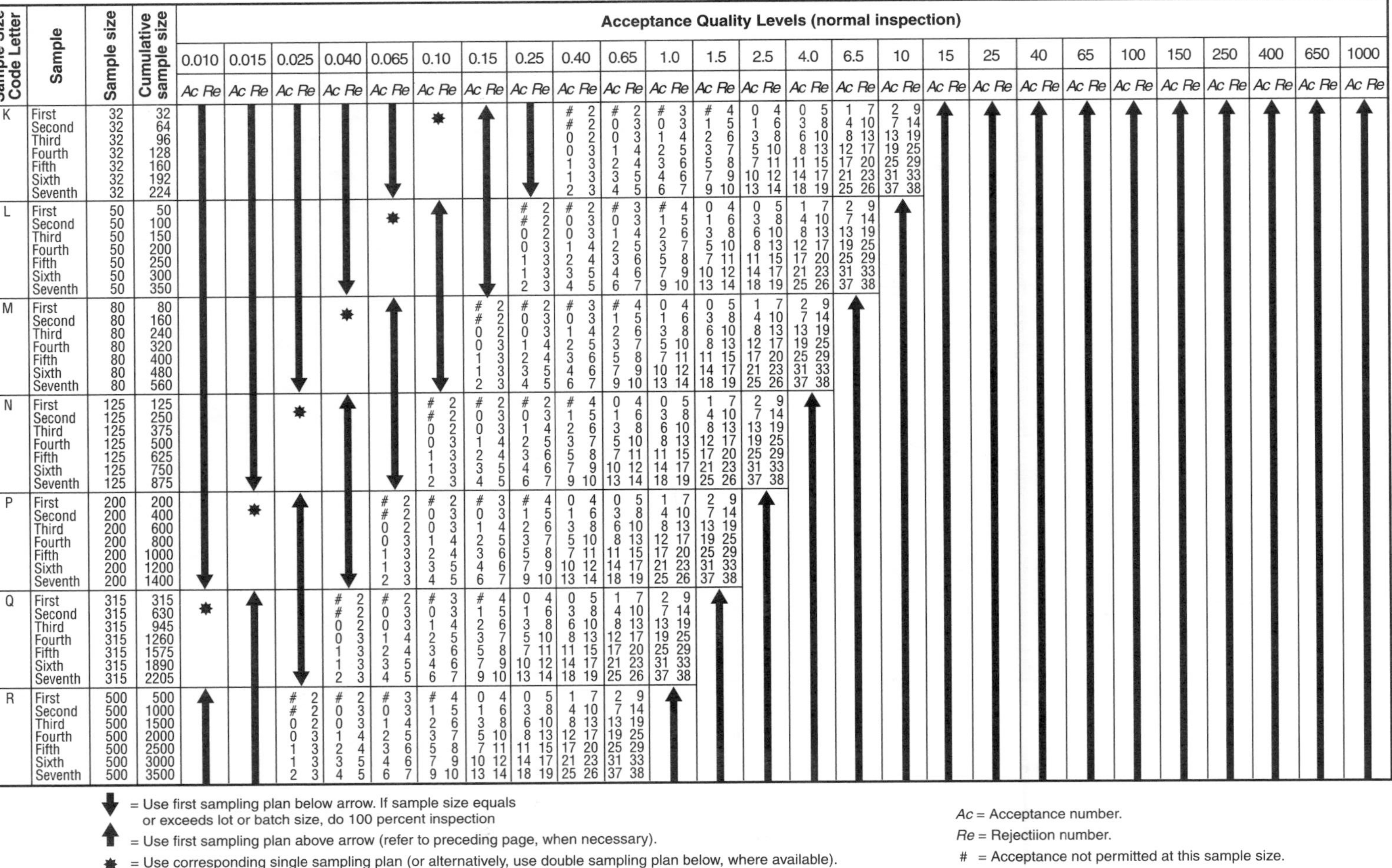

Sample Size Code Letter	Sample	Sample size	Cumulative sample size	Acceptance Quality Levels (normal inspection)																									
				0.010	0.015	0.025	0.040	0.065	0.10	0.15	0.25	0.40	0.65	1.0	1.5	2.5	4.0	6.5	10	15	25	40	65	100	150	250	400	650	1000
				Ac Re	Ac Re	Ac Re	Ac Re	Ac Re	Ac Re	Ac Re	Ac Re	Ac Re	Ac Re	Ac Re	Ac Re	Ac Re	Ac Re	Ac Re	Ac Re	Ac Re	Ac Re	Ac Re	Ac Re	Ac Re	Ac Re	Ac Re	Ac Re	Ac Re	Ac Re
K	First	32	32						*	↑		# 2	# 2	# 3	# 4	0 4	0 5	1 7	2 9	↑	↑	↑	↑	↑	↑	↑	↑	↑	↑
	Second	32	64									# 2	0 3	0 3	1 5	1 6	3 8	4 10	7 14										
	Third	32	96									0 2	0 3	1 4	2 6	3 8	6 10	8 13	13 19										
	Fourth	32	128									0 3	1 4	2 5	3 7	5 10	8 13	12 17	19 25										
	Fifth	32	160									1 3	2 4	3 6	5 8	7 11	11 15	17 20	25 29										
	Sixth	32	192									1 3	3 5	4 6	7 9	10 12	14 17	21 23	31 33										
	Seventh	32	224					↓			↓	2 3	4 5	6 7	9 10	13 14	18 19	25 26	37 38										
L	First	50	50					*	↑		# 2	# 2	# 3	# 4	0 4	0 5	1 7	2 9	↑										
	Second	50	100								# 2	0 3	0 3	1 5	1 6	3 8	4 10	7 14											
	Third	50	150								0 2	0 3	1 4	2 6	3 8	6 10	8 13	13 19											
	Fourth	50	200								0 3	1 4	2 5	3 7	5 10	8 13	12 17	19 25											
	Fifth	50	250								1 3	2 4	3 6	5 8	7 11	11 15	17 20	25 29											
	Sixth	50	300								1 3	3 5	4 6	7 9	10 12	14 17	21 23	31 33											
	Seventh	50	350				↓			↓	2 3	4 5	6 7	9 10	13 14	18 19	25 26	37 38											
M	First	80	80				*	↑		# 2	# 2	# 3	# 4	0 4	0 5	1 7	2 9	↑											
	Second	80	160							# 2	0 3	0 3	1 5	1 6	3 8	4 10	7 14												
	Third	80	240							0 2	0 3	1 4	2 6	3 8	6 10	8 13	13 19												
	Fourth	80	320							0 3	1 4	2 5	3 7	5 10	8 13	12 17	19 25												
	Fifth	80	400							1 3	2 4	3 6	5 8	7 11	11 15	17 20	25 29												
	Sixth	80	480							1 3	3 5	4 6	7 9	10 12	14 17	21 23	31 33												
	Seventh	80	560			↓			↓	2 3	4 5	6 7	9 10	13 14	18 19	25 26	37 38												
N	First	125	125			*	↑		# 2	# 2	# 2	# 4	0 4	0 5	1 7	2 9	↑												
	Second	125	250						# 2	0 3	0 3	1 5	1 6	3 8	4 10	7 14													
	Third	125	375						0 2	0 3	1 4	2 6	3 8	6 10	8 13	13 19													
	Fourth	125	500						0 3	1 4	2 5	3 7	5 10	8 13	12 17	19 25													
	Fifth	125	625						1 3	2 4	3 6	5 8	7 11	11 15	17 20	25 29													
	Sixth	125	750						1 3	3 5	4 6	7 9	10 12	14 17	21 23	31 33													
	Seventh	125	875		↓			↓	2 3	4 5	6 7	9 10	13 14	18 19	25 26	37 38													
P	First	200	200		*	↑		# 2	# 2	# 3	# 4	0 4	0 5	1 7	2 9	↑													
	Second	200	400					# 2	0 3	0 3	1 5	1 6	3 8	4 10	7 14														
	Third	200	600					0 2	0 3	1 4	2 6	3 8	6 10	8 13	13 19														
	Fourth	200	800					0 3	1 4	2 5	3 7	5 10	8 13	12 17	19 25														
	Fifth	200	1000					1 3	2 4	3 6	5 8	7 11	11 15	17 20	25 29														
	Sixth	200	1200					1 3	3 5	4 6	7 9	10 12	14 17	21 23	31 33														
	Seventh	200	1400	↓			↓	2 3	4 5	6 7	9 10	13 14	18 19	25 26	37 38														
Q	First	315	315	*	↑		# 2	# 2	# 3	# 4	0 4	0 5	1 7	2 9	↑														
	Second	315	630				# 2	0 3	0 3	1 5	1 6	3 8	4 10	7 14															
	Third	315	945				0 2	0 3	1 4	2 6	3 8	6 10	8 13	13 19															
	Fourth	315	1260				0 3	1 4	2 5	3 7	5 10	8 13	12 17	19 25															
	Fifth	315	1575				1 3	2 4	3 6	5 8	7 11	11 15	17 20	25 29															
	Sixth	315	1890				1 3	3 5	4 6	7 9	10 12	14 17	21 23	31 33															
	Seventh	315	2205			↓	2 3	4 5	6 7	9 10	13 14	18 19	25 26	37 38															
R	First	500	500	↑		# 2	# 2	# 3	# 4	0 4	0 5	1 7	2 9	↑															
	Second	500	1000			# 2	0 3	0 3	1 5	1 6	3 8	4 10	7 14																
	Third	500	1500			0 2	0 3	1 4	2 6	3 8	6 10	8 13	13 19																
	Fourth	500	2000			0 3	1 4	2 5	3 7	5 10	8 13	12 17	19 25																
	Fifth	500	2500			1 3	2 4	3 6	5 8	7 11	11 15	17 20	25 29																
	Sixth	500	3000			1 3	3 5	4 6	7 9	10 12	14 17	21 23	31 33																
	Seventh	500	3500			2 3	4 5	6 7	9 10	13 14	18 19	25 26	37 38																

↓ = Use first sampling plan below arrow. If sample size equals or exceeds lot or batch size, do 100 percent inspection

↑ = Use first sampling plan above arrow (refer to preceding page, when necessary).

* = Use corresponding single sampling plan (or alternatively, use double sampling plan below, where available).

Ac = Acceptance number.

Re = Rejectiion number.

\# = Acceptance not permitted at this sample size.

Figure IV.18 Continued.

Lot Size			Inspection Levels				
			Special		General		
			S3	S4	I	II	III
2	to	8	B	B	B	B	C
9	to	15	B	B	B	B	D
16	to	25	B	B	B	C	E
26	to	50	B	B	C	D	F
51	to	90	B	B	D	E	G
91	to	150	B	C	E	F	H
151	to	280	B	D	F	G	I
281	to	400	C	E	G	H	J
401	to	500	C	E	G	I	J
501	to	1,200	D	F	H	J	K
1,201	to	3,200	E	G	I	K	L
3,201	to	10,000	F	H	J	L	M
10,001	to	35,000	G	I	K	M	N
35,001	to	150,000	H	J	L	N	P
150,001	to	500,000	H	K	M	P	P
500,001	and	over	H	K	N	P	P

Figure IV.19 ANSI/ASQC Z1.9-1993 Table A-2[2]: Sample size code letters.[1] Used by permission.

[1]Sample size code letters given in body of table are applicable when the indicated inspection levels are to be used.

[2]The theory governing inspection by variables depends on the properties of the normal distribution and, therefore, this method of inspection is only applicable when there is reason to believe that the frequency distribution is normal.

Sample Size Code Letter	Sample Size	Acceptance Quality Levels (normal inspection)											
		T	.10	.15	.25	.40	.65	1.00	1.50	2.50	4.00	6.50	10.00
		k	k	k	k	k	k	k	k	k	k	k	k
B	3	↓	↓	↓	↓	↓	↓	↓	↓	.587	.502	.401	.296
C	4							.651	.598	.525	.450	.364	.276
D	5				↓	↓	.663	.614	.565	.498	.431	.352	.272
E	7			↓	.702	.659	.613	.569	.525	.465	.405	.336	.266
F	10	↓	↓	.916	.863	.811	.755	.703	.650	.579	.507	.424	.341
G	15	1.04	.999	.958	.903	.850	.792	.738	.684	.610	.536	.452	.368
H	25	1.10	1.05	1.01	.951	.896	.835	.779	.723	.647	.571	.484	.398
I	30	1.10	1.06	1.02	.959	.904	.843	.787	.730	.654	.577	.490	.403
J	40	1.13	1.08	1.04	.978	.921	.860	.803	.746	.668	.591	.503	.415
K	60	1.16	1.11	1.06	1.00	.948	.885	.826	.768	.689	.610	.521	.432
L	85	1.17	1.13	1.08	1.02	.962	.899	.839	.780	.701	.621	.530	.441
M	115	1.19	1.14	1.09	1.03	.975	.911	.851	.791	.711	.631	.539	.449
N	175	1.21	1.16	1.11	1.05	.994	.929	.868	.807	.726	.644	.552	.460
P	230	1.21	1.16	1.12	1.06	.996	.931	.870	.809	.728	.646	.553	.462
		.10	.15	.25	.40	.65	1.00	1.50	2.50	4.00	6.50	10.00	
		Acceptance Quality Levels (tightened inspection)											

All AQL values are in percent nonconforming. T denotes plan used exclusively on tightened inspection and provides symbol for identification of appropriate OC curve.

↓ Use first sampling plan below arrow; that is, both sample size as well as k value. When sample size equals or exceeds lot size, every item in the lot must be inspected.

Figure IV.20 ANSI/ASQC Z1.9-1993 Table C-1: Master table for normal and tightened inspection for plans based on variability unknown (single specification limit–form 1). Used by permission.

Q_U or Q_L	Sample Size														
	3	4	5	7	10	15	20	25	30	35	50	75	100	150	200
1.50	0.00	0.00	3.80	5.28	5.87	6.20	6.34	6.41	6.46	6.50	6.55	6.60	6.62	6.64	6.65
1.51	0.00	0.00	3.61	5.13	5.73	6.06	6.20	6.28	6.33	6.36	6.42	6.47	6.49	6.51	6.52
1.52	0.00	0.00	3.42	4.97	5.59	5.93	6.07	6.15	6.20	6.23	6.29	6.34	6.36	6.38	6.39
1.53	0.00	0.00	3.23	4.82	5.45	5.80	5.94	6.02	6.07	6.11	6.17	6.21	6.24	6.26	6.27
1.54	0.00	0.00	3.05	4.67	5.31	5.67	5.81	5.89	5.95	5.98	6.04	6.09	6.11	6.13	6.15
1.55	0.00	0.00	2.87	4.52	5.18	5.54	5.69	5.77	5.82	5.86	5.92	5.97	5.99	6.01	6.02
1.56	0.00	0.00	2.69	4.38	5.05	5.41	5.56	5.65	5.70	5.74	5.80	5.85	5.87	5.89	5.90
1.57	0.00	0.00	2.52	4.24	4.92	5.29	5.44	5.53	5.58	5.62	5.68	5.73	5.75	5.78	5.79
1.58	0.00	0.00	2.35	4.10	4.79	5.16	5.32	5.41	5.46	5.50	5.56	5.61	5.64	5.66	5.67
1.59	0.00	0.00	2.19	3.96	4.66	5.04	5.20	5.29	5.34	5.38	5.45	5.50	5.52	5.55	5.56
1.60	0.00	0.00	2.03	3.83	4.54	4.92	5.08	5.17	5.23	5.27	5.33	5.38	5.41	5.43	5.44
1.61	0.00	0.00	1.87	3.69	4.41	4.81	4.97	5.06	5.12	5.16	5.22	5.27	5.30	5.32	5.33
1.62	0.00	0.00	1.72	3.57	4.30	4.69	4.86	4.95	5.01	5.04	5.11	5.16	5.19	5.21	5.23
1.63	0.00	0.00	1.57	3.44	4.18	4.58	4.75	4.84	4.90	4.94	5.01	5.06	5.08	5.11	5.12
1.64	0.00	0.00	1.42	3.31	4.06	4.47	4.64	4.73	4.79	4.83	4.90	4.95	4.98	5.00	5.01
1.65	0.00	0.00	1.28	3.19	3.95	4.36	4.53	4.62	4.68	4.72	4.79	4.85	4.87	4.90	4.91
1.66	0.00	0.00	1.15	3.07	3.84	4.25	4.43	4.52	4.58	4.62	4.69	4.74	4.77	4.80	4.81
1.67	0.00	0.00	1.02	2.95	3.73	4.15	4.32	4.42	4.48	4.52	4.59	4.64	4.67	4.70	4.71
1.68	0.00	0.00	0.89	2.84	3.62	4.05	4.22	4.32	4.38	4.42	4.49	4.55	4.57	4.60	4.61
1.69	0.00	0.00	0.77	2.73	5.52	3.94	4.12	4.22	4.28	4.32	4.39	4.45	4.47	4.50	4.51
1.70	0.00	0.00	0.66	2.62	3.41	3.84	4.02	4.12	4.18	4.22	4.30	4.35	4.38	4.41	4.42
1.71	0.00	0.00	0.55	2.51	3.31	3.75	3.93	4.02	4.09	4.13	4.20	4.26	4.29	4.31	4.32
1.72	0.00	0.00	0.45	2.41	3.21	3.65	3.83	3.93	3.99	4.04	4.11	4.17	4.19	4.22	4.23
1.73	0.00	0.00	0.36	2.30	3.11	3.56	3.74	3.84	3.90	3.94	4.02	4.08	4.10	4.13	4.14
1.74	0.00	0.00	0.27	2.20	3.02	3.46	3.65	3.75	3.81	3.85	3.93	3.99	4.01	4.04	4.05
1.75	0.00	0.00	0.19	2.11	2.93	3.37	3.56	3.66	3.72	3.77	3.84	3.90	3.93	3.95	3.97
1.76	0.00	0.00	0.12	2.01	2.83	3.28	3.47	3.57	3.63	3.68	3.76	3.81	3.84	3.87	3.88
1.77	0.00	0.00	0.06	1.92	2.74	3.20	3.38	3.48	3.55	3.59	3.67	3.73	3.76	3.78	3.80
1.78	0.00	0.00	0.02	1.83	2.66	3.11	3.30	3.40	3.47	3.51	3.59	3.64	3.67	3.70	3.71
1.79	0.00	0.00	0.00	174	2.57	3.03	3.21	3.32	3.38	3.43	3.51	3.56	3.59	3.62	3.63
1.80	0.00	0.00	0.00	1.65	2.49	2.94	3.13	3.24	3.30	3.35	3.43	3.48	3.51	3.54	3.55
1.81	0.00	0.00	0.00	1.57	2.40	2.86	3.05	31.6	3.22	3.27	3.35	3.40	3.43	3.46	3.47
1.82	0.00	0.00	0.00	1.49	2.32	2.79	2.98	3.08	3.15	3.19	3.27	3.33	3.36	3.38	3.40
1.83	0.00	0.00	0.00	1.41	2.25	2.71	2.90	3.00	3.07	3.11	3.19	3.25	3.28	3.31	3.32
1.84	0.00	0.00	0.00	1.34	2.17	2.63	2.82	2.93	2.99	3.04	3.12	3.18	3.21	3.23	3.25
1.85	0.00	0.00	0.00	1.26	2.09	2.56	2.75	2.85	2.92	2.97	3.05	3.10	3.13	3.16	3.17
1.86	0.00	0.00	0.00	1.19	2.02	2.48	2.68	2.78	2.85	2.89	2.97	3.03	3.06	3.09	3.10
1.87	0.00	0.00	0.00	1.12	1.95	2.41	2.61	2.71	2.78	2.82	2.90	2.96	2.99	3.02	3.03
1.88	0.00	0.00	0.00	1.06	1.88	2.34	2.54	2.64	2.71	2.75	2.83	2.89	2.92	2.95	2.96
1.89	0.00	0.00	0.00	0.99	1.81	2.28	2.47	2.57	2.64	2.69	2.77	2.83	2.85	2.88	2.90

Figure IV.21 ANSI/ASQC Z1.9-1993 Table B-5: Table for estimating the lot percent nonconforming using standard deviation method.[1] Used by permission.

[1]Values tabulated are read in percent.

Sample Size Code Letter	Sample Size	Acceptance Quality Levels (normal inspection)											
		T	.10	.15	.25	.40	.65	1.00	1.50	2.50	4.00	6.50	10.00
		M	M	M	M	M	M	M	M	M	M	M	M
B	3	↓	↓	↓	↓	↓	↓	↓	↓	7.59	18.86	26.94	33.69
C	4	↓	↓	↓	↓	↓	↓	1.49	5.46	10.88	16.41	22.84	29.43
D	5	↓	↓	↓	↓	0.041	1.34	3.33	5.82	9.80	14.37	20.19	26.55
E	7	↓	0.005	0.087	0.421	1.05	2.13	3.54	5.34	8.40	12.19	17.34	23.30
F	10	0.077	0.179	0.349	0.714	1.27	2.14	3.27	4.72	7.26	10.53	15.17	20.73
G	15	0.186	0.311	0.491	0.839	1.33	2.09	3.06	4.32	6.55	9.48	13.74	18.97
H	20	0.228	0.356	0.531	0.864	1.33	2.03	2.93	4.10	6.18	8.95	13.01	18.07
I	25	0.250	0.378	0.551	0.874	1.32	2.00	2.86	3.97	5.98	8.65	12.60	17.55
J	35	0.253	0.373	0.534	0.833	1.24	1.87	2.66	3.70	5.58	8.11	11.89	16.67
K	50	0.243	0.355	0.503	0.778	1.16	1.73	2.47	3.44	5.21	7.61	11.23	15.87
L	75	0.225	0.326	0.461	0.711	1.06	1.59	2.27	3.17	4.83	7.10	10.58	15.07
M	100	0.218	0.315	0.444	0.684	1.02	1.52	2.18	3.06	4.67	6.88	10.29	14.71
N	150	0.202	0.292	0.412	0.636	0.946	1.42	2.05	2.88	4.42	6.56	9.86	14.18
P	200	0.204	0.294	0.414	0.637	0.945	1.42	2.04	2.86	4.39	6.52	9.80	14.11
		.10	.15	.25	.40	.65	1.00	1.50	2.50	4.00	6.50	10.00	
		Acceptance Quality Levels (tightened inspection)											

All AQL values are in percent nonconforming. T denotes plan used exclusively on tightened inspection and provides symbol for identification of appropriate OC curve.

↓ Use first sampling plan below arrow; that is, both sample size as well as k value. When sample size equals or exceeds lot size, every item in the lot must be inspected.

Figure IV.22 ANSI/ASQC Z1.9-1993 Table B-3: Master table for normal and tightened inspection for plans based on variability unknown (double specification limit and form 2–single specification limit). Used by permission.

Endnotes

1. J. A. Simpson, "Foundations of Metrology," *Journal of Research of the National Bureau of Standards* 86, no. 3 (May/June 1981): 36–42.
2. W. J. Darmody, "Elements of a Generalized Measuring System," in *Handbook of Industrial Metrology* (Englewood Cliffs, NJ: Prentice Hall, 1967).
3. Ibid.
4. A. F. Rashed and A. M. Hamouda, *Technology for Real Quality* (Alexandria, Egypt: Egyptian University House, 1974).
5. ASQC Statistics Division, *Glossary and Tables for Statistical Quality Control*, 2nd ed. (Milwaukee: ASQC Quality Press, 1983).
6. American Society for Testing and Materials, *ASTM Standards on Precision and Accuracy for Various Applications* (Philadelphia: ASTM, 1977).
7. Ibid.
8. A. McNish, "The Nature of Measurement." In *Handbook of Industrial Metrology* (Englewood Cliffs, NJ: Prentice Hall, 1967).
9. T. Raz, "Inspection," In *Quality Engineering Handbook,* eds. T. Pyzdek and R. Berger (Milwaukee: ASQC Quality Press; and New York: Marcel Dekker, 1992).
10. Ibid.
11. Ibid.
12. W. E. Deming, *Out of the Crisis* (Cambridge, MA: M.I.T. Center for Advanced Engineering, 1986).
13. See note 5.
14. Ibid.
15. See note 12.

References

ASQC Statistics Division. *Glossary and Tables for Statistical Quality Control*, 2nd ed. Milwaukee: ASQC Quality Press, 1983.

Burr, W. *Statistical Quality Control Methods.* New York: Marcel Dekker, 1976.

Dorris, A. L., and B. L. Foote. "Inspection Errors and Statistical Quality Control: A Survey." *AIIE Transactions* 10, no. 2 (1978): 184–92.

Dovich, R. "Acceptance Sampling." In *Quality Engineering Handbook.* Ed. T. Pyzdek and R. Berger. Milwaukee: ASQC Quality Press and New York: Marcel Dekker, 1992.

Farago, F. T. *Handbook of Dimensional Measurement,* 2nd. ed. New York: Industrial Press, 1982.

Juran, J. M., and F. N. Gryna Jr. *Quality Planning and Analysis.* New York: McGraw-Hill, 1980.

Konz, S., G. Peterson, and A. Joshi. "Reducing Inspection Errors." ASQC *Quality Progress* 14, no. 7 (1981): 24–26.

McKenzie, R. M. "On the Accuracy of Inspectors." *Ergonomics* 1 (1958): 258–72.

Megaw, E. D. "Factors Affecting Visual Inspection Accuracy." *Applied Ergonomics* 10 (1979): 27–32.

Schrader, G. F., and A. K. Elshennawy. *Manufacturing Processes and Materials.* Dearborn, MI: Society of Manufacturing Engineers, 2000.

V

Quality Audits

A. AUDITING TECHNIQUES

1. Principles

The basic components of an audit include the following:

- Preparation
- Performance
- Documentation (that is, record keeping)
- Closure

Preparation

Preparation for any type of quality audit requires consideration of the following:

• *Identification of authorization source.* Formal preparation for an audit normally does not commence until the audit is authorized by an appropriate individual within an organization. Authorization for an audit carries with it the obligation of and responsibility for allocating resources, so audit authorization decisions are normally reserved for management team members who are at or above the director level. While any one of several management team members may have an interest in requesting and authorizing an audit of quality systems, processes, and/or products/services, it is generally the director of quality who actually issues the audit authorization.

Once audit authorization has been issued, documentation of the authorization becomes an important part of the historical records generated as part of the audit process. Such documentation is needed when a contact person is required for other interested parties to learn more about the reasons why an audit may have been authorized, when other interested parties are interested in justification or explanation of system/process/product/service modifications or revisions as a result of corrective actions called for in an audit, or in the case of litigation.

• *Determination of the audit purpose.* An audit may be authorized for one or several purposes. The most common purposes of an audit include qualification of a vendor's quality system, process(es), and/or products/services and in meeting contractual obligations. Common purposes for initiating and authorizing an audit also include continuous improvement, identification and verification of perceived weaknesses, verification of corrective action, verification of adequacy of resources (that is, facilities, equipment, human resources, and so on), verification of new technology and/or methods, and enhancing customer satisfaction.

• *Determination of audit type.* As will be described below, audit types are normally determined as system, process(es), and/or products/services—these three types of audits are the most common and represent the primary audit types. There are, however, other types of audits referred to as secondary audit types that include management reviews and various forms of vendor/supplier surveillance.

• *Determination of audit scope.* Scope of the audit refers to the areas, topics, or entities to be audited—and more importantly, scope of the audit defines the frame of reference wherein auditors are to concentrate their focus and analyses. In other words, scope of the audit sets the limits or boundaries on what gets evaluated and what does not.

Due to a tendency for the scope of an audit to "creep" or get bigger and more encompassing as the audit progresses, it is extremely important to identify very early in the audit preparation the scope of the audit since significant financial and human resources will be required to complete a comprehensive audit, and if scope is allowed to creep, costs of the audit will escalate very quickly. Establishment and documentation of the audit scope then becomes a limitation or constraint that keeps everyone involved (that is, all stakeholders) focused on what was originally intended and authorized by the audit.

• *Determination of resources required.* Consistent with the type and scope of audit to be performed, resources will be required to support the audit process. Primary resources needed to support an audit normally include assignment of auditing and auditee personnel, physical workspace for the audit team—normally a secure workspace, computer/data processing and printing support, and clerical/administrative support. Secondary resources needed to support an audit may include travel funding, per diem for travel-related expenses, lodging/accommodation, and ground transportation.

• *Formation of the audit team.* Formation of an audit team is completed again, in accordance with the type and scope of audit. In most cases, audit team members are selected based on their knowledge of, training and certification in, and experience with auditing methods and practices. When there is not an optimal skill set or talent pool of trained and experienced auditors available, auditors are commonly selected from the most technically competent and knowledgeable personnel available. These auditors normally work under the guidance and direction of one or more experienced auditors and with the further guidance and direction provided by detailed documentation called audit *working papers.*

• *Assignment of audit team roles and responsibilities.* Once key individuals have been selected for an audit team, roles and responsibilities are assigned to facilitate the audit process. In the preparation phase of an audit, it is common practice to select an audit team leader and a small complement of experienced auditors or experts in a given technical area and assign those people responsibility and authority consistent with the audit type and scope. The team leader is normally assigned the role and responsibility of leading the team, facilitating the audit process, coordinating all resources needed to support the audit, and constituting the remainder of an audit team. Other key individuals initially selected for an audit team are normally assigned roles and responsibilities consistent with their areas of expertise either in auditing practices/methods, or in a specific technical area. Other individuals not initially selected for the audit team, but who are subsequently selected by the audit team leader, are assigned roles and responsibilities consistent with their expertise and ability to contribute to the effectiveness of the audit.

- *Identification of requirements.* To successfully complete an audit, everyone involved with the audit must complete their assigned tasks and produce any required deliverables—these assigned tasks and deliverables are referred to as *audit requirements.* While there are general requirements that are consistent with audits in general, there is much flexibility in the level of formality and detail required to "successfully" complete an audit.

Generally expected components of audits include formal documentation of the audit as described throughout this section, a final set of working papers (that is, detailed questions and notes that guided the audit process), a series of debriefings describing the audit process and the findings/results, and a detailed description of any requested/required corrective action(s). Also, generally expected components of audits include documentation of and provision for verification of adequacy and completeness of corrective action(s).

- *Establishment of time schedule.* A final component of an audit is establishment of a time schedule. A time schedule is a critical component for the audit team leader in the preparation of detailed work or project plans to guide the work effort of an audit. The time schedule is also important to management team members as a communications tool and as a coordination device, indicating when and where certain physical or human resources will be needed to support the audit process.

Performance

Audit performance is described by the following set of activities:

- *Managing/administering the audit process.* To properly manage/administer an audit, the team leader is required to complete a set of tasks needed to keep the audit process moving. In part, the team leader is responsible to call for and conduct regularly scheduled meetings with the audit team to discuss preliminary results and findings. During these meetings, the team leader must make decisions regarding the amount and type of communications that may be warranted between the audit team and other stakeholders, possible interventions that may be needed by the audit team, and the effectiveness of the audit process. The team leader is also responsible to call for and conduct, on an as needed basis, meetings with the auditee to discuss audit progress, significant results and findings, and changes in the audit plan (that is, content to be evaluated or the time schedule).

- *Creating a set of working papers.* To ensure complete and thorough scrutiny consistent with the type and scope of audit, working papers are drafted to guide the audit work effort. Working papers consist of predefined sets of auditee interview questions, checklists of specific documents/policies/procedures/instructions to be reviewed, log sheets of personnel contacted as part of the audit, data collection forms, and so on. A more thorough discussion of working papers will be provided in a later section of this chapter.

- *Conducting an opening meeting.* As a normal part of the auditing process, an opening meeting is held wherein both the audit team and management team members and appropriate personnel from the auditee are present to discuss the audit plan. While generally a short meeting, the opening meeting allows the audit team leader the opportunity to review the audit plan, answer questions about the intent of or approach to the audit, discuss the timing and logistics of the audit, as well as address/resolve any conflicts that may have developed in the time between approval of the audit plan and the audit team arriving at the audit site.

- *Collecting data.* Audit team members complete the next step in the audit process by collecting data consistent with data requirements documented in the working papers mentioned above. Data collected to support the audit may encompass design parameters, performance specifications, actual performance data, process documentation, work instructions, policy statements, general quality system documentation, vendor/supplier qualification information, raw material and component part certificates of authenticity/purity, purchasing/acquisition records, defective material disposition records, compliance with selected standards, and perhaps training/certification records.

- *Analyzing data.* Once data are collected, it is necessary for audit team members to sort or categorize the data in some way so as to be able to identify and categorize the results and findings in a manner that indicates some level of importance. Frequently, this means that audit team members create three or more levels of concern, wherein verifiable observations are recorded in what may be categories such as "passes/meets expectations," "marginal pass/questionable response/performance," and "fails to meet expectations."

  Once data are categorized in accordance with a scheme established by the audit team, it is possible for audit team members to analyze the data looking for existing patterns or emerging trends that indicate potential problems.

- *Conducting an exit meeting.* A final step in the completion of an audit is conducting an exit meeting between the audit team and the auditee. At this exit meeting, the primary points of discussion revolve around major findings and results of the audit—note, this is an opportunity for the audit team to share their findings and results with the auditee, not a venue for the audit team to have to justify or debate the findings or results. Also during the exit meeting, any requested or required corrective actions are presented and discussed with particular importance being placed on creation of a corrective action plan, time schedule for the corrective actions, and verification provisions for correcting any potential problems.

Documentation

Documentation associated with an audit includes appropriate correspondence, audit planning documents (that is, authorization, type/scope statements, audit team member assignments, and so on), audit working papers, status reports, preliminary findings and results documentation, debriefing and closure reports, corrective action requests, and follow-up report forms for corrective action verification. By sheer volume, the amount of documentation associated with a quality audit can quickly become very large—particularly when conducting system and multiple process audits.

It is generally specified in planning/authorization documents or procurement contracts how long to maintain copies of audit records. In many cases five years is the required time frame for care and maintenance of audit documents—particularly where the audit involves a large, complex, or distributed quality system (that is, a quality system comprised of a vendor/supplier with multiple facilities/locations). One year is an acceptable time frame for saving audit documents in cases where the time frame for saving audit documentation is not specified for the care and maintenance of audit documents, and where the audit does not involve particularly large or complex quality systems.

Closure

Technically, an audit is considered complete as soon as the final report has been submitted to the authorizing agent and the auditee. However, an emerging trend in auditing is to delay reaching closure on an audit until a set of terms and conditions have been met as defined by the agent authorizing the audit and the auditee. Those terms and conditions related to closure of an audit increasingly focus on resolution of problems related to unfavorable audit results or findings. In the case of one or more unfavorable audit results or findings, the terms and conditions for audit closure specify scope of potential corrective actions and an appropriate time frame for completion of corrective action(s). Under these emerging conditions, an audit is considered closed when both parties involved with the audit are satisfied that all corrective actions have been satisfactorily completed.

2. Applications

Applications of auditing tools and techniques include the following:

- *Audit working papers.* Audit working papers consist of the various data collection forms used to gather, categorize, summarize, and analyze selected audit data. For the audit team, audit working papers represent the formal and informal note sheets and formal question/data sheets that guide and direct audit team members to review specific portions or sections of quality systems.

  While there is no standard for the design of working papers, various forms of check sheets are used to assist auditors in collecting tabular data very quickly while providing auditors some room for detailed note taking and specific data collection. The many qualitative and quantitative quality tools are also used as working papers, when tailored to the collection and analysis of selected audit data.

- *Qualitative quality tools.* Qualitative quality tools encompass tools like the "new" Japanese tools such as relations diagrams, affinity diagrams, systematic diagrams, process decision program charts, and arrow diagrams. To avoid duplication, these tools have not been reintroduced here, and readers are encouraged to review these tools as they appear in other portions of this book.

- *Quantitative quality tools.* Quantitative quality tools encompass tools like the "traditional" Japanese tools such as flowcharting (also used for forward and backward tracing), cause-and-effect diagrams, check sheets, histograms, Pareto diagrams, scatter diagrams, and statistical process control charts. To avoid duplication, these tools have not been reintroduced here and readers are encouraged to review these tools as they appear in other portions of this book.

B. AUDIT TYPES

Several factors contribute to the structure of quality audits, including:

• *Integrity of the audit process.* The intent of any audit is to protect the business, professional, and/or legal interests of the party or person requesting the audit. Implicit in this intent is a requirement that the audit be based on factual data and observations obtained from independent and objective individual(s) performing the audit in keeping with the concept of ". . . management by fact." By extension, then, audits are formal or informal in nature and revolve around analyses of the day-to-day things actually done to meet customer expectations as compared to customer expectations normally documented in the form of some standard or specifications.

• *Parties or individuals to be involved.* There are generally three interests involved in quality audits. The company, party, or person that requests and authorizes the audit is known as the *client.* The company, party, team, or person that actually conducts the audit is known as the *auditor.* And the company, party, facility/location, process, or product/service that is audited is known as the *auditee.*

Who actually performs the audit becomes important, with the level of perceived objectivity being a key consideration. In this context, a client may request or require one or more of three parties to complete any given audit. An audit is known as a *first-party* audit when conducted by the client actually requesting or authorizing the audit—internal audits are first-party audits wherein the client is seeking to protect their business interests as a result of the audit. An audit is known as a *second-party* audit when conducted by someone or an organization other than the client wherein both the client and the auditor have a business interest in the result of the audit—external audits are second-party audits. An audit is known as a *third-party* audit when conducted by someone or an organization other than the client, and the auditor has no business interest in the result of the audit other than maintaining their professional credibility, reputation, and avoidance of legal liability.

• *Scope of the audit.* To be functionally effective, boundaries must be set that define what is to be audited (that is, what is to be considered/evaluated, and what is not)—we call these boundaries the scope of the audit. Audits may be very far-reaching and encompassing, such as systems audits, where virtually all aspects of quality systems are reviewed. Audits may also be more restricted in terms of what is considered part of the audit, such as with process or product/service audits.

• *Type of audit.* There are three primary types of audits that are described as follows:

1. *System audit*: A system audit is a comprehensive audit involving all parts of a quality system to include quality management principles and practices, quality system structure and components, quality system operational procedures and instructions, quality system documentation, quality system performance, and mechanisms for continuous improvement of the quality system. While system audits focus on, and normally reveal, high-level issues related to the design and management of quality systems, quality system audits also encompass audits of selected individual processes as well as products/services.

2. *Process audit*: A process audit is a detailed audit of one or more selected processes that constitute a quality system as it relates to the production of tangible products or the delivery of services. Process audits include process design, work flow, procedures and work instructions, documentation, provisions for the assurance and control of quality, and performance measures and metrics associated with the selected process(es).
3. *Product audit*: A product audit is even more detailed than a process audit with respect to a focus on ensuring the product or service being audited will meet customer expectations. Product or service audits include the product/service design, operational specifications, research and development or test data, trials or performance data, customer satisfaction data (if available), and failure data (internal and/or external). Much of the work of product audits is completed at key milestones called *design reviews* in the development of new products and services. Product audits are, however, commonly completed by business-to-business customers purchasing products/services as a final check or approval following the design and development of these new products/services from another company or other vendor outside their company or by another division, department, or work center within their own company.

• *Source of auditors.* The demand for auditors as sources of independent and objective evaluation is, in many cases, greater than the supply of resources available to provide for these services. This means that individuals who are not formally trained or who are not working day-to-day in general or mainstream quality practices, tools, and techniques, but who have in-depth process and/or product/service knowledge, may be used as auditors. In this case, and to provide greater coverage of audit scrutiny, there has been a general approach developed to the deployment of auditors, wherein system-level audits are normally conducted by auditors from outside the company or organization. These auditors are referred to as *external auditors.* Further, process and/or product/service audits may certainly be conducted by external auditors, but in many cases these audits are conducted by auditors from inside their own company or organization. These auditors are referred to as *internal auditors.* Internal auditors are normally obtained from functions, facilities, processes, or product/service delivery lines different from their day-to-day responsibilities.

As it becomes somewhat more cumbersome and difficult for internal auditors to gain access to the highest levels of individuals and resources within their own organizations, internal auditors are normally not used for system audits—although there is no formal rule preventing this practice. Internal auditors are very frequently deployed, however, to conduct process and product/service audits—particularly where the internal auditors are called upon to audit processes and/or product/services different from their area of primary responsibility.

• *Expected outcomes.* To facilitate the process of ". . . management by fact," the expected outcome of any audit is independent, accurate, verifiable, and traceable facts and observations. These facts and observations are needed and used as input in the management decision-making process wherein steps are planned for, authorized, and taken to assure customer expectations are met or exceeded. Further, these facts and observations are needed and used as input in the areas of continuous improvement, corrective action, and for compliance with various standards.

References

American Society for Quality Control. "Specification of General Requirements for a Quality Program." In *American National Standard*. Milwaukee: ASQC Quality Press, 1996.

Arter, D. *Quality Audits for Improved Performance,* 2nd ed. Milwaukee: ASQC Quality Press, 1994.

Kolarik, W. *Creating Quality: Concepts, Systems, Strategies, and Tools.* New York: McGraw-Hill, 1995.

Mills, C. *The Quality Audit: A Management Evaluation Tool.* New York: McGraw-Hill, 1989.

Russell, J. P. *The Quality Audit Handbook,* 2nd ed. Milwaukee: ASQ Quality Press, 2000.

VI

Preventive and Corrective Action

A. CONTINUOUS IMPROVEMENT TECHNIQUES

Continuous improvement is a theme or concept that is integrally woven into and throughout the CQT Body of Knowledge (BOK). Accordingly, numerous tools and techniques for continuous improvement have been introduced and explained as they were specifically referenced in other sections of the BOK. With respect to the CQT BOK Section VI, Subsection A, it is intended that CQT candidates be able to actually ". . . determine and select areas for improvement . . ." using these tools and techniques. In this case, selection and application of any given continuous improvement tool or technique is situation specific and cannot be explained without repeating major portions of the content already covered in this text. At this point, it is most appropriate in Table VI.1 to introduce a tool designed to help readers select specific tools or techniques based on the type(s) of desired applications.

As can be seen in the Tools Matrix in Table VI.1, many quality tools and techniques are identified in column two. Column one identifies types or areas of application, while the remaining columns are dedicated to identifying the types of information provided by these tools and techniques.

B. NONCONFORMING MATERIAL IDENTIFICATION

In the book *Glossary and Tables for Statistical Quality Control* written by representatives of the American Society for Quality Statistics Division, a nonconforming unit is defined as follows: "A unit of product or service containing at least one nonconformity."[1] And in the same book, a nonconformity is defined as: "A departure of a quality characteristic from its intended level or state that occurs with a severity sufficient to cause an associated product or service to not meet a specification requirement."[2]

A component of any comprehensive quality system is a subsystem designed to effectively deal with nonconforming materials as soon as they are identified—optimally as early in the production process as possible. For purposes of the Certified Quality Technician (CQT) Body of Knowledge (BOK), nonconforming material identification consists of the following:

• *Determining conformance status.* Conformance status is determined in accordance with compliance or noncompliance with a quality standard or specification as compared

Table VI.1 Tool matrix.

	Tool	E/F	Mission	Customer Require-ments	Current State	Oppor-tunities	Root Causes	Changes	Do It	Monitor	Standar-dize	Learn-ings
Idea Creation Tools	Affinity diagram	E/F	X	X	X	X	X	X			X	X
	Brainstorming	E	X	X	X	X	X	X			X	X
	Brainwriting	E	X	X	X	X	X	X			X	X
	Nominal group technique (NGT)	E	X	X	X	X	X	X			X	X
	Relations diagram	E/F		X		X	X	X			X	X
Process Analysis Tools	Cost-of-quality analysis	E			X	X	X					
	Critical-to-quality analysis	E			X	X	X					
	Deployment flowchart	E/F			X	X	X	X	X	X	X	
	Flowchart	E/F		X	X	X	X	X	X	X	X	
	Matrix diagram	F		X	X	X	X	X	X	X	X	
	Relations diagram	E/F		X	X	X	X	X			X	X
	Requirements matrix	E		X	X	X				X	X	
	Requirements-and-measures tree	E		X	X	X				X	X	
	Storyboard	E	X	X	X	X		X	X		X	X
	Top-down flowchart	E/F	X		X	X	X	X	X	X	X	
	Work flow diagram	E			X	X	X	X	X	X	X	

continued

Table VI.1 Tool matrix. *continued*

	Tool	E/F	Mission	Customer Require-ments	Current State	Oppor-tunities	Root Causes	Changes	Do It	Monitor	Standar-dize	Learn-ings
Cause Analysis Tools	Contingency diagram	E				X	X	X	X		X	
	Fishbone diagram	E				X	X					
	Force-field analysis	E				X	X	X	X		X	
	Is–is not matrix	F				X	X					
	Matrix diagram	F		X	X	X	X	X	X	X	X	
	Pareto chart	F				X	X	X		X	X	
	Scatter diagram	F				X	X			X		
	Stratification	F			X	X	X			X	X	
	Tree diagram	E				X	X	X	X		X	
	Why–why diagram	E					X					
Planning Tools	Activity chart	F	X					X	X		X	
	Arrow diagram	F	X					X	X		X	
	Benefits and barriers excercise	E				X	X	X	X		X	X
	Contingency diagram	E				X	X	X	X		X	
	Deployment flowchart	E/F			X	X	X	X	X	X	X	
	Flowchart	E/F	X	X	X	X	X	X	X	X	X	
	Force-field analysis	E				X	X	X	X		X	
	Matrix diagram	F		X	X	X	X	X	X	X	X	
	Mission statement wordsmithing	E/F	X									

Table VI.1 Tool matrix. *continued*

	Tool	E/F	Mission	Customer Require-ments	Current State	Oppor-tunities	Root Causes	Changes	Do It	Monitor	Standar-dize	Learn-ings
Planning Tools *(continued)*	Operational definitions	F	X	X	X	X	X	X	X	X	X	
	Plan–do–check–act cycle	F	X					X	X		X	X
	Relations diagram	E/F		X		X	X	X			X	X
	Storyboard	E	X	X	X	X		X	X		X	X
	Top-down flowchart	E/F	X		X	X	X	X	X	X	X	
	Tree diagram	E				X	X	X	X		X	
	Work flow diagram	E			X	X	X	X	X	X	X	
Evaluation Tools	ACORN test	F	X									
	Continuum of team goals	F	X									X
	Decision matrix	F				X	X	X			X	
	Effective–achievable matrix	F				X	X	X			X	
	List reduction	F	X	X	X	X	X	X			X	X
	Matrix diagram	F		X	X	X	X	X	X	X	X	
	Mission statement checklist	F	X									
	Multivoting	F	X	X	X	X	X	X			X	X
	Plan–results matrix	F								X	X	
	PMI	F	X			X	X	X			X	

Table VI.1 Tool matrix. *continued*

	Tool	E/F	Mission	Customer Require-ments	Current State	Oppor-tunities	Root Causes	Changes	Do It	Monitor	Standar-dize	Learn-ings
Data Collection and Analysis Tools	Box plot	F			X	X	X			X	X	
	Checksheet	F			X	X	X		X	X	X	
	Control charts	F			X	X	X		X	X	X	
	Graphs	F		X	X	X	X		X	X	X	
	Histogram	F			X	X	X			X	X	
	Importance–performance analysis	F		X	X	X				X	X	
	Kolmogorov–Smirnov test	F			X	X	X		X	X	X	
	Normal probability plot	F			X	X	X		X	X	X	
	Operational definitions	F	X	X	X	X	X	X	X	X	X	
	Pareto chart	F				X	X	X		X	X	
	Performance index	F			X	X			X	X	X	
	Process capability	F			X	X				X	X	
	Requirements-and-measures tree	E		X	X	X				X	X	
	Run chart	F			X	X	X		X	X	X	
	Scatter diagram	F				X	X			X		
	Stratification	F			X	X	X			X	X	
	Survey	E/F		X	X	X		X		X	X	

Source: The Quality Toolbox by Nancy R. Tague, ASQC Quality Press, 1995.

to some sort of classification scheme. While the classification schemes may be different from company to company, the important consideration is that gradations or "categories" of seriousness are created as a means for the material review board, and any other stakeholders, to understand the relative importance and magnitude of nonconformities.

- *Identifying nonconforming materials.* Identification of nonconforming materials must be completed in a manner that is readily apparent to anyone coming in contact with the item(s) or material in question. To accomplish the identification, some provision must be made so as to distinguish the physical appearance of the item(s) or material as "nonconforming." The physical nature of the provision refers to altering the appearance of the item(s) or its associated production data documentation with some sort of special coloring (that is, by paint, marker, or a different colored tag). The nonphysical nature of the provision refers to collecting and documenting data related to the nonconformity and attaching that data to the production data documentation accompanying the item(s) or material.

- *Segregating nonconforming materials.* Once identified as nonconforming, any such material must be prevented from entering or continuing in the supply chain. Segregation, then, is an important concern for both suppliers and customers as a means of ensuring product or process quality.

Segregation of nonconforming materials is accomplished by establishing a secure area (that is, a lockable area with strictly limited access). Once inside this secure area, nonconforming materials are not available to access, inspection, further processing, or shipment by anyone other than authorized material review board members or their designees.

C. NONCONFORMING MATERIAL REVIEW PROCESS

Virtually all quality standards require the creation and implementation of a clearly defined and communicated process to follow when "nonconforming" material is identified or detected. The importance of a nonconforming material review process cannot be overstated, as it serves as the mechanism by which to prevent nonconforming material from entering or proceeding in the supply chain. Such a process is most commonly referred to as a *nonconforming material review process.*

While specific components or steps in a nonconforming material review process will vary from company to company, and from quality standard to quality standard, at the most basic level, such a process would consist of the following:

- A cross-functional team called a material review board (MRB) composed of representatives from the quality and engineering functions and, in some cases, customers
- Appropriate quality standards and metrics
- A sampling and inspection protocol/plan
- Policies and procedures addressing when and how to trigger the MRB
- Overall process documentation

As would be expected, the successful operation of a nonconforming material review process is the responsibility of the MRB. Ultimately, the MRB must determine what to do with nonconforming material, and what corrective action to take to prevent further nonconforming material. The "... what to do with nonconforming material ..." portion of the MRB responsibility is commonly referred to as *disposition*. Disposition may take many forms agreed to by the supplier and the customer, described by Berger as[3]:

- Shipped "as is"
- Sort/100 percent inspection
- Downgrade
- Repair
- Rework
- Scrap

D. INVESTIGATION OF ROOT CAUSES

Andersen and Fagerhaug define and describe root cause analysis as "... a collective term to describe a wide range of approaches, tools, and techniques used to uncover causes to problems."[4]

The title of the section of the CQT BOK "... investigation of root causes ..." implies the existence of one or more problem(s) that needs to be resolved. In this context, *root cause analysis* is a structured approach to problem solving that uses all the traditional quality control tools identified in the CQT BOK Section I, Subsection D, such as histograms, Pareto charts, cause-and-effect diagrams, check sheets, scatter diagrams, and control charts. In fact, it can easily be argued that root cause analysis uses even more than the traditional quality control tools identified in Section I, Subsection D to include the nontraditional quality tools and techniques identified by Kolarik,[5] such as affinity diagrams, relations diagrams, systematic diagrams, matrix diagrams, process decision program charts, and arrow diagrams. Additionally, tools and techniques identified by Brassard and Ritter in a book titled *The Memory Jogger II*, such as force-field analysis, interrelationship diagraphs, prioritization matrices, and radar charts can also be applied to the root cause analysis.[6]

Emphasizing that the root cause analysis process is a series of iterative steps taken while solving a problem is important. Since there are many generally accepted approaches to problem solving (that is, PDSA/PDCA, Kepner-Tragoe, and so on), the benefit to be derived from any problem solving approach is in the consistency and rigor involved in the problem solving methodology or protocol.

At issue in this whole notion of problem solving is solving the "right" problem. All too often, a problem that presents itself is the result of another problem, or perhaps several other problems combined. In this case, and in the language of root cause analysis, we say the problem that presents itself as the most apparent is merely the symptom of a more deeply rooted problem. Solving symptomatic problems, therefore, gives rise to other, perhaps seemingly unrelated, problems.

It has long been understood in the quality community that until someone can ask the question "why?" at least five times, they cannot hope to be looking at anything more than symptoms to a problem rather than the actual or root cause problem. This why?, why?, why?, why?, why? questioning methodology, as supported by the many problem solving tools identified above, represents the means by which to separate symptoms from root causes. One would then know that a root cause problem had been identified and solved when other problems disappear or are eliminated automatically as a function of solving the root cause problem.

Endnotes

1. American Society for Quality Control, *Glossary and Tables for Statistical Quality Control,* 3rd ed. (Milwaukee: ASQC Quality Press, 1996).
2. Ibid.
3. R. Berger, et al., *The Certified Quality Engineer Handbook* (Milwaukee: ASQ Quality Press, 2002).
4. B. Andersen and T. Fagerhaug, *Root Cause Analysis* (Milwuakee: ASQ Quality Press, 2000).
5. W. Kolarik, *Creating Quality: Concepts, Systems, Strategies, and Tools* (New York: McGraw-Hill, 1995).
6. M. Brassard and D. Ritter, *The Memory Jogger II* (Metheun, MA: Goal QPC Press, 1994).

References

American Society for Quality Control. *Glossary and Tables for Statistical Quality Control,* 3rd ed. Milwaukee: ASQC Quality Press, 1996.

———. "Specification of General Requirements for a Quality Program." In *American National Standard.* Milwaukee: ASQC Quality Press, 1996.

Andersen, B., and T. Fagerhaug. *Root Cause Analysis.* Milwaukee: ASQ Quality Press, 2000.

Berger, R., et al. eds. *The Certified Quality Engineer Handbook.* Milwaukee: ASQ Quality Press, 2002.

Brassard, M., and D. Ritter. *The Memory Jogger II.* Methuen, MA: Goal QPC Press, 1994.

Kolarik, W. *Creating Quality: Concepts, Systems, Strategies, and Tools.* New York: McGraw-Hill, 1995.

Tague, N. R. *The Quality Toolbox.* Milwaukee: ASQC Quality Press, 1995.

Appendix A
The ASQ Code of Ethics

To uphold and advance the honor and dignity of the profession, and in keeping with high standards of ethical conduct, *I acknowledge that I:*

FUNDAMENTAL PRINCIPLES

- Will be honest and impartial, and will serve with devotion my employer, my clients, and the public.
- Will strive to increase the competence and prestige of the profession.
- Will use my knowledge and skill for the advancement of human welfare, and in promoting the safety and reliability of products for public use.
- Will earnestly endeavor to aid the work of the Society.

RELATIONS WITH THE PUBLIC

1.1 Will do whatever I can to promote the reliability and safety of all products that come within my jurisdiction.

1.2 Will endeavor to extend public knowledge of the work of the Society and its members that relates to the public welfare.

1.3 Will be dignified and modest in explaining my work and merit.

1.4 Will preface any public statements that I may issue by clearly indicating on whose behalf they are made.

RELATIONS WITH EMPLOYERS AND CLIENTS

2.1 Will act in professional matters as a faithful agent or trustee for each employer or client.

2.2 Will inform each client or employer of any business connections, interests, or affiliations which might influence my judgment or impair the equitable character of my services.

2.3 Will indicate to my employer or client the adverse consequences to be expected if my professional judgment is overruled.

2.4 Will not disclose information concerning the business affairs or technical processes of any present or former employer or client without his/her consent.

2.5 Will not accept compensation from more than one party for the same service without the consent of all parties. If employed, I will engage in supplementary employment of consulting practice only with the consent of my employer.

RELATIONS WITH PEERS

3.1 Will take care that credit for the work of others is given to those whom it is due.

3.2 Will endeavor to aid the professional development and advancement of those in my employ or under my supervision.

3.3 Will not compete unfairly with others; will extend my friendship and confidence to all associates and those with whom I have business relations.

Appendix B
Body of Knowledge

I. Quality Concepts and Tools (21 Questions)
   A. Quality Concepts
      1. Customers and suppliers
      2. Basic quality principles
      3. Quality standards, requirements, and specifications
   B. PDCA
   C. Effective Team Function
      1. Conflict resolution
      2. Consensus
      3. Brainstorming
      4. Meeting management
      5. Stages of team development
   D. Quality Control Tools

II. Statistical Techniques (23 Questions)
   A. Basic Statistics
   B. Objectives of Statistical Quality Control
   C. Elementary Concepts of Probability
   D. Frequency Distributions
   E. Statistical Inference
      1. Universe vs. sample
      2. Parameter vs. statistic
      3. Standard deviation
      4. Confidence level
      5. Confidence limits
   F. Control Charts
      1. Control limits vs. specification limits
      2. Techniques and applications of control charts
      3. State of statistical control

        4. Control limits
        5. PRE-control
        6. Process capability
        7. Rational subgroups
        8. Variables charts
        9. Attributes charts
        10. Machine capability
        11. Analysis of charts
        12. Data plotting

III. METROLOGY AND CALIBRATION (13 Questions)

- A. Measurement Tools
    1. Hand tools
    2. Gages
    3. Optical tools
    4. Coordinate measuring machines (CMM)
    5. Electronic measuring equipment
    6. Weights, balances, and scales
    7. Hardness testing equipment
    8. Surface plate methods and equipment
    9. Surface analyzers
    10. Force measurement
    11. Angle measurement
- B. Calibration Procedures
    1. Gage traceability
    2. Calibration status
    3. Effect of calibration error on product acceptance
    4. Gage correlation
    5. Reporting calibration discrepancies

IV. INSPECTION AND TEST (21 Questions)

- A. Measurement Terms and Definitions
- B. Geometric Dimensioning and Tolerancing (GD&T)
- C. Blueprint Reading
- D. Classification of Characteristics and Defects
- E. Inspection Planning
- F. Inspection Points
- G. Inspection Techniques and Processes
    1. Nondestructive testing (NDT) techniques
    2. Gage care, cleaning, and checking
    3. Accuracy and precision; reproducibility and repeatability
    4. Rounding rules
    5. Inspection error

6. Gage selection
7. Types of measurements
8. Measurement scales
9. Product traceability

H. Sampling
1. Selecting samples from lots
2. Sampling types

V. QUALITY AUDITS (11 Questions)

A. Auditing Techniques
1. Principles
2. Applications

B. Audit Types

VI. PREVENTIVE AND CORRECTIVE ACTION (11 Questions)

A. Continuous Improvement Techniques

B. Nonconforming Material Identification

C. Nonconforming Material Review Process

D. Investigation of Root Causes

Appendix C

Areas under Standard Normal Curve

z	Area	z	Area	z	Area	z	Area	z	Area	z	Area	z	Area
0.00	0.5000	0.50	0.3085	1.00	0.1587	1.50	0.0668	2.00	0.0228	2.50	0.0062	3.00	1.35E-03
0.01	0.4960	0.51	0.3050	1.01	0.1562	1.51	0.0655	2.01	0.0222	2.51	0.0060	3.01	1.31E-03
0.02	0.4920	0.52	0.3015	1.02	0.1539	1.52	0.0643	2.02	0.0217	2.52	0.0059	3.02	1.26E-03
0.03	0.4880	0.53	0.2981	1.03	0.1515	1.53	0.0630	2.03	0.0212	2.53	0.0057	3.03	1.22E-03
0.04	0.4840	0.54	0.2946	1.04	0.1492	1.54	0.0618	2.04	0.0207	2.54	0.0055	3.04	1.18E-03
0.05	0.4801	0.55	0.2912	1.05	0.1469	1.55	0.0606	2.05	0.0202	2.55	0.0054	3.05	1.14E-03
0.06	0.4761	0.56	0.2877	1.06	0.1446	1.56	0.0594	2.06	0.0197	2.56	0.0052	3.06	1.11E-03
0.07	0.4721	0.57	0.2843	1.07	0.1423	1.57	0.0582	2.07	0.0192	2.57	0.0051	3.07	1.07E-03
0.08	0.4681	0.58	0.2810	1.08	0.1401	1.58	0.0571	2.08	0.0188	2.58	0.0049	3.08	1.04E-03
0.09	0.4641	0.59	0.2776	1.09	0.1379	1.59	0.0559	2.09	0.0183	2.59	0.0048	3.09	1.00E-03
0.10	0.4602	0.60	0.2743	1.10	0.1357	1.60	0.0548	2.10	0.0179	2.60	0.0047	3.10	9.68E-04
0.11	0.4562	0.61	0.2709	1.11	0.1335	1.61	0.0537	2.11	0.0174	2.61	0.0045	3.11	9.36E-04
0.12	0.4522	0.62	0.2676	1.12	0.1314	1.62	0.0526	2.12	0.0170	2.62	0.0044	3.12	9.04E-04
0.13	0.4483	0.63	0.2643	1.13	0.1292	1.63	0.0516	2.13	0.0166	2.63	0.0043	3.13	8.74E-04
0.14	0.4443	0.64	0.2611	1.14	0.1271	1.64	0.0505	2.14	0.0162	2.64	0.0041	3.14	8.45E-04
0.15	0.4404	0.65	0.2578	1.15	0.1251	1.65	0.0495	2.15	0.0158	2.65	0.0040	3.15	8.16E-04
0.16	0.4364	0.66	0.2546	1.16	0.1230	1.66	0.0485	2.16	0.0154	2.66	0.0039	3.16	7.89E-04
0.17	0.4325	0.67	0.2514	1.17	0.1210	1.67	0.0475	2.17	0.0150	2.67	0.0038	3.17	7.62E-04
0.18	0.4286	0.68	0.2483	1.18	0.1190	1.68	0.0465	2.18	0.0146	2.68	0.0037	3.18	7.36E-04
0.19	0.4247	0.69	0.2451	1.19	0.1170	1.69	0.0455	2.19	0.0143	2.69	0.0036	3.19	7.11E-04
0.20	0.4207	0.70	0.2420	1.20	0.1151	1.70	0.0446	2.20	0.0139	2.70	0.0035	3.20	6.87E-04
0.21	0.4168	0.71	0.2389	1.21	0.1131	1.71	0.0436	2.21	0.0136	2.71	0.0034	3.21	6.64E-04
0.22	0.4129	0.72	0.2358	1.22	0.1112	1.72	0.0427	2.22	0.0132	2.72	0.0033	3.22	6.41E-04
0.23	0.4090	0.73	0.2327	1.23	0.1093	1.73	0.0418	2.23	0.0129	2.73	0.0032	3.23	6.19E-04
0.24	0.4052	0.74	0.2296	1.24	0.1075	1.74	0.0409	2.24	0.0125	2.74	0.0031	3.24	5.98E-04
0.25	0.4013	0.75	0.2266	1.25	0.1056	1.75	0.0401	2.25	0.0122	2.75	0.0030	3.25	5.77E-04
0.26	0.3974	0.76	0.2236	1.26	0.1038	1.76	0.0392	2.26	0.0119	2.76	0.0029	3.26	5.57E-04
0.27	0.3936	0.77	0.2206	1.27	0.1020	1.77	0.0384	2.27	0.0116	2.77	0.0028	3.27	5.38E-04

continued

continued

z	Area	z	Area	z	Area	z	Area	z	Area	z	Area	z	Area
0.28	0.3897	0.78	0.2177	1.28	0.1003	1.78	0.0375	2.28	0.0113	2.78	0.0027	3.28	5.19E-04
0.29	0.3859	0.79	0.2148	1.29	0.0985	1.79	0.0367	2.29	0.0110	2.79	0.0026	3.29	5.01E-04
0.30	0.3821	0.80	0.2119	1.30	0.0968	1.80	0.0359	2.30	0.0107	2.80	0.0026	3.30	4.83E-04
0.31	0.3783	0.81	0.2090	1.31	0.0951	1.81	0.0351	2.31	0.0104	2.81	0.0025	3.31	4.67E-04
0.32	0.3745	0.82	0.2061	1.32	0.0934	1.82	0.0344	2.32	0.0102	2.82	0.0024	3.32	4.50E-04
0.33	0.3707	0.83	0.2033	1.33	0.0918	1.83	0.0336	2.33	0.0099	2.83	0.0023	3.33	4.34E-04
0.34	0.3669	0.84	0.2005	1.34	0.0901	1.84	0.0329	2.34	0.0096	2.84	0.0023	3.34	4.19E-04
0.35	0.3632	0.85	0.1977	1.35	0.0885	1.85	0.0322	2.35	0.0094	2.85	0.0022	3.35	4.04E-04
0.36	0.3594	0.86	0.1949	1.36	0.0869	1.86	0.0314	2.36	0.0091	2.86	0.0021	3.36	3.90E-04
0.37	0.3557	0.87	0.1922	1.37	0.0853	1.87	0.0307	2.37	0.0089	2.87	0.0021	3.37	3.76E-04
0.38	0.3520	0.88	0.1894	1.38	0.0838	1.88	0.0301	2.38	0.0087	2.88	0.0020	3.38	3.62E-04
0.39	0.3483	0.89	0.1867	1.39	0.0823	1.89	0.0294	2.39	0.0084	2.89	0.0019	3.39	3.50E-04
0.40	0.3446	0.90	0.1841	1.40	0.0808	1.90	0.0287	2.40	0.0082	2.90	0.0019	3.40	3.37E-04
0.41	0.3409	0.91	0.1814	1.41	0.0793	1.91	0.0281	2.41	0.0080	2.91	0.0018	3.41	3.25E-04
0.42	0.3372	0.92	0.1788	1.42	0.0778	1.92	0.0274	2.42	0.0078	2.92	0.0018	3.42	3.13E-04
0.43	0.3336	0.93	0.1762	1.43	0.0764	1.93	0.0268	2.43	0.0075	2.93	0.0017	3.43	3.02E-04
0.44	0.3300	0.94	0.1736	1.44	0.0749	1.94	0.0262	2.44	0.0073	2.94	0.0016	3.44	2.91E-04
0.45	0.3264	0.95	0.1711	1.45	0.0735	1.95	0.0256	2.45	0.0071	2.95	0.0016	3.45	2.80E-04
0.46	0.3228	0.96	0.1685	1.46	0.0721	1.96	0.0250	2.46	0.0069	2.96	0.0015	3.46	2.70E-04
0.47	0.3192	0.97	0.1660	1.47	0.0708	1.97	0.0244	2.47	0.0068	2.97	0.0015	3.47	2.60E-04
0.48	0.3156	0.98	0.1635	1.48	0.0694	1.98	0.0239	2.48	0.0066	2.98	0.0014	3.48	2.51E-04
0.49	0.3121	0.99	0.1611	1.49	0.0681	1.99	0.0233	2.49	0.0064	2.99	0.0014	3.49	2.42E-04

Appendix D
Control Limit Formulas

VARIABLES CHARTS

$\bar{x}$ and R chart: Averages Chart: $\bar{\bar{x}} \pm A_2\bar{R}$ Range Chart: $LCL = D_3\bar{R}$ $UCL = D_4\bar{R}$

$\bar{x}$ and s chart: Averages Chart: $\bar{\bar{x}} \pm A_3\bar{s}$ Std. Dev. Chart: $LCL = B_3\bar{s}$ $UCL = B_4\bar{s}$

Individuals & Moving Range Chart (two - value moving window):

Individuals Chart: $\bar{x} \pm 2.66\bar{R}$ Moving Range: $UCL = 3.267\bar{R}$

Moving Average and Moving Range (2 - value moving window):

Moving Average: $\bar{\bar{x}} \pm 1.88\bar{R}$ Moving Range: $UCL = 3.267\bar{R}$

ATTRIBUTE CHARTS

p - chart: $\bar{p} \pm 3\sqrt{\frac{\bar{p}(1-\bar{p})}{n}}$

np chart: $n\bar{p} \pm 3\sqrt{n\bar{p}(1-\bar{p})}$

c - chart: $\bar{c} \pm 3\sqrt{\bar{c}}$

u - chart: $\bar{u} \pm 3\sqrt{\frac{\bar{u}}{n}}$

Appendix E

Constants for Control Charts

Subgroup Size n	A_2	d_2	D_3	D_4	A_3	c_4	B_3	B_4	E_2	A_2 for Median Charts
2	1.880	1.128	–	3.267	2.659	0.798	–	3.267	2.660	1.880
3	1.023	1.693	–	2.574	1.954	0.886	–	2.568	1.772	1.187
4	0.729	2.059	–	2.282	1.628	0.921	–	2.266	1.457	0.796
5	0.577	2.326	–	2.114	1.427	0.940	–	2.089	1.290	0.691
6	0.483	2.534	–	2.004	1.287	0.952	0.030	1.970	1.184	0.548
7	0.419	2.704	0.076	1.924	1.182	0.959	0.118	1.882	1.109	0.508
8	0.373	2.847	0.136	1.864	1.099	0.965	0.185	1.815	1.054	0.433
9	0.337	2.970	0.184	1.816	1.032	0.969	0.239	1.761	1.010	0.412
10	0.308	3.078	0.223	1.777	0.975	0.973	0.284	1.716	0.975	0.362

Appendix F

Standard Normal Distribution for Select Values of Z

Z	Area to Left of Z	Area to Right of Z	Parts per Million Right of Z
0	0.5000000	0.5000000	500000.0002
0.1	0.5398279	0.4601721	460172.1045
0.2	0.5792597	0.4207403	420740.3128
0.3	0.6179114	0.3820886	382088.6425
0.4	0.6554217	0.3445783	344578.3034
0.5	0.6914625	0.3085375	308537.5326
0.6	0.7257469	0.2742531	274253.0649
0.7	0.7580364	0.2419636	241963.5785
0.8	0.7881447	0.2118553	211855.3339
0.9	0.8159399	0.1840601	184060.0917
1	0.8413447	0.1586553	158655.2598
1.1	0.8643339	0.1356661	135666.1015
1.2	0.8849303	0.1150697	115069.7317
1.3	0.9031995	0.0968005	96800.5495
1.4	0.9192433	0.0807567	80756.71126
1.5	0.9331928	0.0668072	66807.22879
1.6	0.9452007	0.0547993	54799.28945
1.7	0.9554346	0.0445654	44565.43178
1.8	0.9640697	0.0359303	35930.26551
1.9	0.9712835	0.0287165	28716.49286
2	0.9772499	0.0227501	22750.06204
2.1	0.9821356	0.0178644	17864.35742
2.2	0.9860966	0.0139034	13903.39891
2.3	0.9892759	0.0107241	10724.08106
2.4	0.9918025	8.1975289E-03	8197.528869
2.5	0.9937903	6.2096799E-03	6209.679859
2.6	0.9953388	4.6612218E-03	4661.221783

continued

continued

Z	Area to Left of *Z*	Area to Right of *Z*	Parts per Million Right of *Z*
2.7	0.9965330	3.4670231E-03	3467.023053
2.8	0.9974448	2.5551906E-03	2555.190642
2.9	0.9981341	1.8658801E-03	1865.88014
3	0.9986500	1.3499672E-03	1349.967223
3.1	0.9990323	9.6767124E-04	967.6712356
3.2	0.9993128	6.8720208E-04	687.2020808
3.3	0.9995165	4.8348254E-04	483.4825366
3.4	0.9996630	3.3698082E-04	336.9808229
3.5	0.9997673	2.3267337E-04	232.6733737
3.6	0.9998409	1.5914571E-04	159.1457138
3.7	0.9998922	1.0783015E-04	107.8301454
3.8	0.9999276	7.2372434E-05	72.37243427
3.9	0.9999519	4.8115519E-05	48.11551887
4	0.9999683	3.1686035E-05	31.68603461
4.1	0.9999793	2.0668716E-05	20.66871577
4.2	0.9999866	1.3354097E-05	13.35409733
4.3	0.9999915	8.5460212E-06	8.546021191
4.4	0.9999946	5.4169531E-06	5.416953054
4.5	0.9999966	3.4008031E-06	3.400803062
4.6	0.9999979	2.1146434E-06	2.114643376
4.7	0.9999987	1.3023157E-06	1.302315654
4.8	0.9999992	7.9435267E-07	0.794352669
4.9	0.9999995	4.7986955E-07	0.479869547
5	0.9999997	2.8710500E-07	0.287105
5.1	0.9999998	1.7012231E-07	0.170122314
5.2	0.9999999	9.9834400E-08	0.0998344
5.3	0.9999999	5.8022066E-08	0.058022066
5.4	1.0000000	3.3396123E-08	0.033396123
5.5	1.0000000	1.9036399E-08	0.019036399
5.6	1.0000000	1.0746217E-08	0.010746217
5.7	1.0000000	6.0076532E-09	0.006007653
5.8	1.0000000	3.3260517E-09	0.003326052
5.9	1.0000000	1.8235793E-09	0.001823579
6	1.0000000	9.9012187E-10	0.000990122

Glossary

A

acceptable quality level (AQL): The maximum percentage or proportion of variant units in a lot or batch that, for purposes of acceptance sampling, can be considered satisfactory as a process average.

acceptance sampling: Sampling inspection in which decisions are made to accept or not accept product or service; also, the methodology that deals with procedures by which decisions to accept or not accept are based on the results of the inspection of samples.

accuracy: The closeness of alignment between an observed value and an accepted reference value.

action plan: The detailed plan to implement the actions needed to achieve strategic goals and objectives.

activity: An action of some type that requires a time duration for accomplishment.

activity network diagram (AND) (arrow diagram): A management and planning tool used to develop the best possible schedule and appropriate controls to accomplish the schedule; the critical path method (CPM) and the program evaluation review technique (PERT) make use of arrow diagrams.

advanced product quality planning and control plan (APQP): APQP is a comprehensive quality planning and control system specifying protocols for product and process design and development, validation, assessment, and corrective action.

advanced quality planning (AQP): A comprehensive system of applying quality disciplines during a product or process development effort; sometimes also called advanced product quality planning (APQP).

analytical study: A study which uses theory and a model in order predict future outcomes or to lead to a change in outcomes.

assignable cause: A factor that contributes to variation and that is feasible to detect and identify.

assumptions: Conditions that must be true in order for a statistical procedure to be valid.

attributes data: Data that is categorized for analysis or evaluation. (Attribute data may involve measurements as long as the measurements are used only to place a given piece of data in a category for further analysis or evaluation. Contrasted to variables data.)

auditee: The individual or organization being audited.

availability: A measure of the degree to which an item is in the operable and committable state at the start of the mission, when the mission is called for at an unknown (random) time.

average outgoing quality (AOQ): The expected quality of outgoing product following the use of an acceptance sampling plan for a given value of incoming product quality.

average outgoing quality limit (AOQL): For a given acceptance sampling plan, the maximum AOQ over all possible levels of incoming quality.

average sample number: The average number of sample units per lot used for making decisions (acceptance or nonacceptance).

B

benchmark: An organization, part of an organization, or measurement that serves as a reference point or point of comparison.

benefit–cost analysis: A collection of the dollar value of benefits derived from an initiative divided by the associated costs incurred.

block diagram: A diagram that describes the operation, interrelationships, and interdependencies of components in a system. Boxes, or blocks (hence the name), represent the components; connecting lines between the blocks represent interfaces. There are two types of block diagrams: a functional block diagram, which shows a system's subsystems and lower-level products, their interrelationships, and interfaces with other systems, and a reliability block diagram, which is similar to the functional block diagram except that it is modified to emphasize those aspects influencing reliability.

brainstorming: A problem-solving tool that teams use to generate as many ideas as possible related to a particular subject. Team members begin by offering all their ideas; the ideas are not discussed or reviewed until after the brainstorming session.

C

calibration: The comparison of a measurement instrument or system of unverified accuracy to a measurement instrument or system of known accuracy to detect any variation from the true value.

causal factor: A variable which when changed or manipulated in some manner serves to influence a given effect or result.

chance cause variation: Variation due to chance causes. Also known as common cause or random variation.

change agent: The person who takes the lead in transforming a company into a quality organization by providing guidance during the planning phase, facilitating implementation, and supporting those who pioneer the changes.

characteristic: A property that helps to differentiate between items of a given sample or population.

client: A person or organization requesting the audit.

conflict resolution: A process for resolving disagreements in a manner acceptable to all parties.

consensus: Finding a proposal acceptable enough that all team members can support the decision and no member opposes it.

consumer's risk (β): For a sampling plan, refers to the probability of acceptance of a lot, the quality of which has a designated numerical value representing a level that is seldom desirable. Usually the value will be the lot tolerance percent defective (LTPD). Also called beta risk or type II error.

continuous variable: A variable whose possible values form an interval set of numbers such that between each two values in the set another member of the set occurs.

control plan: A document that may include the characteristics for quality of a product or service, measurements, and methods of control.

coordinate measuring machine (CMM): Coordinate measuring machines (CMM) can most easily be defined as physical representations of a three-dimensional rectilinear coordinate system. Coordinate measuring machines now represent a significant fraction of the measuring equipment used for defining the geometry of different shaped workpieces.

corrective action: Action taken to eliminate the root cause(s) and symptom(s) of an existing deviation or nonconformity to prevent recurrence.

Crawford slip method: Refers to a method of gathering and presenting anonymous data from a group.

critical defect: A critical defect is a defect that judgment and experience indicate is likely to result in hazardous or unsafe conditions for the individuals using, maintaining, or depending on the product; or a defect that judgment and experience indicate is likely to prevent performance of the unit.

critical path: The sequence of tasks that takes the longest time and determines a project's completion date.

critical path method (CPM): An activity-oriented project management technique that uses arrow-diagramming techniques to demonstrate both the time and cost required to complete a project. It provides one time estimate—normal time.

criticality: An indication of the consequences which are expected to result from a failure.

cross-functional team: A group consisting of members from more than one department that is organized to accomplish a project.

cycle time: Refers to the time that it takes to complete a process from beginning to end.

D

defect: A departure of a quality characteristic from its intended level or state that occurs with a severity sufficient to cause an associated product or service not to satisfy intended normal or reasonably foreseeable usage requirements.

dependent events: Two events A and B are dependent if the probability of one event occurring is higher given the occurrence of the other event.

deployment: To spread around. Used in strategic planning to describe the process of cascading plans throughout the organization.

descriptive statistics: Techniques for displaying and summarizing data.

design of experiments (DOE), designed experiment: The arrangement in which an experimental program is to be conducted, and the selection of the versions (levels) of one or more factors or factor combinations to be included in the experiment.

design review: Documented, comprehensive, and systematic examination of a design to evaluate its capability to fulfill the requirements for quality.

detection: The likelihood of detecting a failure once it has occurred. Detection will be evaluated based on a 10-point scale. In the lowest end of the scale (1) it is assumed a design control will detect a failure with certainty. In the highest end of the scale (10) it is assumed a design control will not detect a failure if a failure occurs.

discrete variable: A variable whose possible values form a finite or at most countably infinite set.

DMAIC: An acronym denoting a sequence used in the methodology associated with Six Sigma: define, measure, analyze, improve, control.

E

empowerment: A condition whereby employees have the authority to make decisions and take action in their work areas, within stated bounds, without prior approval.

entity: Item that can be individually described and considered.

error: 1. Error in measurement is the difference between the indicated value and the true value of a measured quantity. 2. A fault resulting from defective judgment, deficient knowledge, or carelessness. It is not to be confused with measurement error which is the difference between a computed or measured value and the true or theoretical value.

expected value: The mean of a variable.

external failure costs: Costs associated with defects found during or after delivery of the product or service.

F

facilitator: An individual who is responsible for creating favorable conditions that will enable a team to reach its purpose or achieve its goals by bringing together the necessary tools, information, and resources to get the job done.

factor: An assignable cause that may affect the responses (test results) and of which different versions (levels) are included in the experiment.

failure: The termination, due to one or more defects, of the ability of an item, product, or service to perform its required function when called upon to do so. A failure may be partial, complete, or intermittent.

failure modes and effects analysis (FMEA): A procedure in which each potential failure mode in every sub-item of an item is analyzed to determine its effect on other sub-items and on the required function of the item.

filters: Relative to human-to-human communication, those perceptions (based on culture, language, demographics, experience, and so on) that affect how a message is transmitted by the sender and how a message is interpreted by the receiver.

flowchart: A graphical representation of the steps in a process. Flowcharts are drawn to better understand processes. The flowchart is one of the seven tools of quality.

foolproofing: A process of making a product or process immune to foolish errors on the part of user or operator. Is synonymous with error proofing.

G

Gantt chart: A type of bar chart used in process/project planning and control to display planned work and finished work in relation to time. Also called a "milestone chart."

gatekeeping: The role of an individual (often a facilitator) in a group meeting in helping ensure effective interpersonal interactions (for example, someone's ideas are not ignored due to the team moving on to the next topic too quickly).

gauging: Gauging is a procedure that determines product conformance with specifications, with the aid of measuring instruments such as calipers, micrometers, templates, and other mechanical, optical, and electronic devices.

goal: A statement of general intent, aim, or desire; it is the point toward which the organization (or individual) directs its efforts; goals are often nonquantitative.

H

hierarchical relationship: A set of relationships which can be ordered or arranged from general to specific.

hold point: A point, defined in an appropriate document, beyond which an activity must not proceed without the approval of a designated organization or authority.

I

independent events: Two events A and B are called independent if the probability that they both occur is the product of the probabilities of their individual occurrence. That is, $P(A\&B) = P(A)P(B)$.

inferential statistics: Techniques for reaching conclusions about a population based on analysis of data from a sample.

information system: Technology-based systems used to support operations, aid day-to-day decision making, and support strategic analysis (other names often used include: management information system, decision system, information technology (IT), data processing).

inspection: The process of measuring, examining, testing, gauging, or otherwise comparing the unit with the applicable requirements.

internal failure costs: Costs associated with defects found before the product or service is delivered.

intervention: An action taken by a leader or a facilitator to support the effective functioning of a team or work group.

K

***kaizen* blitz/event:** An intense, short time frame, team approach to employ the concepts and techniques of continuous improvement (for example, to reduce cycle time, increase throughput).

L

leader: An individual, recognized by others, as the person to lead an effort. One cannot be a "leader" without one or more "followers." The term is often used interchangeably with "manager" (see "manager"). A "leader" may or may not hold an officially designated management-type position.

leadership: An essential part of a quality improvement effort. Organization leaders must establish a vision, communicate that vision to those in the organization, and provide the tools, knowledge, and motivation necessary to accomplish the vision.

levels: In experimental design, the possible values of a factor.

lot tolerance percent defective (LTPD): LTPD, expressed in percent defective, is the poorest quality in an individual lot that should be accepted.

M

maintainability: The measure of the ability of an item to be retained or restored to specified condition when maintenance is performed by personnel having specified skill levels, using prescribed procedures and resources, at each prescribed level of maintenance and repair.

major defect: A defect that will interfere with normal or reasonable foreseeable use, but will not cause a risk of damage or injury.

material control: A broad collection of tools for managing the items and lots in a production process.

materials review board: A quality control committee or team, usually employed in manufacturing or other materials-processing installations, that has the responsibility and authority to deal with items or materials that do not conform to fitness-for-use specifications.

mean time between failures (MTBF): A basic measure of reliability for repairable items: The mean number of life units during which all parts of item perform within their specified limits, during a particular measurement interval under stated conditions.

mean time to failure (MTTF): A basic measure of system reliability for nonrepairable items: The total number of life units for an item divided by the total number of failures within that population, during a particular measurement interval under stated conditions.

mean time to repair (MTTR): A basic measure of maintainability: The sum of corrective maintenance times at any specific level of repair, divided by the total number of failures within an item repaired at that level, during a particular interval under stated conditions.

measurement: 1. The process of evaluating a property or characteristic of an object and describing it with a numerical or nominal value. 2. A series of manipulations of physical objects or systems according to a defined protocol that results in a number.

measurement process: Repeated application of a test method using a measuring system.

measuring system: In general, the elements of a measuring system include the instrumentation, calibration standards, environmental influences, human operator limitations, and features of the workpiece or object being measures.

milestone: A point in time when a critical event is to occur; a symbol placed on a milestone chart to locate the point when a critical event is to occur.

milestone chart: Another name for a Gantt chart.

minor defect: A defect which may cause difficulty in assembly or use of the product, but will not prevent the product from being properly used, nor pose any hazard to users.

mistake: Is similar to an error, but with the implication that it could be prevented by better training or attention.

multi-voting: A decision-making tool that enables a group to sort through a long list of ideas to identify priorities.

Myers-Briggs Type Indicator: A method and instrument for assessing personality type based on Carl Jung's theory of personality preferences.

N

nominal group technique: A technique similar to brainstorming, used by teams to generate and make a selection from ideas on a particular subject. Team members are asked to silently come up with as many ideas as possible, writing them down. Each member is then asked to share one idea, which is recorded. After all the ideas are recorded, they are discussed and prioritized by the group.

nonconformity: A departure of a quality characteristic from its intended level or state that occurs with a severity sufficient to cause an associated product or service not to meet a specification requirement.

O

observation: The process of determining the presence or absence of attributes or making measurements of a variable. Also, the result of the process of determining the presence or absence of attributes or making a measurement of a variable.

objective: A quantitative statement of future expectations and an indication of when the expectations should be achieved; it flows from goal(s) and clarifies what people must accomplish.

objective evidence: Verifiable qualitative or quantitative observations, information, records, or statements of fact pertaining to the quality of an item or service or to the existence and implementation of a quality system element.

observational study: Analysis of data collected from a process without imposing changes on the process.

occurrence: The likelihood of a failure occurring. Occurrence will be evaluated based on a 10-point scale. In the lowest end of the scale (1) it is assumed the probability of a failure is unlikely. In the highest end of the scale (10) it is assumed the probability of a failure is nearly inevitable.

operating characteristic (OC) curve: For a sampling plan, the OC curve indicates the probability of accepting a lot based on the sample size to be taken and the fraction defective in the batch.

organization: Company, corporation, firm, enterprise, or institution, or part thereof, whether incorporated or not, public or private, that has its own functions and administration.

P

parameter: A constant or coefficient that describes some characteristic of a population.

payback period: The number of years it will take the results of a project or capital investment to recover the investment from net cash flows.

poka-yoke: A term that means to mistake-proof a process by building safeguards into the system that avoid or immediately find errors. The term comes from Japanese terms *poka*, which means "error," and *yokeru*, which means "to avoid."

policy: A high-level overall plan embracing the general goals and acceptable practices of a group.

population: The totality of items or units of material under consideration.

precision: The closeness of agreement between randomly selected individual measurements or test results.

process: An activity or group of activities that takes an input, adds value to it, and provides an output to an internal or external customer; a planned and repetitive sequence of steps by which a defined product or service is delivered.

process improvement team (PIT): A natural work group or cross-functional team whose responsibility is to achieve needed improvements in existing processes. The lifespan of the team is based on the completion of the team purpose and specific tasks.

process mapping: The flowcharting of a work process in detail, including key measurements.

producer's risk (α): For a sampling plan, refers to the probability of not accepting a lot, the quality of which has a designated numerical value representing a level that is generally desirable. Usually the designated value will be the acceptable quality level. Also called alpha risk or type I error.

product identification: A means of marking parts with labels, etching, engraving, ink, or other means so that different part numbers and other key attributes can be identified.

program evaluation and review technique (PERT): An event-oriented project management planning and measurement technique that utilizes an arrow diagram or road map to identify all major project events and demonstrates the amount of time (critical path) needed to complete a project. It provides three time estimates: optimistic, most likely, and pessimistic.

project lifecycle: A typical project lifecycle consists of five sequential phases in project management: concept, planning, design, implementation, and evaluation.

project management: The entire process of managing activities and events involved throughout a project's lifecycle.

project plan: All the documents that comprise the details of why the project is to be initiated, what the project is to accomplish, when and where it is to be implemented, who will have responsibility, how implementation will be carried out, how much it will cost, what resources are required, and how the project's progress and results will be measured.

Q

quality assurance: All the planned or systematic actions necessary to provide adequate confidence that a product or service will satisfy given needs.

quality audit: A systematic, independent examination and review to determine whether quality activities and related results comply with planned arrangements and whether these arrangements are implemented effectively and are suitable to achieve the objectives.

quality audit observation: Statement of fact made during a quality audit and substantiated by objective evidence.

quality auditor: Person qualified to perform quality audits.

quality control: The operational techniques and the activities that sustain a quality of product or service that will satisfy given needs; also the use of such techniques and activities.

quality council: Sometimes referred to as a "quality steering committee." The group driving the quality improvement effort and usually having oversight responsibility for the implementation and maintenance of the quality management system; operated in parallel with the normal operation of the business.

quality function deployment (QFD): A structured method in which customer requirements are translated into appropriate technical requirements for each stage of product development and production. The QFD process is often referred to as listening to the voice of the customer.

quality improvement: Actions taken throughout the organization to increase the effectiveness and efficiency of activities and processes in order to provide added benefits to both the organization and its customers.

quality management: The totality of functions involved in organizing and leading the effort to determine and achieve quality.

quality manual: A document stating the quality policy and describing the quality system of an organization.

quality planning: The activity of establishing quality objectives and quality requirements.

quality policy: Top management's formally stated intentions and direction for the organization pertaining to quality.

quality surveillance: Continual monitoring and verification of the status of an entity and analysis of records to ensure that specified requirements are being fulfilled.

quality system: The organizational structure, procedures, processes, and resources needed to implement quality management.

R

random sampling: The process of selecting units for a sample in such a manner that all combinations of units under consideration have an equal or ascertainable chance of being selected as the sample.

random variable: A variable whose value depends on chance.

readability: Readability is the ease of reading the instrument scale when a dimension is being measured.

record: A document or electronic medium which furnishes objective evidence of activities performed or results achieved.

reinforcement: The process of providing positive consequences when an individual is applying the correct knowledge and skills to the job. It has been described as "catching people doing things right and recognizing their behavior." Caution: less than desired behavior can also be reinforced unintentionally.

reliability: The probability that an item can perform its intended function for a specified interval under stated conditions.

repeatability: How close the measurements of an instrument are to each other if such measurements are repeated on a part under the same measuring conditions.

replication: The repetition of the set of all the treatment combinations to be compared in an experiment. Each of the repetitions is called a replicate.

reproducibility: Reproducibility is a measure of the degree of agreement between two single test results made on the same object in two different, randomly selected measuring locations or laboratories.

resource requirements matrix: A tool to relate the resources required to the project tasks requiring them (used to indicate types of individuals needed, material needed, subcontractors, and so on).

response variable: The variable that shows the observed results of an experimental treatment.

return on investment (ROI): An umbrella term for a variety of ratios measuring an organization's business performance and calculated by dividing some measure of return by a measure of investment and then multiplying by 100 to provide a percentage. In its most basic form, ROI indicates what remains from all money taken in after all expenses are paid.

robust designs: Products or processes that continue to perform as intended in spite of manufacturing variation and extreme environmental conditions during use.

robustness: The condition of a product or process design that remains relatively stable with a minimum of variation even though factors that influence operations or usage, such as environment and wear, are constantly changing.

S

sample: A group of units, portions of material, or observations taken from a larger collection of units, quantity of material, or observations that serves to provide information that may be used as a basis for making a decision concerning the larger quantity.

sample integrity: Samples are maintained in a unique manner to avoid corruption or confusion with others.

scribe: The member of a team assigned the responsibility for recording minutes of meetings.

self-directed work team (SDWT): A team that requires little supervision and manages itself and the day-to-day work it does; self-directed teams are responsible for whole work processes and schedules with each individual performing multiple tasks.

sensitivity: Sensitivity can be defined as the least perceptible change in dimension detected by the measuring tip and shown by the indicator.

severity: An indicator of the severity of a failure should a failure occur. Severity can be evaluated based on a 10-point scale. In the lowest end of the scale (1) it is assumed a failure will have no noticeable effect. In the highest end of the scale (10) it is assumed a failure will impact safe operation or violate compliance with regulatory mandate.

Six Sigma approach: A quality philosophy; a collection of techniques and tools for use in reducing variation; a program of improvement which focuses on strong leadership tools and an emphasis on bottom-line financial results.

special causes: Causes of variation that arise because of special circumstances. They are not an inherent part of a process. Special causes are also referred to as assignable causes.

sponsor: A member of management who oversees, supports, and implements the efforts of a team or initiative.

stable process: A process for which no special causes of variation are present.

stages of team growth: The four development stages through which groups typically progress: forming, storming, norming, and performing. Knowledge of the stages help team members accept the normal problems that occur on the path from forming a group to becoming a team.

stakeholders: People, departments, and organizations that have an investment or interest in the success or actions taken by the organization.

standard: A statement, specification, or quantity of material against which measured outputs from a process may be judged as acceptable or unacceptable.

statement of work (SOW): A description of the actual work to be accomplished. It is derived from the work breakdown structure and, when combined with the project specifications, becomes the basis for the contractual agreement on the project (also referred to as scope of work).

statistic: A quantity calculated from a sample of observations, most often to form an estimate of some population parameter.

statistical control: A process is considered to be in a state of statistical control if variations among the observed sampling results from it can be attributed to a constant system of chance causes.

statistical process control (SPC): The application of statistical techniques to control a process.

steering committee: A group responsible for overall selection of continuous improvement projects.

strategic planning: A process to set an organization's long range goals and identify the actions needed to reach the goals.

substitute quality characteristic: A producer's view/expression of what constitutes quality in a product or service.

subsystem: A combination of sets, groups, and so on which performs an operational function within a system and its major subdivision of the system.

surface metrology: Surface metrology may be broadly defined as the measurement of the difference between what the surface actually is and what it is intended to be. It may involve other terms such as surface roughness and surface finish.

supply chain: The series of processes and/or organizations that are involved in producing and delivering a product to the final user.

SWOT analysis: An assessment of an organization's key strengths, weaknesses, opportunities, and threats. It considers factors such as the organization's industry, the competitive position, functional areas, and management.

system: A composite of equipment and skills, and techniques capable of performing or supporting an operational role, or both. A complete system includes all equipment, related facilities, material, software, services, and personnel required for its operation and support to the degree that it can be considered self-sufficient in its intended operating environment.

T

team: A group of two or more people who are equally accountable for the accomplishment of a purpose and specific performance goals; it is also defined as a small number of people with complementary skills who are committed to a common purpose.

team building: The process of transforming a group of people into a team and developing the team to achieve its purpose.

testing: A means of determining the capability of an item to meet specified requirements by subjecting the item to a set of physical, chemical, environmental, or operating actions and conditions.

timekeeper: A member of a team who monitors progress against a predefined schedule during meetings.

traceability, gage: A process intended to quantify measurement uncertainty in relation to national standards. Evidence of gage traceability typically consists of certificates and reports on calibration.

traceability, product: The ability to trace the history, application, or location of an item or activity and like items or activities by means of recorded identification.

traceability system, product: A formal set of procedures, usually implemented in a computerized database, which allows the manufacturer of a unit to trace it and its components back to the source.

treatment: A combination of the versions (levels) of each of the factors assigned to an experimental unit.

true quality characteristic: A customer's view/expression of what constitutes quality in a product or service.

type I error: The incorrect decision that a process is unacceptable when, in fact, perfect information would reveal that it is located within the zone of acceptable processes.

type II error: The incorrect decision that a process is acceptable when, in fact, perfect information would reveal that it is located within the zone of rejectable processes.

V

value: The net difference between customer-perceived benefits and burdens, sometimes expressed as a ratio of benefits to burdens or a ratio of worth to cost.

variables data: Data resulting from the measurement of a parameter or a variable. The resulting measurements may be recorded on a continuous scale. (Contrasted to attributes data.)

W

work breakdown structure (WBS): A project management technique by which a project is divided into tasks, subtasks, and units of work to be performed.

work group: A group composed of people from one functional area who work together on a daily basis and whose goal is to manage and improve the processes of their function.

Index

Note: Italicized page numbers indicate illustrations.

D